It seems with every book I've read
The pages get inside my head.
The latest book that I checked out
Came with pirates strewn about.

Pages in My Head

I turned the page to chapter four
Where I was handed down an oar
And rowed until my hands were raw.
Then the rocky coast I saw.

It loomed against the darkening sky;
A castle bold was standing high.
See how with the books I've read
The pages get inside my head?

—Nancy Bopp

Reading 5 Worktext
Answer Key

Second Edition

bju press®

Greenville, South Carolina

D1157439

NOTE:
The fact that materials produced by other publishers may be referred to in this volume does not constitute an endorsement of the content or theological position of materials produced by such publishers. Any references and ancillary materials are listed as an aid to the student or the teacher and in an attempt to maintain the accepted academic standards of the publishing industry.

READING 5 Worktext Teacher's Edition
Second Edition

Project Coordinators	**Project Editors**	**Designers**
Dorothy Buckley	Carolyn Cooper	Wendy Searles
Debra White	Debbie L. Parker	Noelle Snyder

Contributing Writers
Wendy M. Harris
Janice A. Joss
Carol S. Lotter
Amy Miller
L. Michelle Rosier
Diana Simms

Composition
Carol Larson

Project Manager
Martin Grove

Design Coordinator
Duane Nichols

Cover
Ellyson Kalagayan

Illustration Coordinator
Mary Ann Lumm

The following individuals have contributed to the illustrations included in this textbook.

Tim Banks	Cory Godbey	Keith Neely	Dana Thompson
John Bjerk	Preston Gravely Jr.	Duane Nichols	Del Thompson
Jim Brooks	Dyke Habegger	Kathy Pflug	Stephanie True
Roger Bruckner	Jim Hargis	John Roberts	Sanela Tutaris
Paula Cheadle	Chris Koelle	Lynda Slattery	Tara Warrington
Tim Davis	Sam Laterza	Melissa Smith	
Johanna Ehnis	Mary Ann Lumm	Noelle Snyder	
Justin Gerard	John Muessen	Julie Speer	

Produced in cooperation with the Bob Jones University
School of Education and Bob Jones Academy.

© 2002 BJU Press
Greenville, South Carolina 29614

First Edition © 1986 BJU Press

Printed in the United States of America
All rights reserved

ISBN 978-1-57924-444-6

15   14   13

CONTENTS

Introduction

This Worktext accompanies the student text for *READING 5 for Christian Schools*® (Second Edition) and is an integral part of the Bob Jones University Press Reading program. It contains interesting activities to focus on specific reading skills. These pages are meant to be completed under the teacher's guidance. The Skill Day section includes systematic teaching of structural analysis, study skills, and literature skills. The Author Scrapbook section introduces a listening strategy as well as information about various authors. The Phonics Critters section provides phonics review for students who can benefit from review or remedial help.

The "Useful for grading" label found in the upper right corner of some Worktext pages assists the teacher in selecting pages for evaluation. The first time a particular skill is taught, the page is labeled "Skill introduction" to alert the teacher that the activity is provided for student practice rather than evaluation. Pages labeled "Optional" may be used for advanced students, or as a group activity, or not at all.

Undercover Work

NOTE: It is correct to put quotation marks around story titles, but this early in the school year the students may not remember to do so.

The **table of contents** and the **index** are valuable tools in helping you find information in a book.

▶ **Use the table of contents in your reader to answer the questions.**

1. The first unit or division title is Lessons. What are the titles of the other five units?
   Viewpoints, Regions, Creatures Great and Small, Endeavors, Reflections

2. What is the title of the first story in the Endeavors unit? _____ *"Moses and Joshua"*

3. Who is the author of the selection entitled "Some Special Day" found in the Regions unit?
   Marie C. Poley

4. In which division or unit might you expect to read stories about animals?
   Creatures Great and Small

5. On which page does the Glossary begin? _____ *page 515*

6. Which of Aesop's fables can you read about? *"The Birds, the Beasts, and the Bat";*
   "The Field of Corn"; "The Sick Stag"; "The Rose and the Clay";
   "The Maid and Her Milk Pail"

7. On what page does the Index begin? _____ *page 547*

▶ **Use the index in your reader to find the beginning page numbers for each item.**

1. "Venture to Mierow Lake"—page _____ *232*

2. selection written by David McCord—page _____ *230*

3. selections written by Henry Becker—
   pages _____ *84, 324, 370*

4. "Doubting Castle"—page _____ *416*

5. selection by Hans Christian Andersen—page _____ *52*

6. "A Wonderful Man"—page _____ *12*

7. "The King and the Shirt"—page _____ *51*

Reading 5: "Lessons," p. 1, Lesson 1
Study skills: using the table of contents and index to locate information

1

▶Read the following paragraphs and state the author's main purpose for each.

to inform	to entertain
to persuade	to teach a lesson

> Authors may have several different purposes in their writing. Some of the most common purposes are to inform, to entertain, to persuade, and to teach a lesson.

Katie loved to collect shells. She decided to find out what kinds of shells she had. Looking in the encyclopedia, Katie realized that most of her shells were mollusks. Mollusks love to be in the ocean, in fresh water, and on land.

1. _____ *to inform* _____

Daniel knew that he was putting his own life in danger. He knew that his life could be quickly ended because of the king's decree. But he also knew that he could not go back on his God. Pressure didn't affect his personal time with God.

2. _____ *to teach a lesson* _____

The Kountry Klub for Kids is a fantastic group. If you are not a member or have never even visited, you need to! It's the most well-rounded club I've ever known.

3. _____ *to persuade* _____

The sour pickles were after Mort the mushroom. Mort jumped into a toaster slot. The pickles turned the toaster on in hopes of sizzling Mort. One pickle realized the plan was failing and poked his knife down into the slots. Zzzzzzap! A charge of electricity sizzled through the surprised pickle.

4. _____ *to entertain* _____

Some people think that monkeys and chimpanzees are the same animal, but that's not true. There are several ways to tell these animals apart, but perhaps the easiest way is to look for a tail. If you can see a tail, you're looking at a monkey. If there is no tail, it's a chimp. Also, a monkey's arms are generally shorter than its legs, but a chimp's arms are longer than its legs.

5. _____ *to inform* _____

Janwahr whistled high and long and loud. Just behind them the river burst open with a great rush and a horrible roar. The silver horn gleamed as the water streamed off the giant creature. Danzee saw the armies and raised himself a hundred feet out of the water, shaking his head and screaming.

6. _____ *to entertain* _____

Reading 5: "Lessons," p. 1, Lesson 1
Literature: identifying the author's purpose in paragraphs

▶**Read each paragraph. Underline all the first-person pronouns. Circle the number of each paragraph that is told from the first-person point of view.**

> A **first-person narrative** is a story that is told by one of the story's characters. The pronouns **I, me, my, we, our,** and **us** help to determine that it is a first-person narrative.

① The only good thing about going to a new school was that my new classmates didn't know how fast I could run. So, when we lined up for the year's first race, I could run like turbocharged lightning right through the finish line. Then I would listen to the amazed comments of the kids as I pretended not to be breathing hard.

2 The football teams jogged onto the field from under the stadium bleachers. The game was about to begin. The noisy crowd rose to sing the national anthem. The teams went into a quick huddle. The referee signaled for the kickoff. The Mustang fans jumped up with a cheer as the ball hurtled down the field.

③ We were playing Red Rover at recess. I was running toward the clenched arms of my friends. Their arms were so tight against me that the last thing I remember is going up into the air. The next thing I heard was the doctor saying, "Little lady, what's your name?" I answered her, wincing at the pain and squinting my eyes.

④ The cage door rattled as the huge tiger batted it with his paw. My little brother and I were enjoying the scene. With a clang, the door flew open and the beautiful cat bounded to the floor. My little brother's eyes opened wide, and so did his mouth. I pulled him behind a big glass case as the crowd scattered.

> An **acronym** is a word made of the initial letters or parts of a word or words.

▶**Match each acronym with its meaning. Write the correct letter.**

__C__ 1. Rachel lived with her grandparents in their **RV.**

__A__ 2. The hard drive on my **PC** crashed.

__E__ 3. The **scuba** equipment helped the diver reach the sunken vessel.

__B__ 4. Dad watched the national election returns on **TV.**

__D__ 5. My favorite hymn is not on my sister's **CD.**

A. personal computer

B. television

C. recreational vehicle

D. compact disk

E. self-contained underwater breathing apparatus

Reading 5: "Runaway Friends," pp. 2-7, Lesson 2
Literature: recognizing first-person point of view
Vocabulary: matching acronyms and meanings

Useful for grading

▶**Answer the questions in complete sentences.** *Wording may vary.*

1. What was Rachel's usual formula for making friends at each new school? _____

   _____*Rachel astonished everyone with how fast she could run.*_____

2. When Rachel saw Kyle out of the corner of her eye in the first race, what did she do?

   _____*Rachel sped up faster than ever.*_____

3. When Kyle was in a terrible accident, what did the whole school do? _____

   _____*They rooted for him and prayed for him daily.*_____

4. What advice did Grandma give Rachel for making new friends? _____

   _____*She told Rachel to ask about their families and hobbies.*_____

5. When Chrissy asked Rachel to spend time talking at recess, what decision did Rachel

   make about running? ___*She wanted friends*___

   _____*more than she wanted to beat Kyle.*_____

6. When Rachel fell in the Fall Field Day relay race, what did Kyle do? _____

   _____*Kyle came to see how she was and stayed away from*_____

   _____*the finish line for the rest of the day.*_____

PROVERBS 17:17
A friend loveth at all times.

▶**Match each contraction with its meaning. Write the correct letter.**

___C___ 1. didn't   A. they would

___A___ 2. they'd   B. could not

___F___ 3. let's   C. did not

___B___ 4. couldn't   D. I will

___D___ 5. I'll   E. I would

___H___ 6. wasn't   F. let us

___E___ 7. I'd   G. do not

___G___ 8. don't   H. was not

4

Reading 5: "Runaway Friends," pp. 8-11, Lesson 3
Comprehension: identifying solutions to problems
Vocabulary: matching contractions and meanings

> **Alliteration** is the repetition of the same beginning sound in two or more words. Authors use alliteration to make the text more enjoyable.

▶**Write the words that have alliteration in each of these lines from "The Star-Spangled Banner."**

1. "Oh! say, can you see, by the dawn's early light,"

   _____*say, see*_____

2. "Whose broad stripes and bright stars, thro'

   the perilous fight,"

   _____*broad, bright, stripes, stars*_____

3. "And the rockets' red glare, the bombs bursting in air,"

   _____*rockets', red, bombs, bursting*_____

4. "Where the foe's haughty host in dread silence reposes,"

   _____*haughty, host*_____

▶**Circle the words with the same vowel sounds in these lines of poetry from the Psalms.**

> The repetition of vowel sounds within words in a line of poetry is called **assonance.**

1. (Teach me) thy way, O Lord, and (lead me) in a plain path (Psalm 27:11).

2. (Bow down) thine ear to me (Psalm 31:2).

3. (Thy) word have (I) hid in (mine) heart (Psalm 119:11).

4. (I) will (delight myself) in (thy) statutes (Psalm 119:16).

5. (Great) is the Lord, and (greatly) to be (praised) in the city of our God (Psalm 48:1).

Which Is It?

▶Circle the word that tells which verb tense is used in each of the paragraphs below.

My father carries a pearl-handled knife. It has three steel blades. He whittles me whistles, darts, and sailboats from sticks.

past   (present)

At the fairgrounds the huge Ferris wheel goes round and round. Slowly it stops, and children jump out, giggling and screaming.

past   (present)

People liked to be friends with me once they knew I was the fastest kid my age on two feet. It happened the same way every year.

(past)   present

Roger is on his last lap. He approaches the finish line. We wonder if he can really pull ahead and make it across the line first.

past   (present)

"Run to the fence," Mr. Herman explains. "Touch the fence. Then turn around and run back. And may the best team win!"

past   (present)

Yesterday was a long day. Nothing went as planned, and the beating sun was almost more than I could bear.

(past)   present

> When comparing two things or ideas, use the *-er* form of the word. When comparing more than two things or ideas, use the *-est* form of the word.

▶Add *-er* or *-est* to the adjectives below. Write the correct form of an adjective in each blank to complete the sentence.

long	high	sharp	noisy	bushy	large

1. My father carves the ___*sharpest / longest*___ arrows in our village.

2. Walking on wood shavings is ___*noisier*___ than walking on grass.

3. Nathan whittled the whistle from the ___*longest / sharpest / largest*___ stick in the box.

4. The bass drum is ___*larger / noisier*___ than the snare drum.

5. The piccolo can play ___*higher*___ tunes than the flute.

6. A raccoon has a ___*bushier / larger*___ tail than a mouse.

Reading 5: "A Wonderful Man," pp. 12-13, Lesson 5
Comprehension: distinguishing between present and past verb tense
Vocabulary: using comparatives and superlatives

6

▶**Write the letter of the emotion at the right that tells how each line from the story should be read.**

___D___ 1. Billy said, "He's some horse, ain't he?"

___A___ 2. Billy made a wild grab for the saddle horn.

___E___ 3. Time and again Billy's hand reached down as if to grab for the saddle horn, but he kept away from it.

___C___ 4. "I don't think you'd better ride him any more today, Sonny," Lem said.

___F___ 5. Lem said, "You go after him this time."

___B___ 6. Billy had ridden his first bronc.

A. fear

B. pride

C. concern

D. admiration

E. determination

F. encouragement

▶**Use the definitions to fill in the crossword puzzle.**

Across
1. a small, wild, or partly tamed horse
4. a rope halter used to break horses
7. a rope used to prevent free movement of an animal

Down
2. to jump with stiff legs
3. to annoy, make resentful
4. to want to have or do something
5. to fasten firmly to a saddle with a strap
6. a fenced-off area for animals
8. to train a horse to respond to human commands

Crossword:
- 1 Across: BRONC
- 4 Across: HACKAMORE
- 7 Across: HOBBLE
- 2 Down: CRWHHOP (CROWHHOP)
- 3 Down: PEEVE
- 4 Down: HANKER
- 5 Down: CINCH
- 6 Down: CORRAL
- 8 Down: BREAK

Reading 5: "His First Bronc," pp. 14-18, Lesson 6
Comprehension: identifying emotional responses of characters
Vocabulary: matching words and definitions

In a story, one event or circumstance (the **cause**) often results in another event or circumstance (the **effect**).

▶**Choose the correct effect.**

1. **Cause:** If Billy can break the black horse,
   Effect:
   ● then he can have the horse.
   ○ then he can become a cowboy.

2. **Cause:** As a result of Billy taking the blindfold off the horse,
   Effect:
   ● he began riding the horse.
   ○ he saddled the horse.

3. **Cause:** Because Billy paid more attention to what his father was saying,
   Effect:
   ○ Billy cinched the saddle tighter.
   ● Billy was loosened the first jump by the horse.

4. **Cause:** As a result of Billy grabbing his hat and waving it in the air,
   Effect:
   ○ Billy broke the horse.
   ● Billy fell off the horse.

5. **Cause:** Because Billy's father held to cowboy traditions in bronc riding,
   Effect:
   ● he told Billy not to grab the saddle horn.
   ○ he told Billy not to ride the horse again.

6. **Cause:** Because Billy turned and saw the horse challenging him,
   Effect:
   ○ Billy ran the horse around the corral.
   ● Billy blindfolded the horse and climbed on again.

7. **Cause:** Since Lem told Billy to make the pony think he was a wolf,
   Effect:
   ● Billy had confidence to ride the horse.
   ○ Billy fell off the horse.

8. **Cause:** Because Billy broke the horse,
   Effect:
   ● Billy was all smiles and proud as a peacock.
   ○ Billy became a wolf and turned challenger.

Reading 5: "His First Bronc," pp. 14-18, Lesson 7
Comprehension: determining cause-and-effect relationships
Literature: identifying the function of setting in cause-and-effect relationships

Name_____

▶**Look at the author catalog card on reader page 20. Answer the questions.**

___b___ 1. What is the call number for this book?
a. 1963
b. F Hen
c. PZ10.3H43

___c___ 2. Who is Wesley Dennis?
a. author
b. publisher
c. illustrator

___a___ 3. In which section of the library would you find this book?
a. fiction
b. biography
c. nonfiction

___c___ 4. In which drawer of the card catalog would you find this card?
a. A-Av
b. Gr-Ha
c. He-Ib

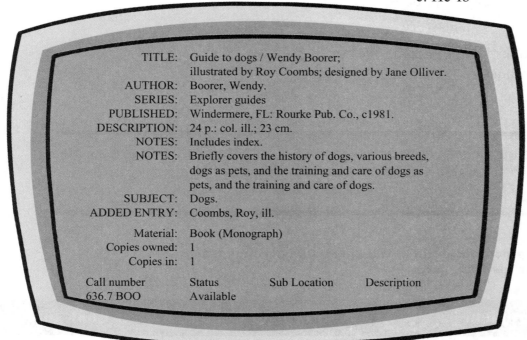

TITLE: Guide to dogs / Wendy Boorer; illustrated by Roy Coombs; designed by Jane Olliver.
AUTHOR: Boorer, Wendy.
SERIES: Explorer guides
PUBLISHED: Windermere, FL: Rourke Pub. Co., c1981.
DESCRIPTION: 24 p.: col. ill.; 23 cm.
NOTES: Includes index.
NOTES: Briefly covers the history of dogs, various breeds, dogs as pets, and the training and care of dogs as pets, and the training and care of dogs.
SUBJECT: Dogs.
ADDED ENTRY: Coombs, Roy, ill.

Material: Book (Monograph)
Copies owned: 1
Copies in: 1

Call number   Status   Sub Location   Description
636.7 BOO   Available

▶**Use the computer screen to answer the questions.**

___c___ 1. Which number will help you locate the book?
a. 24 p.
b. c1981
c. 636.7 BOO

___a___ 2. 1981 is the year that the
a. book was published.
b. author traveled.
c. library bought the book.

___a___ 3. Who is the author?
a. Wendy Boorer
b. Roy Coombs
c. Jane Olliver

___c___ 4. In which section of the library would you find this book?
a. fiction
b. biography
c. nonfiction

Reading 5: "Skill Lesson: Card Catalog," pp. 19-23, Lesson 8
Study skills: using the card catalog to locate books and information in a library

9

▶ 1. **Help each person with his book problem. Fill in the chart with the type of catalog card needed in the search—*author, subject,* or *title*.**

2. **Write the information each person would look for to find the answer to his problem.**

Problem	Type of Card	Look for
Loren likes to read about unusual fish.	*subject*	*fish*
Mrs. Gelhausen needs to find the book <u>Robinson Crusoe</u>.	*title*	<u>*Robinson Crusoe*</u>
Juanita would like to read more books by Elizabeth Yates.	*author*	*Elizabeth Yates*
"Are there any books about robots in the library?" Jesse wonders.	*subject*	*robots*

> The name of every book is recorded on at least three cards in the card catalog. You can search for any book by its *title,* by its *author,* or by at least one *subject* heading.

▶ **Repeat the same procedure to fill in this chart. One person has two choices. Be sure to give him both.**

Problem	Type of Card	Look for
Harold needs <u>The Buffalo Trace</u> by Virginia S. Eifert for a book report.	*title* *author*	<u>*The Buffalo Trace*</u> *Virginia S. Eifert*
Preston likes the book <u>Rikki-Tikki-Tavi</u>. Did Rudyard Kipling write any other books?	*author*	*Rudyard Kipling*
Allegra wants to know who wrote <u>The Hundred Dresses</u>.	*title*	<u>*The Hundred Dresses*</u>
Julie is writing a state report about Utah.	*subject*	*Utah*

Reading 5: "Skill Lesson: Card Catalog," pp. 19-23, Lesson 8
Study skills: using the card catalog to locate books and information in a library

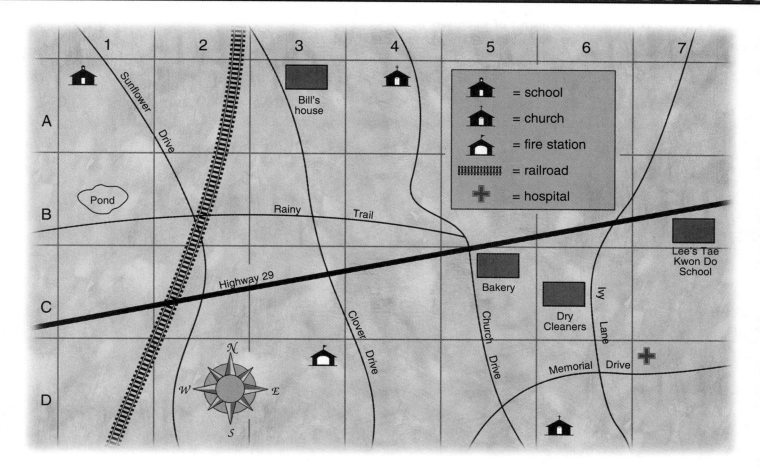

▶ **Use the map to answer the questions.**

1. What is located in Section 3A?

   Bill's house

2. What important place is located in 7B?

   Lee's Tae Kwon Do School

3. What roads do the railroad tracks cross?

   Rainy Trail, Sunflower Drive,

   Highway 29

4. If someone went from the hospital to Mr. Lee's school, what direction would he go?

   north

Mapmakers place numerals and letters on the outside edges of maps. These map coordinates provide points of reference for locating specific places on a map.

5. Which direction would Bill walk to the nearest church? _____*east*_____

6. The fire station is what direction from the church in 6D? _____*west*_____

7. In what section do Ivy Lane and Highway 29 cross? _____*6B*_____

8. On what street is the school located?

   Sunflower Drive

Reading 5: "Lessons from Mr. Lee," pp. 24-27, Lesson 9
Study skills: determining location on a map using coordinates, a map key, and a compass rose

11

▶**Choose the correct meaning of each word.
You may look up the word in the story if you need to.**

1. **Martial arts** are (page 24)
   ○ art done by marshals.
   ○ exercises for Martians.
   ● oriental methods of combat.

2. **Tae kwon do** is (page 24)
   ○ a way of spinning around in karate.
   ● a martial art.
   ○ a karate teacher.

3. **Zen** is (page 24)
   ○ a form of karate.
   ○ a Korean emperor.
   ● a religion.

4. **Taoism** is (page 24)
   ● a religion.
   ○ a form of karate.
   ○ a karate instructor.

5. A **bodyguard** is (page 24)
   ● a protector for an emperor.
   ○ a kind of armor.
   ○ a kind of deodorant.

6. **Calisthenics** are (page 26)
   ○ calluses.
   ○ calls made by animals.
   ● exercises to build muscles.

7. **Allegiance** means (page 26)
   ● loyalty.
   ○ leadership qualities.
   ○ friends or allies.

8. A ***gi*** is (page 27)
   ○ a soldier.
   ○ a slang name for a man.
   ● a uniform used in the martial arts.

9. **Spar** means (page 28)
   ○ a faraway star.
   ● to practice fighting techniques.
   ○ extra.

10. A ***dojo*** is (page 28)
    ● a school for teaching karate.
    ○ a technique in karate.
    ○ an extinct bird.

▶**Reread the first three paragraphs of "Lessons from Mr. Lee." Answer the questions.**

____*a*____ 1. How do these paragraphs make you feel?
   a. somber and quiet
   b. bustling and upset
   c. tired and worried

____*b*____ 2. What were Bill's feelings when he heard the boys laughing and saw them making fun of his arm?
   a. He didn't care.
   b. He was ashamed.
   c. He was angry.

3. Write the sentence from the story that tells you how Bill felt.

"I looked down at my feet and kept going."

Reading 5: "Lessons from Mr. Lee," pp. 28-31, Lesson 10
Comprehension: identifying emotional responses of characters
Vocabulary: matching words and definitions
Literature: identifying mood

▶Answer each question, look up each Scripture verse, and then
choose the verse that backs up your answer.

1. On what part of himself was Bill
placing too much importance?

his appearance
_____

● I Samuel 16:7
○ Galatians 6:7

2. Why shouldn't Bill have been ashamed
of the way he was made?

because God made him
_____

the way He wanted him to be
_____

○ James 1:12
● Psalm 139:14

3. What lesson did Mr. Lee try to teach
Bill about his own worth?

that he was of value to God
_____

○ Proverbs 6:6
● Luke 12:6-7

4. Even when Bill fell and got tired, he
kept on working hard on his tae kwon
do. What character trait had he
developed?

determination
_____

○ Ecclesiastes 7:1
● Galatians 6:9

▶1. Write the names of the two main characters in the story in the
correct ovals.

2. Use the phrases to complete the chart, showing how the characters
acted at the beginning and end of the story. A phrase may be used
more than once.

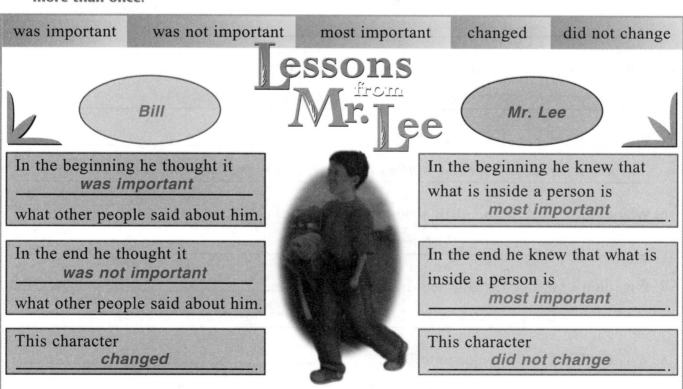

| was important | was not important | most important | changed | did not change |

Lessons from Mr. Lee

Bill

In the beginning he thought it *was important* what other people said about him.

In the end he thought it *was not important* what other people said about him.

This character *changed*.

Mr. Lee

In the beginning he knew that what is inside a person is *most important*.

In the end he knew that what is inside a person is *most important*.

This character *did not change*.

Reading 5: "Lessons from Mr. Lee," pp. 32-34, Lesson 11
Comprehension: recalling facts and details; inferring facts and details; supporting personal
conclusions with biblical truth; determining character change

13

Sometimes a **motive**, or why a person says or does something, isn't stated but just hinted at or implied.

▶ **Answer the questions in complete sentences.**

Wording may vary.

1. Why didn't Bill tell Mr. Lee the real reason he wanted to take karate?

   He didn't think Mr. Lee would like it if he told him he wanted

   to fight the boys who made fun of him.

2. Why was Mr. Lee surprised when Bill said he didn't play baseball? _____

   He probably thought every young American boy played baseball.

3. Mr. Ryan said he wanted to take Bill home because of the rain.

   What do you think was his real motive? _____

   He knew Bill was tired because he had

   worked so hard in class.

   I SAMUEL 16:7

   For man looketh on the outward appearance, but the Lord looketh on the heart.

4. Why did Bill wince when his mother called him "Billy"? _____

   He wanted to feel more grown up than his name sounded when she said it.

5. Why did Bill feel better when he rode with Mr. Ryan? _____

   Mr. Ryan didn't let the bullies bother him; he looked and acted strong.

6. Why did Mr. Lee question Bill about riding to the school? _____

   He was afraid Bill was trying to hide from the other boys.

7. Why didn't Mr. Lee tell Bill he was testing him? _____

   Bill probably would have been more tense and nervous.

8. Why did Bill finally decide to walk? _____

   He decided he was ready for his test with the boys.

Reading 5: "Lessons from Mr. Lee," pp. 24-34, Lesson 12
Comprehension: inferring motives of characters

Nail Soup

One day in a marketplace in Turkey, a traveling musician came along begging for a little food in exchange for some singing. Alas, they were a suspicious people who would not even look at him.

"A man must make do," he said with a loud sigh. "I suppose I can get by with a pot full of nail soup." At these words, many of the passersby stopped and stared at him in surprise. He filled his pot with water, set it over his fire, and dropped a nail into it. As he stirred it, he said, "It looks very good, but I wish I had some carrots." A woman hurriedly gave him some carrots and watched him cut them up and drop them into the pot.

"Splendid! Splendid! There's nothing like good, hot nail soup!" he exclaimed. "Dear me, a potato would be nice."

"I wouldn't eat nail soup for anything," one man in the crowd said. "But here, take these potatoes." And he stared while the musician chopped them up and put them in.

"Delicious! Delicious!" the musician cried, tasting the broth.

"Would you like to try some?" the musician invited an astonished boy.

"Oh, no, but here, take this piece of beef to add flavor."

"Thank you, thank you." The musician ate up all the soup in front of the astonished crowd. When he found the nail in the bottom of the pot, he wiped it off and put it in his pocket. "The best part about nail soup," he told the crowd, "is that you can use the same nail for weeks!"

★ The Contest

Once upon a time the Hare and the Pig held a contest to see which could leap across a ditch.

The Hare tried first but fell short by an inch. Then the Pig tried, but his short legs carried him only half the way.

After that, they both began to argue as to which was the better animal. Finally, they called the Fox in to settle the dispute. The Fox said, "Both in the ditch; Can't say which." *You cannot boast if you miss the mark.*

▶**Follow the directions.**

1. Circle the title of the story that tells you the setting.

2. Put a star by the title of the story that has animal characters.

3. Put a box around the title of the story that has a moral stated at the end.

4. Write the name of the story that is a fable. _____*"The Contest"*_____

5. Write the name of the story that is a folktale. _____*"Nail Soup"*_____

Reading 5: "Literature Lesson: Fables and Folktales," pp. 35-37, Lesson 13
Literature: identifying elements of fables and folktales; distinguishing between fables and folktales

15

Understanding the Glossary

▶ Write the words from the word box on the lines to label
the glossary parts correctly.

pronunciation	entry word
part of speech	definition
guidewords	word form

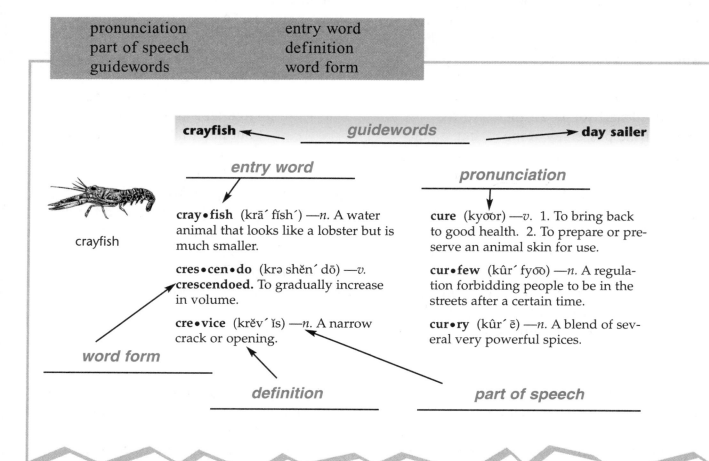

crayfish ◀——— *guidewords* ———▶ **day sailer**

entry word

pronunciation

crayfish

cray•fish (krā′ fĭsh′) —*n*. A water
animal that looks like a lobster but is
much smaller.

cres•cen•do (krə shĕn′ dō) —*v*.
crescendoed. To gradually increase
in volume.

cre•vice (krĕv′ ĭs) —*n*. A narrow
crack or opening.

cure (kyo͝or) —*v*. 1. To bring back
to good health. 2. To prepare or preserve an animal skin for use.

cur•few (kûr′ fyo͞o) —*n*. A regulation forbidding people to be in the
streets after a certain time.

cur•ry (kûr′ ē) —*n*. A blend of several very powerful spices.

word form

definition

part of speech

▶ Use the glossary page to identify the glossary part needed to
find the information.

1. To find out if the word *curfew* is a noun or a verb _____ *part of speech*

2. To determine how many syllables are in *crescendo* _____ *entry word*

3. To get the meaning of the word *crayfish* _____ *definition*

4. To determine quickly if a word would be on a page _____ *guidewords*

5. To decide how to spell the past form of *crescendo* _____ *word form*

6. To decide if *crevice* has a long vowel sound _____ *pronunciation*

Reading 5: "Literature Lesson: Fables and Folktales," pp. 35-37, Lesson 13
Study skills: using the parts of a glossary to determine information

How You Say Dat?

A **dialect** is a variation of a language used by a certain group of people. An author may use dialect to give personality to his characters and flavor to his story.

▶Read each sentence. Choose the phrase that best explains the meaning of the phrase in bold print.

1. "I just thought I'd **fetch it out to you.**"

   - ● bring it to you
   - ○ kick it to you
   - ○ write it out for you

2. They **ain't got no business layin' a mince meat pie 'round loose.**

   - ○ don't have any reason to sit on a mince meat pie
   - ● don't have any reason to leave a mince meat pie uneaten
   - ○ don't have any reason to hang a mince meat pie around the neck

3. They got done **howdyin' and askin' after one another's family.**

   - ○ saying goodbye to every family
   - ○ saying hello and goodbye to each other's family
   - ● saying hello and seeing how each family was doing

4. **"Who goin' to do the foolin',"** says Brer Fox.

   - ● Who is going to play the joke?
   - ○ Who is going to dig the grave?
   - ○ Who is going to play the game?

5. Brer Fox and Brer Wolf **they sorter talked on,** they did.

   - ○ they sorted out their conversation
   - ● they held a lengthy conversation
   - ○ they figured out the nouns and verbs

6. "Where are **your mournin' clothes,** Brer Wolf?" says Brer Rabbit.

   - ○ the clothes that you wear in the morning
   - ○ the clothes that you cried over
   - ● the clothes you wear for a funeral

7. "Dead folks **raise a leg and hollers wahoo!**"

   - ○ raise a leg and dig a hole
   - ● lift up a leg and yell *wahoo!*
   - ○ raise the leg of the table and yell *wahoo!*

8. "Too many friends **spoils the dinner,**" says Brer Rabbit; "which one's this?"

   - ○ cause the dinner to get moldy
   - ● another friend is not needed at dinner
   - ○ there is enough for everyone

Reading 5: "Mr. Wolf Makes a Failure," pp. 38-40, Lesson 14
Comprehension: interpreting words nonliterally; interpreting dialect

▶**Answer the questions.**

1. What did Uncle Remus say when the boy gave him a pie?
   - ○ "This here my fav'rit' kind in the whole world."
   - ● "They ain't got no business layin' a mince meat pie 'round loose."
   - ○ "Did you he'p make it?"

2. What did Uncle Remus say about the pie?
   - ○ "This jus' what I needs to take 'way that empty feelin'."
   - ○ "This will make me as happy as a laughin' brook."
   - ● "This here pie will give me strength to pursue on after Brer Fox en Brer Rabbit and the other beastesses."

3. What did Brer Fox say about Brer Wolf's plan?
   - ● "How you goin' get him there?"
   - ○ "I don't think your plan goin' to work."
   - ○ "You 'speck him to fall for that?"

4. What did Brer Wolf tell Brer Fox to do?
   - ● "You run along home, and get on the bed, and make like you're dead."
   - ○ "Go fetch some straw and stuff some of your clothes with it."
   - ○ "You hide under the bed and grab his laig."

5. What did Brer Rabbit say when Brer Wolf told him he was his friend?
   - ○ "Since when you my friend?"
   - ○ "Look out. I'm goin' to faint away."
   - ● "Too many friends spoils the dinner."

6. What was Brer Wolf's bad news?
   - ○ "Your bruthuh took sick."
   - ● "Brer Fox died this mornin'."
   - ○ "Somebody took over yo' briar patch."

7. What did Brer Rabbit say about staying with Brer Fox?
   - ○ "Don't believe I feels like stayin' with no dead folks."
   - ○ "I believe this a trick to catch me."
   - ● "It's the busy season with me, but I'll set up with him."

8. What did Brer Rabbit say about dead people?
   - ○ "I ain't never heard 'bout no dead folks what talks."
   - ● "Dead folks always raises up a leg and hollers *wahoo!*"
   - ○ "If they grab you, you cain't never get 'way."

Reading 5: "Mr. Wolf Makes a Failure," pp. 38-40, Lesson 14
Comprehension: interpreting dialect; recalling facts and details

Froggy Lessons

▶**Choose the correct moral for each fable.**

Two frogs lived together in a marsh. One hot summer day the marsh dried up. The frogs left the marsh to look for another place to live. You see, frogs like damp places if they can find them.

By and by the frogs came to a deep well. One of them looked down into the well and said, "This looks like a nice cool place. Let's jump in and settle here."

But the other frog, who had the wiser head on his shoulders, replied, "Not so fast, my friend. Suppose this well is dried up like the marsh. How shall we get out again?"

○ One good turn deserves another.
● Look before you leap.
○ Little by little does the trick.

A frog was hopping around a farmyard, when he decided to investigate the barn. Being somewhat careless, and maybe a little too curious, he ended up falling into a pail half-filled with fresh milk.

As he swam about attempting to reach the top of the pail, he found that the sides of the pail were too high and too steep to reach. He stretched his back legs to push off the bottom of the pail. He found the milk pail too deep.

The frog was determined not to give up and continued to struggle. He kicked and squirmed and kicked and squirmed. At last, all his churning about turned the milk into a big hunk of butter. The butter was now solid enough for him to climb onto and get out of the pail!

● Never give up!
○ Misery loves company.
○ Try before you trust.

The hares were so persecuted by the other beasts that they did not know where to go. As soon as they saw a single animal approach them, off they would run.

One day they saw a troop of wild horses stampeding about. In quite a panic all the hares scuttled off to a nearby lake. They were determined to drown themselves rather than live in such a continual state of fear.

Just as the hares arrived at the bank of the lake, a troop of frogs, frightened in their turn by the approach of the hares, scuttled off. The troop of frogs jumped into the water.

"Truly," said one of the hares, "things are not as bad as they seem."

○ Do not attempt too much at once.
● There is always someone worse off than yourself.
○ Honesty is the best policy.

Reading 5: "Aesop's Fables," pp. 41-44, Lesson 16
Literature: identifying the moral of a fable

▶**Use the pronunciation key to answer the following questions.**

1. Find and circle the pronunciation key.

2. Write the pronunciation for *mullet.*

    mŭl´ ĭt

3. Which entry word has an *a* with the sound of *a* in *pay?*

    navigate

4. Which entry word has the sound of *ər* as in *butter?*

    muster

5. Which entry word has an *o* with the sound of *o* in *for?*

    moral

6. Write the pronunciation for *musty.*

    mŭs´ tē

7. Which entry word has the same vowel sound as the *u* in *abuse?*

    mutiny

8. Which entry word has the same vowel sound as *book?*

    mooring line

9. Which entry word has the same sound as the *o* in *atom?*

    molest

All the letters and symbols used in a dictionary pronunciation are shown in a **pronunciation key.**

navigate

mo•lest (mə lĕst´) —*v.* To bother or destroy.

moor•ing line (moor´ ĭng līn) —*n.* A line used to tie up or anchor a boat.

moral (môr´əl) —*n.* The lesson taught by a fable, story, or event; the basic message.
—*adj.* 1. Conforming to a standard of right conduct. 2. Teaching what is right conduct or behavior.

muck (mŭk) —*n.* A moist, sticky mixture, especially of mud and filth.

muff (mŭf) —*n.* A tube of fur or cloth into which hands can be put to keep them warm.

mull (mŭl) —*v.* **mulled.** To ponder.

mul•let (mŭl´ĭt) —*n.* A type of edible fish.

mur•ky (mûr´kē) —*adj.* Stirred up; muddy.

mus•lin (mŭz´lĭn) —*n.* A cotton cloth with a plain weave.

mus•ter (mŭs´tər) —*v.* **mustered.** To gather; to assemble.
—*n.* A gathering, especially of troops.

must•y (mŭs´tē) —*adj.* Stale in odor or taste.

mu•ti•ny (myoot´n ē) —*n.* Open rebellion against leaders, especially by sailors.

N

nav•i•gate (năv´ĭ gāt) —*v.* To plan, guide, and control the course of a ship or aircraft.

muff

ă	pat	ĕ	pet
ā	pay	ē	be
âr	care	ĭ	pit
ä	father	ī	pie
îr	fierce	oi	oil
ŏ	pot	oo	book
ō	go	oo	boot
ô	paw,	yoo	abuse
	for	ou	out
ŭ	cut	ə	ago,
ûr	fur		item,
th	the		pencil,
th	thin		atom,
hw	which		circus
zh	vision	ər	butter

20

Reading 5: "Aesop's Fables," pp. 41-44, Lesson 16
Study skills: using a pronunciation key; determining information from a dictionary

▶**Choose all the characteristics that match each character.**

King Bauakas ("A Just Judge")

- ○ greedy
- ● wise
- ● generous
- ○ foolish

peasant ("Three Rolls and a Pretzel")

- ○ content
- ○ wise
- ○ generous
- ● foolish

beggar ("A Just Judge")

- ● greedy
- ● dishonest
- ● ungrateful
- ○ humble

happy man ("The King and the Shirt")

- ○ greedy
- ○ dishonest
- ○ generous
- ● content

judge ("A Just Judge")

- ○ greedy
- ● wise
- ● fair
- ● content

▶**Choose four words from the box and write an original sentence for each. Be sure that your sentence makes the meaning of each word clear. You may use your glossary.**

rogue	seize	alms	scholar	deftly	emissary

1. _____ *Answers will vary.* _____

_____

2. _____

_____

3. _____

_____

4. _____

_____

Reading 5: Tolstoy's Stories, pp. 45-51, Lesson 17
Comprehension: identifying character traits
Composition: writing sentences to convey word meaning

21

Chart the Stories

▶Put an *X* in each box to see how the following
stories are alike or different.

Charts can help you organize information.

STORY COMPARISONS

	Realistic Characters	Talking Animal Characters	Fable	Folktale	First-Person Narrator	Setting in Western U.S.
"Runaway Friends"	X				X	X
"His First Bronc"	X					X
"Lessons from Mr. Lee"	X				X	
Aesop's fables		X	X			
Tolstoy's stories				X		

▶**Answer the questions in complete sentences.**

1. List two ways that "Runaway Friends" and "His First Bronc" are similar and one way they are different. _____ *The two stories both have realistic characters*

_____ *and are set in the western United States.*

_____ *Only "Runaway Friends" is told in first-person narrator.*

2. What type of story may use talking animal characters to teach a lesson?

_____ *A fable may use talking animal characters to teach a lesson.*

_____

_____

Reading 5: Tolstoy's Stories, pp. 45-51, Lesson 17
Study skills: reading a chart; completing a chart; comparing and contrasting information

▶ **Write the letter of each character that you think would fit each description. Some may have more than one answer.** *Some answers will vary.*

a. Father	b. Franz	c. Ludwig	d. Hans

__d__ 1. would take you to see a gurgling brook

__d__ 2. would be easy to get along with

__a, b, c__ 3. would be hard to get along with

__d__ 4. would listen to your problems

__b, c__ 5. would be upset if you beat him at a game

__d__ 6. would help you if you were in trouble

__a, b, c__ 7. would be more concerned about money than people

__d__ 8. would willingly lend you his favorite possession

▶ **Write a word from the box that matches the definition. When you are finished, the shaded letters spell another name for a kingdom.**

simpleton	arrogant	vain	conceited	ambitious

1. __A__ __R__ __R__ __O__ __G__ __A__ __N__ __T__

2. __C__ __O__ __N__ __C__ __E__ __I__ __T__ __E__ __D__

3. __V__ __A__ __I__ __N__

4. __S__ __I__ __M__ __P__ __L__ __E__ __T__ __O__ __N__

5. __A__ __M__ __B__ __I__ __T__ __I__ __O__ __U__ __S__

1. proud; feeling that one is more important than everyone else
2. having too high an opinion of oneself and one's abilities
3. of no real worth; thinking too much of oneself or one's appearance
4. a person who is felt to have a lack of good sense
5. eager for success, fame, money, or power

Reading 5: "Hans Clodhopper," pp. 52-57, Lesson 19
Comprehension: identifying character traits; distinguishing differences among characters
Vocabulary: matching words and definitions

Gracious Speaking

▶ **Underline the word that tells the right way to say each line from the play "Hans Clodhopper."**

Father: *(excitedly / impatiently)* The messenger said the king's daughter is to be married.

Father: *(impatiently / doubtfully)* Don't be silly. You do not have the brains to win the princess.

Hans: *(seriously / bored)* Father, I want to go to the court and talk to the princess, too.

Hans: *(happily / doubtfully)* Here, I have sand in my pocket. Will you lunch with me?

Franz: *(meekly / proudly)* I shall win her.

Girl II: *(happily / scornfully)* How silly he looks.

Princess: *(excitedly / scornfully)* Get out! Did any of those stuck-up fools think I would marry him?

Princess: *(happily / impatiently)* I will have you for a husband.

▶ **Use the suffixes to help you to choose the correct meaning of each of the words.**

1. ambitious
   - ● abounding in ambition
   - ○ without ambition

2. backward
   - ● moving toward the back
   - ○ moving away from the back

3. famous
   - ● full of great fame
   - ○ full of secrecy

4. scornful
   - ● full of contempt
   - ○ full of admiration

5. fearful
   - ○ full of wonder
   - ● full of fright

6. fearless
   - ● having no fear
   - ○ having less fear

> **Suffixes** are word parts added to the end of a base word.

Suffix	Meaning
-ous	full of; abounding in
-ful	full of
-ward	in the direction of
-less	without; having no; that does not

Reading 5: "Hans Clodhopper," pp. 52-57, Lesson 20
Comprehension: identifying emotional responses of characters; identifying voice expressions
Vocabulary: determining word meaning from suffixes

Friend or Foe?

▶**Circle the correct meaning of the colored word or phrase. You may look in your reader if you need to.**

1. "What are you laughing about?" said Pinocchio, taken aback.

   (surprised)   walking away

2. At the sound of the money the Fox involuntarily stretched his leg that was paralyzed.

   on purpose   (without meaning to)

3. "Because of my passion for studying I have lost a leg."

   (great love of)   great fear of

4. "Another time he will know that he ought not to meddle with other people's business."

   (bother with)   work with

5. Pinocchio thought a little and then said resolutely: "No, I will not go."

   (with determination)   doubtfully

6. "Then," said the Fox, "you want to go home? All right! Go home, but it will be the worse for you."

   (You'll be sorry.)   Life will be worse at home now than it was before.

7. "A present to us!" cried the Fox disdainfully as if he were offended.

   loudly   (with disgust)

▶**Look up the following verses in the Bible. Read the Bible principles. Match each principle with the statement from the story that it fits.**

__A__ 1. A Blackbird flies near them and says, "Pinocchio, do not listen to the counsel of bad companions."

__D__ 2. Pinocchio pulls his money out of his pocket, allowing the Cat and the Fox to see it.

__C__ 3. After seeing Pinocchio's money, the Cat and the Fox both try to become his friends.

__E__ 4. The Fox said, "Should you like to double your money?"

__B__ 5. Pinocchio believes money can grow on trees.

A. Psalm 1:1

B. Proverbs 14:15

C. Proverbs 19:4

D. Proverbs 29:11

E. I Timothy 6:10

Reading 5: "Pinocchio and the Gold Coins," pp. 58-61, Lesson 22
Vocabulary: matching words and definitions
Study skills: locating Bible verses
Comprehension: relating story content to biblical truth

▶ **Choose the idea that the words or actions tell you about each character.**

1. Pinocchio said, "Poor Papa! But he will tremble no more after today." Pinocchio
   - ○ knew that his papa would buy a coat.
   - ● wanted to take care of his papa.

2. The Cat also laughed, but in order not to be seen laughing he stroked his mustache with his two front paws. The Cat was
   - ● sly.
   - ○ shy.

3. At the sound of the money the Fox involuntarily stretched his leg that was paralyzed. The Fox
   - ● didn't really have a paralyzed leg.
   - ○ was frightened by the sudden clanking of the money.

4. "Look at me!" said the Fox; "because of my passion for studying I have lost a leg." The Fox
   - ● wanted to cheat Pinocchio out of studying.
   - ○ wanted to help Pinocchio with his studies.

5. Before the Blackbird had time to say "Oh!" the Cat ate him up, feathers and all. Then the Cat cleaned his mouth and closed his eyes and became as blind as he was at first. The Cat
   - ○ could tell where the Blackbird was even though he was blind.
   - ● wasn't really blind.

6. The Fox said, "Should you like to make of those miserable five pieces, ten? a hundred? a thousand?" The Fox
   - ○ wanted to help Pinocchio work some magic.
   - ● wanted to make Pinocchio feel greedy.

7. "Oh, how beautiful!" cried Pinocchio, dancing with joy. "When I have all those gold pieces I will give you five hundred of them and I will take the other two thousand to my papa." Pinocchio was
   - ● generous.
   - ○ good at math.

8. "A present to us!" cried the Fox disdainfully as if he were offended. "No, indeed! We work only to enrich others." The Fox
   - ○ didn't care about himself.
   - ● was lying to Pinocchio.

Reading 5: "Pinocchio and the Gold Coins," pp. 58-61, Lesson 22
Comprehension: recognizing the development of characters through speech and actions

Who Says What?

▶Write the name of the character that would probably have made each statement below.

"Now look here, my boy, there's a world of pleasure out there!"	"That's right, that's right. A world of pleasure."	"Oh, boy! I'd love to do exciting things!"	"Beware. You'll end up in a place you don't want to be."
Fox	*Cat*	*Pinocchio*	*Talking Cricket*

Fox **Pinocchio** **Cat** **Talking Cricket**

"I'm so tired of people always bossing me around."	"Just come with us, and we'll show you things you never dreamed of."	"Never dreamed of."	"I don't care what anybody says! I'm going!"
Pinocchio	*Fox*	*Cat*	*Pinocchio*

▶Write *S* in front of each sentence that contains a simile.

____*S*____ 1. A little creature shone with a pale opaque light like a candle behind a globe of transparent porcelain.

_____ 2. They walked and walked until they arrived at the Red Lobster Inn, tired to death.

_____ 3. The assassins slipped and fell to the ground, rubbing the skin off their legs and hands as they dropped.

____*S*____ 4. The pine tree took fire and blazed like a candle blown by the wind.

____*S*____ 5. Pinocchio began to run across the fields with the assassins after him, like two dogs after a rabbit.

> A **simile** compares two *unlike* things using the words *like* or *as*.

Reading 5: "Pinocchio and the Gold Coins," pp. 62-66, Lesson 23
Comprehension: predicting characters' speech
Literature: identifying similes

Remember the following sentence from "Runaway Friends." "Grandpa sighed a deep sigh and pulled in to the Flyin' High RV Park in Albuquerque, New Mexico." This sentence does not tell us that Grandpa is ready to settle down and live in one city. But when it is mentioned at the end of the story, we are not surprised. We remember the hint that we were given earlier.

▶▶▶▶▶▶

An author uses **foreshadowing** when he gives you a *hint* ahead of time about something that will happen in the story.

▼▼▼▼

▶**Choose the correct answer.**

1. Which selection foreshadowed that Pinocchio would be cheated by the Fox and the Cat?

   ◉ A Blackbird flew near them and said, "Pinocchio, do not listen to the counsel of bad companions. If you do, you will be sorry."

   ○ "You a great, rich man!" said the Fox, and he laughed aloud.

2. Which selection foreshadowed that the host of Red Lobster Inn, the Fox, and the Cat would trick Pinocchio?

   ◉ "All right, sir," replied the host; and he winked his eye at the Fox and the Cat, as if to say, "We understand each other."

   ○ Then Pinocchio asked the landlord, "Did they say where I should meet them?"

3. Which selection foreshadowed that Pinocchio would be sorry for trying to get something for nothing?

   ◉ "Remember that boys who always do what they want to will sooner or later repent."

   ○ "Tomorrow my papa will be a very rich man because these four pieces will become two thousand."

▶**Read the first paragraph on reader page 67. Answer the question in a complete sentence.**

What did the description of the city called Stupid-catchers foreshadow about what would happen to Pinocchio in the Field of Wonders?

Answers will vary, but should include the idea that Pinocchio would

not become rich but poor and sick like those in Stupid-catchers.

▶You must be able to follow directions to make a puppet.
Follow these directions to make your own leap frog.

1. Fold a whole sheet of notebook paper diagonally so that the two edges meet.

 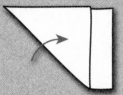

2. Cut off the extra part so that you have a folded triangle. Unfold the paper.

3. Fold the paper into fourths to make four squares. Open the paper.

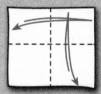

4. Fold each corner to the center.

5. Fold each upper edge to the center line.

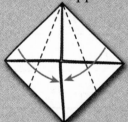

6. With the longer pointed end at the top, fold up the bottom triangle.

7. Fold each outer corner to meet in the middle of the bottom edge.

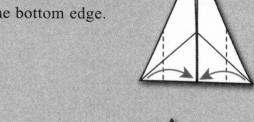

8. Fold lower straight edge up along line shown in diagram.

9. Fold straight edge in half toward the bottom.

10. Fold down head.

11. Turn the puppet over and decorate the face with eyes. The frog is completed. When you press on the frog's back, he jumps. Perhaps you will want to have a frog race.

▶Listed below are ten books and the call numbers found on their title cards. Use the call numbers to help you decide which section of the library the book would be found in.

The Dewey Decimal System

000-099	General works (encyclopedias)
100-199	Philosophy and Psychology (ways of thinking)
200-299	Religion (spiritual beliefs)
300-399	Social Sciences (human society)
400-499	Philology (languages, dictionaries)
500-599	Natural Science (things in nature)
600-699	Useful Arts (practical things, technology)
700-799	Fine Arts (painting, music)
800-899	Literature (stories, poetry)
900-999	History and Geography (events, places)

Book	**Section**
1. 972 *The Aztecs*	1. History and Geography
2. 743 *Drawing Sharks and Whales*	2. Fine Arts
3. 808 *Favorite Poems for Children*	3. Literature
4. 551 *Disastrous Earthquakes*	4. Natural Science
5. 179 *Acts of Courage*	5. Philosophy and Psychology
6. 628 *Fire Engines*	6. Useful Arts
7. 071 *The Newspapers*	7. General Works
8. 468 *More Fun with Spanish*	8. Philology
9. 230 *Systematic Theology*	9. Religion
10. 398 *Aesop's Fables*	10. Social Sciences

Nonfiction books are shelved according to call numbers using the **Dewey decimal system.**

Reading 5: "How to Make a Puppet," pp. 71-77, Lesson 25
Study skills: using the Dewey decimal system

Untangle the Strings

▶1. Read the details from "Almost Real."
2. Select three supporting details for each main idea from the box at the bottom of the page.
3. Write them on the lines under the appropriate headings.

Information is sometimes organized according to main ideas. Each main idea is supported with details.

practicing hundreds of hours

working on the bridge above the puppet stage

portrayed stories from Scripture

practicing puppet's character

use the words <u>puppet</u> and <u>marionette</u> interchangeably

controlled by strings or wires

speaking for the puppet to the audience

responding to fellow puppets

practicing puppet's emotion and actions

Order may vary under each heading.

String Puppets

portrayed stories from Scripture

_____

controlled by strings or wires

_____

use the words <u>puppet</u> and <u>marionette</u> interchangeably

_____

Practice and Imagination

practicing hundreds of hours

_____

practicing puppet's character

_____

practicing puppet's emotion and actions

_____

On-Stage Performances

working on the bridge above the puppet stage

_____

responding to fellow puppets

_____

speaking for the puppet to the audience

_____

Reading 5: "Almost Real," pp. 78-82, Lesson 26
Study skills: locating supporting details; organizing information

The **main idea** of a paragraph tells the reader what the paragraph is about.

▶ **Underline the topic sentence in each paragraph. Choose the main idea.**

A marionette is a jointed puppet controlled by strings or wires attached to various parts of its body. The strings make it possible for the puppet to move and gesture like a real person. The number of strings varies from puppet to puppet. The more strings, the more elaborate the movement can be. Each marionette has its own control to which all of the strings are attached.

○ Strings move and cause a marionette to gesture.
○ Each marionette has its own control.
● A marionette is controlled by strings or wires.

Because a marionette's face cannot move, the puppeteer must show the puppet's emotion through other movements of his body. Allowing the head to fall forward lets the audience know that the puppet is shedding tears or is embarrassed. Moving both arms up at the same time can show surprise. Laughter can be shown by moving the control to cause the puppet to shake all over.

○ Both arms up can show surprise.
● A puppeteer shows the puppet's emotion through body movements.
○ The puppet shakes all over to show laughter.

The life put into a marionette comes down the strings from the puppeteer. As the puppet moves to the master's hand, the marionette can become happy or sad, funny or angry, energetic or tired. And once it moves, a puppet can seem, for a moment, like a "real live boy."

● A puppeteer gives life to a marionette through the strings.
○ The puppet moves to the master's hand.
○ Each puppet must look, act, and respond naturally.

Reading 5: "Almost Real," pp. 78-82, Lesson 27
Study skills: locating the topic sentence in a paragraph; determining the main idea of a paragraph

Name_____

Each problem in a story is called a **con...**
The action or events that happen to solve
the problem are called the **solution.**

▶**Mark two answers to show what Timothy
should have done to solve each problem.**

1. **Problem:** Timothy doesn't understand
   what to do about his older brother being
   mentally disabled.

   Possible solutions: Timothy should

   ● do the best he can to help Brad.
   ○ ask his parents to put Brad in a
     mental hospital.
   ● praise the Lord for Brad.
   ○ ignore Brad as much as he can.

2. **Problem:** Mike started making fun
   of Brad.

   Possible solutions: Timothy should

   ○ tell him to get lost.
   ○ beat him up.
   ● walk away and take Brad with him.
   ● tell him Brad is a special blessing.

3. **Problem:** Brad was crying and could
   hardly walk.

   Possible solutions: Timothy should

   ○ jerk him to make him walk faster.
   ○ tell him to be quiet.
   ● take him to see the puppy.
   ● reassure Brad that it will be all right.

[Pro]blem: Brad and the baby were both
[cry]ing.

Possible solutions: Timothy should

○ stay in his room.
● comfort Brad.
○ go outside.
● hold the baby.

PROVERBS 20:11

*Even a child is known
by his doings, whether
his work be pure, and
whether it be right.*

▶**Underline the pronouns that refer to Brad.**

   My brother's name is Brad. <u>He</u>'s
fourteen, but <u>he</u> doesn't go to school
anywhere. Mom and Dad work with <u>him</u> at
home a lot. <u>He</u>'s getting to where <u>he</u> can
almost tie <u>his</u> shoes. But <u>he</u> moves funny
and doesn't talk very well. <u>He</u> can't read
right now, but Mom and Dad hope <u>he</u> will
be able to someday.

▶**Underline the pronouns that refer to Mother.**

   Brad was still crying and that was
making the baby cry, so Mom had <u>her</u>
hands full; but I just didn't feel like going
out there to help <u>her</u>. And <u>she</u> never asked
me to come. I guess <u>she</u> probably talked to
Brad about how those bad boys didn't
understand how special he was and stuff
like that.

Reading 5: "Big Brother," pp. 84-88, Lesson 29
Comprehension: identifying solutions to problems; identifying pronoun references

"Come in!" greeted Mrs. Shultz. She seated the friends in a booth and brought mugs of hot cocoa. Jolene, Patty, and Troy were drenched and cold from the rain.

Suddenly, Troy pointed. "Look, it's Marty Thomas!" Marty was standing under the Shultz Dairy's awning, gazing in wistfully. "Boy, he looks sorry enough as it is—and rain sure doesn't help!" Patty joked.

Marty didn't even have a jacket on. Jolene remembered what Mother had told her—Marty's dad had left his mother when he was small. And once when he was a baby, his dad had beaten him so badly that Marty's eardrums had ruptured. Marty was in the special deaf class at their school, Bethany Christian.

"You know what I heard?" Patty whispered. "The Thomases have oatmeal for dinner every night. Mrs. Thomas doesn't work—she's lazy!" said Patty scornfully.

Jolene was puzzled. "I thought she was laid off."

"Not working, laid off— whatever you want to call it—"

"Anyway," inserted Troy, "I'm glad he's in the rain—it's about time he had a shower!" Patty giggled, then said, "Hey, what's wrong, Jolene?"

"I don't think we should make fun of Marty—he can't help it that they are poor.

My mom said he's not even saved. He comes to our school 'cause someone pays his way."

Mrs. Shultz saw Marty. She beckoned to him to come in and led him to the booth. "You're soaked to the skin! Sit here with these nice kids. I'll bring you some hot cocoa."

Jolene moved over and whispered shyly. "Here, you can sit by me."

Troy and Patty laughed. "It's okay— he's just had his shower for the month— remember?" said Troy.

"Troy!" Jolene was shocked at his rudeness.

"Don't worry about it—he can't hear us! Who's going to pay for his hot cocoa anyway?" Patty asked.

Jolene started to speak, but then she saw Mrs. Shultz at the counter looking over at their booth with a thoughtful expression on her face. She wondered if Mrs. Shultz knew what they were saying. She wasn't really making fun of Marty— not like Patty and Troy—but she still felt funny. Her mother had been witnessing to Mrs. Shultz for a long time, and she said that Mrs. Shultz always talked about how nice the Bethany Christian students were. Jolene wondered what Mrs. Shultz thought about them now.

▶**Choose two of the following questions. On a sheet of notebook paper, write four or five sentences to answer the two questions.**

Answers will vary.

What do you think will happen if . . .
1. Mrs. Shultz has heard what they said?
2. Jolene tells Troy and Patty what she knows about Marty?
3. Someone tries to witness to Marty?
4. Jolene's mother tries to witness to Mrs. Shultz again?

Reading 5: "**Big Brother,**" pp. 84-88, Lesson 29
Comprehension: predicting outcomes
Composition: writing outcomes

▶**Compare the stories "Lessons from Mr. Lee" and "Big Brother."**
Answer the questions in complete sentences. You may use your reader.

1. What did Bill think his problem was? _____

    His arm was deformed.

2. What did Timothy think his problem was? _____

    His brother was mentally disabled.

3. What did the other boys do to Bill and to Timothy's brother?

    They laughed and made fun of them.

4. What was Bill's reaction to the boys? _____

    He looked down and hurried away.

5. What was Timothy's reaction to the boys? _____ *He fought them.* _____

6. What did Bill decide to do about the boys after they made fun of him? _____

    He wanted to learn to fight.

7. What did Timothy have to do about the boys after he fought with them? _____

    He had to apologize to them.

8. How do you think the ending of "Lessons from Mr. Lee" would have changed if Bill had

    attacked the older boys? _____ *Answers will vary.* _____

9. How do you think the ending of "Big Brother" would have changed

    if Timothy had refused to ever walk with Brad again? _____

    Answers will vary.

10. How were both Bill's and Timothy's lessons alike? _____

    They both learned not to worry about what others think.

Why? Because!

▶Circle the key word that lets you know that this statement tells about a cause-and-effect relationship. If the *cause* is shaded, write C in the blank. If the *effect* is shaded, write E.

_E_ 1. Timothy felt dissatisfied having Brad as a brother (because) Brad was mentally disabled.

_E_ 2. *National Geographic* has colorful pictures, (so) Brad liked to look at them.

_C_ 3. Timothy started taking Brad for his walks (because) Mom had a new baby now.

_C_ 4. (Since) Brad liked animals, Timothy took him to the pet store.

_E_ 5. Brad could hardly walk (because) he was crying so hard.

_C_ 6. (Since) Timothy kept being nice to Gino Borelli, Gino finally agreed to come visit him.

> Words like *so*, *since*, and *because* can help tell you about a cause-and-effect relationship. They let you know which part of the statement is the **cause** and which part is the **effect**.

> A **prefix** is a group of letters placed at the beginning of a base word, or root, to change the meaning or use of the word.

Prefix	Meaning
dis-	not, opposite of, lack of
in-	not, without
re-	again, back

▶Write the definition of the colored word.

1. Because of Brad's inability to explain, I told Mom what happened. _____*without ability*_____

2. Dad and Mom's displeasure with the incident was obvious. _____*opposite of pleasure*_____

3. I waited in my room wishing I could recall my wrong actions. _____*call back*_____

4. "I disobeyed the Lord yesterday when I hit you." _____*lack of obedience*_____

Reading 5: "Big Brother," pp. 89-91, Lesson 30
Comprehension: identifying cause-and-effect relationships
Vocabulary: determining word meaning from prefixes

▶**Read the paragraph and the poem. Answer the questions.**

The shores of the backwater below the dam are overgrown with tall rushes and other water plants. There are many, many ducks, as far as you can see. All you can see of the ducks are their tails and their bright yellow feet wiggling above the surface of the water. You know that the ducklings, the mother ducks, and the drakes are all busy in the water looking for food even though you can't see them actually doing it.

Ducks' Ditty
Kenneth Grahame

All along the backwater,
Through the rushes tall,
Ducks are a-dabbling
Up tails all!
Ducks' tails, drakes' tails,
Yellow feet a-quiver,
Yellow bills all out of sight
Busy in the river.

1. What is the setting of the paragraph?
   the backwater below the dam

2. What grows along the backwater?
   tall rushes, water plants

3. What are the ducks doing?
   looking for food

4. What is the setting of the poem?
   the backwater

5. What grows along the backwater?
   tall rushes

6. What are the ducks doing?
   eating food / a-dabbling

7. How many words are in the paragraph?
   79

8. How many words are in the poem?
   31

9. Do the paragraph and the poem give the same information?
   yes

10. Which is more concise (has fewer words)?
    the poem

Reading 5: "The Quarrel," pp. 92-93, Lesson 31
Literature: appreciating the conciseness of poetry; determining setting
Comprehension: identifying facts and details

▶Choose the correct meaning for each idiom in bold type.

1. The quarrel led to a **falling out**.

   ⬤ disagreement
   ◯ fall out the window

2. The boys were **dead beat** after the hard work.

   ◯ beaten to death
   ⬤ completely exhausted

3. The storm left them **all in the same boat**.

   ⬤ all in the same situation
   ◯ living in a houseboat

4. The house fire meant we had to start from **scratch**.

   ⬤ the beginning
   ◯ building with our fingernails

5. Nathan **hit the nail on the head** with that answer.

   ◯ hit the nail with a hammer
   ⬤ was absolutely right

> An **idiom** is a phrase or an expression that has a meaning different from the meanings of the individual words.

6. Kory acts like **a chip off the old block**.

   ◯ piece of the fire log
   ⬤ his father

"Be careful with that ax, Chip!"

"All right, Dad."

> **Antonyms** are two words with opposite meanings.

▶Write an antonym for each word in bold print.

failure	loved	strong	sitting	wrong	slowly

1. The start of the quarrel was **slight**. _____ *strong*

2. My brother said he was **right**. _____ *wrong*

3. The siblings **hated** to argue. _____ *loved*

4. He **quickly** ended the argument. _____ *slowly*

5. Don't pout while **standing** in the corner! _____ *sitting*

6. The agreement was a **success**. _____ *failure*

Reading 5: "The Quarrel," pp. 92-93, Lesson 31
Literature: interpreting idioms
Vocabulary: determining antonyms

Lively Words

▶ **Write the letter of the synonym to replace the bold word.**

__b__ 1. The **cadence** of the drums rumbled through the street.
a. silence
b. rhythm

__b__ 2. Gramps packed his fishing gear aboard the **trawler.**
a. bus
b. boat

__a__ 3. The twins secured the boat and **stowed** the sails.
a. stored
b. opened

__a__ 4. The song of the bottles **crescendoed** with the wind.
a. intensified
b. softened

__b__ 5. Jennifer was **lulled** by the steady cadence of the surf.
a. troubled
b. relaxed

> Looking at how a word is used in a sentence can help the reader decide the meaning of that word.

> An author searches for the right verb to describe the action and to help the reader form a mental picture of the action.

▶ **For each numbered word, write a lively synonym that can help you "see" the action better.** *Answers will vary. Sample responses are given.*

Tony ¹walked across the wet sand, laughing as

waves rippled toward him and ²touched his toes.

He spotted a pink and white shell ³floating in the

water. The shell ⁴moved away. As he lunged toward

it, he slipped and ⁵fell into the water. Tony ⁶got to

his feet, triumphantly ⁷lifting the shell up high. "I

²got it!" he ⁸yelled. "And it's a real beauty!"

1. _____ *ambled* _____

2. _____ *tickled* _____

3. _____ *drifting* _____

4. _____ *scooted* _____

5. _____ *toppled* _____

6. _____ *scrambled* _____

7. _____ *raising* _____

8. _____ *shouted* _____

Reading 5: "Adventure on Gull Island," pp. 94-98, Lesson 33
Vocabulary: identifying synonyms to develop word meaning
Composition: writing synonyms to enhance the use of verbs

boom (boom) —*noun* A long pole used to stretch out the bottom of a sail.

bow (bou) —*noun* The front of a boat.

cen•ter•board (sĕn´ tər bôrd´) —*noun* A narrow board that can be lowered into the water to prevent the boat from drifting across the water.

jib (jĭb) —*noun* A triangular sail attached to the mast and the bow and controlled by a rope.

main•sail (mān´ səl) —*noun* The larger sail, attached to the boom and the top of the mast.

mast (măst) —*noun* The vertical pole used to support the sails.

tack (tăk) —*noun* A change of direction to bring the sailboat into the wind.

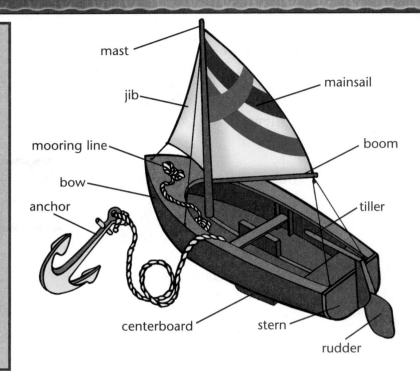

▶**Use the sample glossary above and the diagram to answer the questions. You may use reader pages 99-101. You may also want to look up the words *mooring line, stern,* and *tiller* in the reader glossary.**

1. To steer the boat, Jen would sit in the
   ○ tiller.
   ● stern.

2. The anchor is dropped from the
   ● bow.
   ○ stern.

3. What is used to lock a boat at a dock?
   ● mooring lines
   ○ anchor

4. The mainsail and the jib are both attached to the
   ● mast.
   ○ boom.

5. When a sailor tacks, he is
   ○ keeping the same direction.
   ● changing directions.

6. If you were stuck on a sandbar and wanted to get off, you would first move the
   ○ mooring line.
   ● centerboard.

7. The rear of a boat is the
   ○ bow.
   ● stern.

8. The hinged metal plate attached to the tiller which directs the course of the boat is the
   ○ bow.
   ● rudder.

9. What do you think would happen if the mooring lines were not cast off (untied) when the sails were raised on a windy day? *Answers will vary.*

   The wind might cause

   the ropes to break / the stern

   might go under water /

   the dock might be torn away.

Reading 5: "Adventure on Gull Island," pp. 99-101, Lesson 34
Study skills: using the glossary to develop vocabulary; reading a diagram
Comprehension: inferring facts and details; drawing conclusions

Adventurous Sailing

One event or circumstance (the **cause**) often results in another event or circumstance (the **effect**).

I JOHN 1:7
But if we walk in the light, as he is in the light, we have fellowship one with another.

▶ **Match the cause with its effect.**

Causes

__B__ 1. Sunlight glinted off Tony's glasses.

__D__ 2. Jeremy and Tony went off without Jennifer.

__E__ 3. Tony took Jennifer's job on the boat.

__A__ 4. The lighthouse was built in 1798.

__C__ 5. Jennifer kicked the stool.

__F__ 6. Gramps gave Jennifer a Bible verse.

Effects

A. Only a few shipwrecks have occurred since then.

B. The children couldn't see his eyes.

C. The pieces of the game were scattered.

D. Jennifer was angry.

E. Gramps let Jennifer steer the tiller.

F. Jennifer learned what fellowship is.

▶ **Use the suffixes and their meanings to help you to choose the correct meaning for each of the words.**

1. navigator
   - ● one who guides the course of a ship
   - ○ one who follows the opera

2. novelist
   - ○ one who sings
   - ● one who writes novels

3. beggar
   - ● one who begs
   - ○ one who is rich

4. mariner
   - ● one who operates a ship
   - ○ one who leads a marching band

5. sailor
   - ○ one who sells
   - ● one who works on a ship

6. shipper
   - ○ one who examines rocks
   - ● one who delivers goods

Suffixes are word parts added to the end of a base word.

Suffix	Meaning
-ar -er -or -ist	one who

Reading 5: "Adventure on Gull Island," pp. 102-7, Lesson 35
Comprehension: determining cause-and-effect relationships
Vocabulary: determining word meaning from suffixes

Walk in the Light

▶ **Answer the questions. Choose the Bible verses from the box below.**

When Mrs. Gwang asked Juan to show the new student around, Juan frowned. New students were a bother. They stumbled around trying to find things and made everyone late. They never knew the answers to the games—which meant Juan's team would lose today. Juan looked at the happy, bright-eyed newcomer. "Maybe this one will be different," he thought. Aloud he said disgustedly, "Come on; let's go!"

1. What was the new student's attitude toward school?
   - ● He was excited and eager.
   - ○ He was disgusted and unhappy.

2. How did the author let you know Juan's attitude toward helping the new student adjust to school?
   - ○ He stumbled around.
   - ● He frowned and spoke disgustedly.

3. Which Bible verse might help Juan change his attitude?

   John 15:12

   I Thessalonians 5:18
   Psalm 139:23
   John 15:12

Aimee slumped in her seat as the last character for the school program was assigned. "Stuck in the chorus again!" she muttered. "I never get any of the good parts!"

When Mrs. Schmit asked the class to take out their math books, Aimee obeyed. She stared at her open book. The teacher's voice faded as Aimee imagined herself acting out the lead part in the play. In her mind she could hear the roar of applause from the audience. "Aimee! Aimee!" they called.

1. What was Aimee's attitude when she didn't get a major part in the play?
   - ○ She was obedient and happy.
   - ● She was sullen and grumpy.

2. What is one way Aimee showed her attitude?
   - ○ She acted out the lead part.
   - ● She slumped in her chair.

3. Which Bible verse might help Aimee change her attitude?

   I Thessalonians 5:18

Characters in books, like real people, reveal their attitudes through their actions, thoughts, and speech.

MATTHEW 12:34*b*
For out of the abundance of the heart the mouth speaketh.

Reading 5: "Adventure on Gull Island," pp. 108-12, Lesson 36
Comprehension: evaluating character attitudes
Study skills: locating Bible verses

Which Is It?

▶ **Label each sentence as fact (F) or opinion (O).**

__O__ 1. Henry Witstanley was the best person to build the Eddystone lighthouse.

__F__ 2. Some lighthouse keepers live in the tower.

__F__ 3. Lighthouses were hard to build.

__O__ 4. The English Channel has the most dangerous coastline in the world.

__F__ 5. Light bulbs are easier to keep lit than oil lamps are.

__O__ 6. Being a lighthouse keeper is pleasant work.

__F__ 7. Sailors are safer since lighthouses have been built.

__O__ 8. Electronic lighthouses are better than ones with keepers.

> Remember that a **fact** is something that is true. An **opinion** is what a person thinks about something.

▶ **Look at the picture. Write one factual statement and one opinion statement.**

Factual statement:

_____ *Answers will vary.* _____

_____

Opinion statement:

_____ *Answers will vary.* _____

_____

Reading 5: "Beacons and Bells," pp. 113-17, Lesson 37
Comprehension: distinguishing fact from opinion; interpreting a picture
Composition: writing a fact and an opinion

Get It Straight

▶ **Number the blanks in each column in order.**

Lights	Sounds	Inventors and Inventions
__4__ use of light bulbs	__3__ use of foghorns	__2__ Henry Witstanley
__3__ use of oil lamps	__1__ use of cannons	__1__ Pharos
__1__ use of bonfires	__2__ use of fog bells	__3__ Thomas Edison
__2__ use of candles		

> Divide words into syllables between consonants: *VC/CV.*
> Divide compound words into syllables between the base words.
> crack•shot   bas•ket•ball

▶ 1. **Place a dot between the syllables.**
 2. **Look up four words in your glossary to check the syllable divisions. Circle the four words.**

bil•low	her•ring	var•mint
cur•few	view•point	mem•brane
stick•ball	up•land	hay•wire
ges•ture	crow•hop	hob•by•horse
stag•nant	share•crop•per	john•ny•cake

Reading 5: "Beacons and Bells," pp. 113-17, Lesson 37
Comprehension: sequencing events
Structural analysis: applying Syllable Division Rules 1 and 2—*VC/CV* pattern and compound words
Study skills: using a glossary

44

Lighthouses!

▶ Circle the key word that lets you know that each statement tells about a cause-and-effect relationship. If the *cause* is shaded, write C in the blank. If the *effect* is shaded, write E.

_____E_____ 1. The boat was safe (because) the lighthouse was shining.

_____C_____ 2. Lighthouses were built (so) that ships wouldn't crash on the rocks.

_____C_____ 3. The ship crashed (because) the pilot couldn't see in the dark.

_____E_____ 4. (Since) Philip had heard about the wreck, he was heavy-hearted.

_____E_____ 5. Mr. Rinehold was upset (because) the keeper had been careless.

▶ Complete the crossword puzzle.

Across
4. deceptively dangerous
5. in a quick manner

Down
1. a figure of speech comparing one thing with another
2. to guide, plan, and control the course of a ship
3. a container for storing liquids

> Remember that words like *so, since,* and *because* can help you tell about a cause-and-effect relationship.

metaphor
navigate
promptly
reservoir
treacherous

Crossword solution:
- 1 Down: METAPHOR
- 2 Down: NAVIGATE
- 3 Down: RESERVOIR
- 4 Across: TREACHEROUS
- 5 Across: PROMPTLY

Reading 5: "The Gospel Light," pp. 118-19, Lesson 38
Comprehension: identifying cause-and-effect relationships
Vocabulary: matching words and definitions

45

What It Represents

Identify the metaphors from the song "Let the Lower Lights Be Burning."

_E_ 1. lighthouse   A. Christians

_B_ 2. dark night   B. sin

_D_ 3. fainting, struggling seaman   C. problems in life

_A_ 4. lower lights   D. unsaved person

_C_ 5. angry billows   E. God

> A **metaphor** is figurative language that creates a word picture by comparing one thing to another. It does **not** use the words *like* or *as* when comparing.

MATTHEW 5:14
Ye are the light of the world.

Read the following sentences that use metaphors. Answer the questions.

1. Jesus Christ is the Bread of Life.

   What is Jesus compared to? __the Bread of Life__

2. The Bible is sharper than a two-edged sword.

   What is the Bible compared to? __a two-edged sword__

3. My tears are rain droplets off the leaves of the tree.

   What are the tears compared to? __rain droplets__

4. The clouds are gigantic cotton balls hanging in the sky.

   What are the clouds compared to? __cotton balls__

5. The little girl was an ice cube from shoveling snow.

   What is the little girl compared to? __an ice cube__

6. My brother's stomach is a bottomless pit.

   What is the brother's stomach compared to? __a bottomless pit__

7. A typewriter is a computer without a brain.

   What is a typewriter compared to? __a computer__

Reading 5: "The Gospel Light," pp. 118-19, Lesson 38
Literature: identifying metaphors

▶ **Write the letter of the best resource tool to use for each description.**

A. atlas   B. dictionary   C. encyclopedia

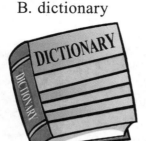

_B_ 1. etymology of a word

_A_ 2. rainfall and climate maps

_B_ 3. pronunciation of a word

_C_ 4. informative articles

_C_ 5. complete explanations

_B_ 6. brief, accurate definitions

_A_ 7. geography and description

_C_ 8. many illustrations

_A_ 9. detailed maps

The **etymology** of a word tells how the word came into existence. It is often put in brackets at the end of a dictionary entry.

▶ **Use the dictionary entries to answer the following questions.**

as•cend (ə sĕnd´) –verb **asc~~ended~~, asc~~ending~~** To go or move upward; rise; climb: *We watched the balloon ascend higher and higher. The hikers ascended the mountain.*

as•say (ă sā´) –verb **assayed** To try to do something.

as•ton•ish•ment (ə stŏn´ ĭsh mənt) –noun Great surprise; amazement; wonder: ~~The circus audience was filled with astonishment when the lion tamer put his head inside the lion's mouth.~~

★ **at•mo•sphere** (ăt´ mə sfîr´) –noun, plural **atmospheres** ①.The gas that surrounds a body in space, especially the air around the earth: *The earth's atmosphere is different from the atmosphere of Mars.* 2. The climate of a place: *the dry atmosphere of the desert.* [New Latin atmosphaera: atmos, vapor + -SPHERE.]

1. Put a star by the entry word that has this definition: "the climate of a place."

2. Put a box around the pronunciation of *assay.*

3. Circle the number of the definition of *atmosphere* as used in the following sentence: *What is the atmosphere of the sun?*

4. Put an X on the word forms that are given for the entry word *ascend.*

5. Cross out the sample sentence for the word *astonishment.*

6. Underline the etymology of the word *atmosphere.*

7. The word *atmosphere* came from a word of what origin?

New Latin

Reading 5: "Skill Lesson: Reference Tools," pp. 120-23, Lesson 39
Study skills: identifying reference tools; using the dictionary; identifying the parts of a dictionary entry

red

Florida

Florida *purple*

Florida is a land of swaying palm trees and warm ocean breezes. There are more than forty million visitors each year. Much of Florida is a 460-mile peninsula that juts into the sea. The northwestern part of the state, called the Panhandle, extends along the northern shore of the Gulf of Mexico. The coastline of Florida is longer than the coastline of any other state except Alaska. Spanish explorers first claimed Florida, but later the United States bought Florida. In 1845 Florida became the twenty-seventh state.

Resources *blue*

Tourists are important to the economy. Farming, fishing, and manufacturing provide jobs for most of the people. Florida farmers grow four-fifths of the orange and grapefruit crops in the United States. Most of the frozen orange juice produced in the United States is processed in Florida.

Population and Climate *blue*

About four million people live in the nearly 60,000 square miles of Florida. Rainfall averages about fifty-three inches yearly in most parts of the state. The sandy beaches and warm temperatures of Florida make it a popular resort and retirement area for older people.

Everglades National Park is the permanent habitat of the spoonbill. *green*

Topography *blue*

The Everglades cover a large part of Florida. Some of the Everglades consists of a prairie covered by shallow water and saw grass, a sharp-pointed tall grass. Almost half of Florida is forests that include more than 300 different kinds of trees. Some of the state is gently rolling hills.

Lakes *blue*

Lake Okeechobee is the largest lake in Florida. It is the second largest natural body of fresh water found wholly in the United States. It covers about 680 square miles. Central Florida contains about 30,000 shallow lakes.

▶**Read the sample encyclopedia article. Follow the directions.**

1. Circle the guideword in purple.
2. Circle the title of the article in red.
3. Draw a blue box around each subtitle.
4. Underline the caption of the picture in green.

Memories of Tal-Omega

Name_____

▶**Answer the questions in complete sentences.**

Wording will vary.

1. When do you think this story takes place?

It is sometime in the future.

_____

2. How did Mitchell and Simmons differ in their attitudes toward Bruce?

Simmons didn't want to hurt him, but Mitchell didn't care.

_____

3. How did Mitchell and Simmons think that Bruce would feel about the mutiny?

They thought that he would be on their side.

_____

4. Why was Bruce's memory of Simmons and Mitchell's conversation blurry?

He was under anesthesia.

_____

5. How do you know from Dr. Hanson's behavior with Bruce that he was a kind man?

He offered to stay with him in sickbay.

He ruffled Bruce's hair and spoke kindly to him.

6. What did Bruce fear about Dr. Hanson when he put his hand over Bruce's mouth?

He feared that Dr. Hanson was also a mutineer.

_____

7. Why do you think Bruce was on the captain's side instead of the mutineers'?

His sense of honesty and fair play compelled him to do what was right.

Bruce wanted to get to Jupiter 2.

Reading 5: "The *Tal-Omega*," pp. 124-29, Lesson 40
Comprehension: recalling facts and details; inferring facts and details; drawing conclusions

49

Before the Mutiny

▶**Complete the crossword puzzle.**

Across
2. to disorder; to scramble
4. to destroy impurities or pollution
6. a highly focused beam of light
7. a vague feeling of fear and unhappiness
8. to breathe in
9. open rebellion against leaders
10. a small room or enclosed area

Down
1. an opening in the deck of a ship leading to a lower deck
3. too quiet to be heard
5. to give someone or something a numbing drug

anesthetize	decontaminate	inaudible
angst	garble	inhale
cubicle	hatch	laser
		mutiny

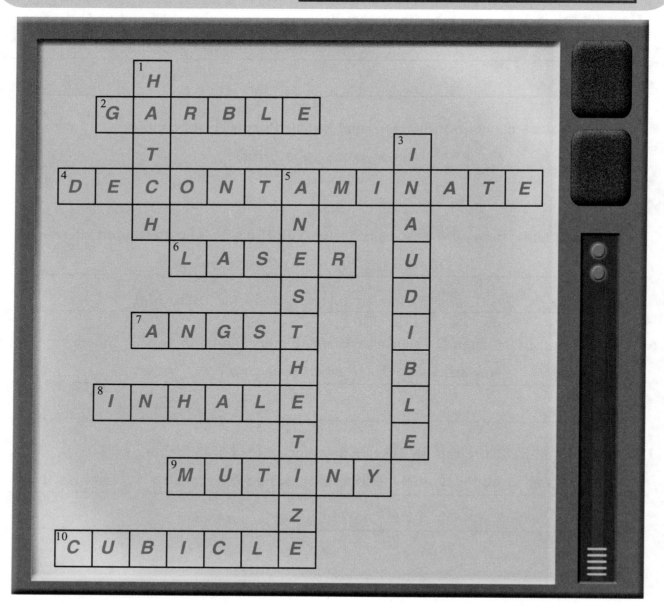

Reading 5: "The *Tal-Omega*," pp. 124-29, Lesson 40
Vocabulary: matching words and definitions

What Does It Mean?

▶ **Rewrite each of the following sentences to explain what the hyperbole in each one means.**

Wording may vary.

1. "He thought his heart would crack from the strain."

   _____*He was straining very hard.*_____

2. I glued the broken part a thousand times.

   _____*I glued the broken part many times.*_____

3. I was hopping mad at misspelling an easy word.

   _____*I was upset at misspelling an easy word.*_____

4. Mother nearly died laughing at my joke.

   _____*Mother laughed a lot at my joke.*_____

"*Tal-Omega—Tal-Omega.* Seven days out from orbit. 0600 hours. Crew roster is as follows: Captain John Denton, helm. Lieutenant Laurence Richards, navigation. Lieutenant Dwight Finelli, communication and survey. All levels acknowledge."

Bruce was already accustomed to the computer's daily request.

Dr. Hanson looked up. "Sickbay acknowledges." He turned to Bruce. "I'm going to anesthetize you, Bruce."

The **setting** of a story tells where and when the story takes place.

▶ **Follow the directions.**

1. Circle the words below that are clues to the setting.

   (orbit)   (anesthetize)   request

   (sickbay)   roster   (Dr.)

2. Circle the setting.

   a ship in the Pacific   the planet Mars

   (sickbay in space)   an airplane

Reading 5: "The *Tal-Omega*," pp. 130-36, Lesson 41
Literature: interpreting hyperboles; identifying the elements of setting

51

The Space Force Academy

Skill introduction

A **schedule** is a plan for performing tasks. It gives the times and order of events.

	Monday	Tuesday	Wednesday	Thursday	Friday
6:00-6:55 A.M.	calisthenics	calisthenics	calisthenics	calisthenics	calisthenics
7:00-7:25 A.M.	breakfast	breakfast	breakfast	breakfast	breakfast
7:30-7:55 A.M.	inspection	inspection	inspection	inspection	inspection
8:00-8:55 A.M.	Astronomy	History of Space Travel	Astronomy	History of Space Travel	Astronomy
9:00-9:55 A.M.	Algebra	Algebra	Algebra	Algebra	Algebra
10:00-10:55 A.M.	Earth History	Earth Geography	Earth History	Earth Geography	Earth History
11:00-11:55 A.M.	Weightlifting	Self-defense	Weightlifting	Self-defense	Weightlifting
12:00-12:55 P.M.	lunch	lunch	lunch	lunch	lunch
1:00-1:55 P.M.	Space Mechanics	Laser Technology	Space Mechanics	Laser Technology	Space Mechanics
2:00-2:55 P.M.	Computer Science	Computer Science	Computer Science	Computer Science	Computer Science

PSALM 97:6

The heavens declare his righteousness, and all the people see his glory.

▶**Answer the questions using Bruce's schedule for the Space Force Academy.**

1. How many times a week does Bruce have a class in Earth Geography? _____ *2*

2. What time does breakfast begin? _____ *7:00 A.M.*

3. What time does lunch end? _____ *12:55 P.M.*

4. With what activity does Bruce start his day? _____ *calisthenics*

5. When does Bruce begin his last class? _____ *2:00 P.M.*

6. Which classes does Bruce have five times a week? _____ *Algebra, Computer Science*

7. How long does inspection last? _____ *25 minutes*

8. How many times a week does Bruce go to a history class? _____ *5*

Reading 5: "The *Tal-Omega*," pp. 137-41, Lesson 42
Study skills: reading and interpreting a schedule

▶**Match the people with the words you think they might have said.**

Widow

Captain

Goodman

Sailor

Physician

Elizabeth

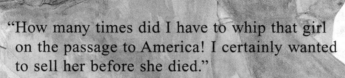

"The girl was sick, near to death, she was. I wouldn't have taken her for anything. Besides, I had plenty of servants as it was."

"The girl was alive when we got to shore, but just barely. The captain wanted to get her off his hands as quickly as he could."

"Be careful, Widow. He wouldn't lose one minute's sleep if she died the moment you bought her."

"How many times did I have to whip that girl on the passage to America! I certainly wanted to sell her before she died."

"The price may be high, but with the Lord's help, I'll pay it. You will not be a slave as long as you live under my roof."

"I will not go with you! Even your whipping cannot make me."

▶**Choose the correct answer to each question.**

1. What did the minister and the Widow have in common?

   ● Both were Christians.
   ○ Both were hot-tempered.
   ○ Both were old.

2. What were characteristics of the physician?

   ○ He was cruel and unkind.
   ● He was good-hearted but firm.
   ○ He was soft-spoken and timid.

3. What were characteristics of the Widow?

   ● She was soft-hearted but firm.
   ○ She was soft-spoken and timid.
   ○ She was good-hearted but hot-tempered.

4. What were characteristics of the goodman?

   ○ He was good-hearted and loving.
   ● He was shrewd and suspicious.
   ○ He was pleasant but stubborn.

5. What were Elizabeth's characteristics at the beginning of the story?

   ○ She was timid but sweet.
   ○ She was helpful but impatient.
   ● She was angry and bitter.

6. How were the captain and physician different?

   ○ The captain was brave, while the physician was timid.
   ● The captain was cruel, while the physician was kind.
   ○ The captain was greedy, while the physician was hotheaded.

Reading 5: "Fees of Indenture," pp. 142-49, Lesson 43
Comprehension: identifying character traits and actions; comparing and contrasting
character traits

53

A Maze of Alleys

From above, the alleyways of Old Philadelphia would have looked very much like a maze. The streets twisted and turned at odd angles.

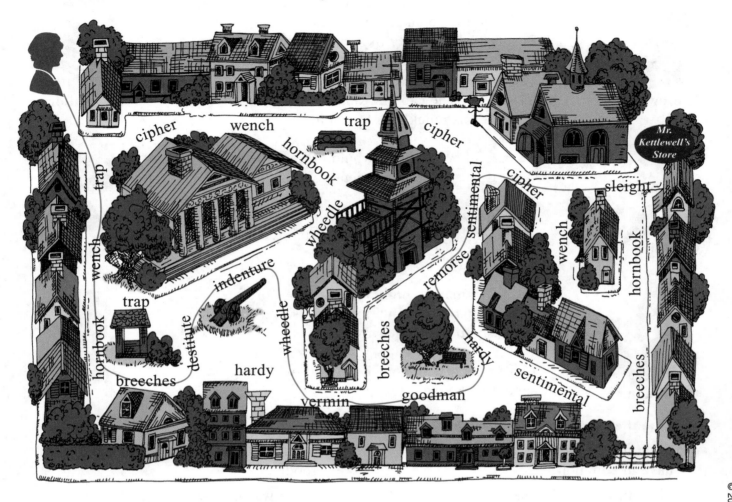

▶Help Elizabeth find her way to Mr. Kettlewell's store by connecting the words from the story in the same order that their definitions appear below. Sometimes there may seem to be more than one choice, but only one path will lead to the store.

1. a light, two-wheeled carriage
2. a young woman or peasant girl
3. an early reading book covered with a hard, clear material
4. short trousers that are fastened at or just below the knee
5. not having anything
6. a contract binding service on one person to another
7. to persuade by flattery or deceit
8. small animals that are annoying or harmful
9. a courteous, old-time title for a man who was not a noble
10. strong and healthy; robust
11. sorrow or regret
12. easily moved by feeling or emotion
13. to figure basic math equations
14. cleverness, especially in tricking people

Reading 5: "Fees of Indenture," pp. 150-55, Lesson 44
Vocabulary: matching words and definitions
Comprehension: following directions

Name_____

Smuggling

In the sixteenth century, Queen Mary Tudor ordered all English people to attend Catholic worship. Bibles printed in English were forbidden to the people, and Protestants had to meet secretly or risk being burned at the stake.

One day Thomas Smithson, a village black-smith, strolled down the lane toward London. He had his hand buried in his tunic. Edward Baker stood at the corner and fell in step with Thomas.

"Where are you going, friend? Mind if I join you?" he boomed to Thomas as though they were strangers. He picked up his staff, and they walked together. Thomas slipped his hand out of his shirt. He was clutching a sheaf of papers. Without a word, without seeming to notice, Edward took the papers and crammed them into his own jacket.

"'Tis a Bible," Thomas whispered out of the side of his mouth. "You must get it to some of the Protestants who are hiding in London—"

Suddenly, two men sprang from behind a tree. "Halt, in the queen's name!" they cried. "You are under arrest for smuggling Bibles written in English!"

"Run!" Thomas called, pushing Edward forward. "Run! I will hold them off! You must get that Bible to the Protestants!"

The **setting** of a story tells the time and the place. Sometimes the setting is important. At other times it is not important.

▶**Choose the correct answer.**

1. The time the story took place is
   - ● stated in the story.
   - ○ unstated in the story.

2. The time is
   - ● sixteenth century.
   - ○ Sunday.
   - ○ unstated in the story.

3. The setting of the story is
   - ● stated in the story.
   - ○ unstated in the story.

4. The setting is
   - ○ on a road somewhere.
   - ● on a road leading to London.
   - ○ unstated in the story.

5. The setting in this story
   - ○ isn't important because you don't need to know the setting to read about the Bible.
   - ● is important because you have to know why men would be smuggling Bibles.
   - ○ is important because setting is always very important.

Reading 5: "Fees of Indenture," pp. 142-55, Lesson 45
Literature: identifying elements of setting; determining whether setting is important or unimportant to the story

Sleight of Hand

"Watch this!" Doug exclaimed. He tossed a coin into the air, caught it, and opened his hand. The coin was gone.

"How did you do that?" Phil asked.

"I read it in a book. It's called sleight of hand, and it's easy." He pulled the coin out of his sleeve, tossed it up, and made it disappear again. When he pulled it out of his sleeve and tossed it, this time Phil caught it. Phil opened his hand, and the coin was gone.

"I read that book last year!" Phil said with a grin.

▶Choose the correct answer.

1. The time the story took place is
   ○ stated in the story.
   ● unstated in the story.

2. The time is
   ○ morning.
   ○ night.
   ● unstated in the story.

3. The setting of the story is
   ○ stated in the story.
   ● unstated in the story.

4. The setting is
   ○ the bedroom.
   ○ the playground.
   ● unstated in the story.

5. The setting in this story
   ○ isn't important because the story is short.
   ● isn't important because you don't need to know about it to read about coin tricks.
   ○ is important because you have to know why the boys would be doing coin tricks.

A well-written **headline** gives the reader the main idea of the article.

▶Read each newspaper excerpt. Check the best headline for each.

The city of Greenville has commissioned Doug Young to sculpt a life-sized statue of baseball legend Shoeless Joe Jackson. Young has already made a miniature version of the statue. He will use 200 to 300 pounds of clay, black pipes, and Styrofoam to make the statue. It will be the first statue to be erected of Shoeless Joe Jackson.

_____ Miniature Statue Built

✔ Young to Sculpt Jackson Statue

French chefs began the art of ice sculpturing more than 200 years ago. The first sculptures were designed to hold food and to keep it cold during buffets. It is a new art form in America. Each ice sculpture is unique and not made from a mold. The artist begins with a block of clear ice. He uses a variety of tools such as ice dogs, chain saws, and chisels.

_____ Chain Saws and Chisels

✔ Art of Ice Sculpturing

Reading 5: "Fees of Indenture," pp. 142-55, Lesson 45
Literature: identifying elements of setting; determining whether setting is important or unimportant
Comprehension: identifying the headline for a newspaper article

Vibrant Vocabulary

Name_____

▶ Complete each sentence with an alliterative verb.
You may also add other words to the sentence.
Answers will vary. Suggestions are given.

Example: The swamp sunflower swallowed the sunshine.

> Remember that **alliteration** is having two or more words that contain the same beginning sound.

1. The magnificent magnolias _____*mumbled*_____.

2. The big bachelor's button _____*brought a bag lunch*_____.

3. A snazzy snapdragon _____*sank into the sand*_____.

4. A tall thistle _____*told a tall tale*_____.

5. My partridge pea _____*picked up a pickle*_____.

▶ Write a word from the box that matches each definition. When you are finished, the shaded letters will spell the name of another flower.

keel	calamity	yammer
regale	titter	prattle

1. a disaster
2. to complain or whine
3. to chatter meaninglessly
4. to giggle
5. to fall down
6. to entertain

1. C A L A **M** I T Y
2. Y **A** M M E R
3. P **R** A T T L E
4. T **I** T T E R
5. K E E **L**
6. R **E** G A L E

▶ **Look at the picture and caption. Answer the questions.**

1. What is shown in this picture?

   a galax plant

2. What is the plant doing?

   growing

3. Where is the plant growing?

   along the Rim of the Gap Trail

   in northern South Carolina

*A solitary **galax plant** grows along the Rim of the Gap Trail in northern South Carolina.*

A **caption** is a title, short explanation, or description that explains a picture or illustration. It provides information at a glance.

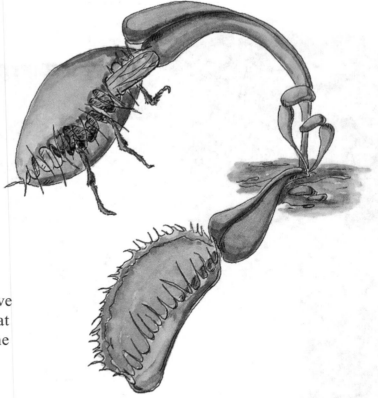

▶ **Read the paragraph. Write a caption for the picture.**

Insects like to take a closer look at the leaves of a Venus's-flytrap. The leaves serve as traps that secrete a smelly substance that attracts insects. When the insects touch one of the six special trigger-hairs in the trap, the hinged leaves fold up. The insects are trapped inside.

Captions will vary.

Reading 5: "Floradora Doe," pp. 156-57, Lesson 46
Study skills: reading captions
Composition: writing captions

What Makes You Laugh?

Good humor is a blessing. The Bible tells about a merry heart being good like a medicine. Families and friends need to enjoy good humor together. Many times a good laugh will relieve a tense situation or "break the ice" when people are getting acquainted.

But there are other times when it isn't good to laugh. Humor isn't good unless it's good for everyone involved. It isn't good to laugh at things that will hurt other people. Little accidents like falls or spills often appear to be funny. It's all right for observers to laugh at those things only if the people involved in the accident laugh too. A person with self-control will be able to determine when such incidents are humorous and when they are too embarrassing or sensitive to be funny.

Sin is never a laughing matter. The Bible calls a man a fool if he laughs at things that should make him feel shame. A Christian with spiritual wisdom will not find sin a funny thing.

PROVERBS 17:22

A merry heart doeth good like a medicine.

▶ **Put a smile in the circle in front of each idea that could be the subject of good humor.**

☺ Both boys rolled over in the snow, laughing as their empty sled sped on down the hill without them.

◯ A drunken old man tottered down the street right past the mission door.

☺ The puppy frisked its way through the pile of crisp leaves, scattering them wildly.

◯ While Grace's family was enjoying a special dinner at a restaurant, the waitress accidentally dropped a plate of spaghetti on Grace's new dress.

☺ The lanky principal laughed uncontrollably as he slipped on the icy sidewalk and landed in the snow in front of the school door.

☺ Jack popped his head out of the closet just as his dad reached in to get something out of it.

◯ Both old men leaned heavily on wobbly canes as they set out on their daily walk from the nursing home to the park.

☺ Three clowns, like three jugglers' balls, bounced rhythmically on the trampoline.

☺ Dozens of small brown monkeys chattered and called as they raced from one tree to another on "monkey island."

☺ "Next time you get the downhill side of the picnic table," Mike teased as he jumped from his seat. His little sister's spilled lemonade ran toward his empty seat.

In "The Beginning of the Armadillos," Kipling poked fun at the theory of evolution and showed us how silly it is. Yet today, much of the world looks upon the evolution theory as truth. Most scientists believe in evolution, and they also make fun of other scientists who believe that God created the world. The science textbooks that these evolutionary scientists write present evolution as fact and present Creation as an old-fashioned fairy tale or legend.

Evolutionists claim that they have a lot of clear evidence that supports their theory. For instance, they have fossils— bone remains from ancient animals and plants that are imbedded in rock—which, they say, show the different stages that man went through as he evolved from apes. From these small fossil fragments they have invented whole skeletons with plaster. These skeletons, which were made mostly from the scientists' imaginations, are used to try to prove evolution.

One of these fossil skeletons was called the Nebraska man. According to evolutionists, the Nebraska man was part man, part ape. They claimed that he was undeniable proof that evolution was true. Several years later, a scientific expedition went back to the place where they found the fossils of the Nebraska man to do some more digging. As they dug up more and more bones, they realized that the fossils did not belong to an "ape-man" at all—but to an extinct species of pig!

Over one hundred years ago, a Dutch doctor found six bones on the banks of a river in the small Asian country of Java. Although these bones had been found scattered apart over distances larger than half a basketball court, he claimed that these bones were a primitive ancestor of man which he named *Pithecanthropus erectus,* which means "ape-man who walked erect." Before he died, the doctor admitted that the bones were monkey bones, but the Java man is still looked upon today as evidence of evolution.

Scientists used to claim that our most recent ancestor was the Cro-Magnon man. They found fossils that looked like men with square faces, deep eyes, and straight jawbones and named them Cro-Magnon men. People believed for years that the Cro-Magnon man was the last link between ape and man. Imagine how embarrassed they were when they discovered that there are still people that fit this description living in Southern France, Wales, and Germany!

The reason evolutionists try so hard to support their theory is that they want to believe that man is the most important being in the world—that there is no God. If they could ever prove that man evolved, they would have won a victory over the "foolish" people who believe that God created all things. But Romans 1:22 says that when men thought they were wise, they really became fools. It is the people who refuse to believe in Almighty God as the Creator who are the real fools.

GOD CREATED

Reading 5: "The Beginning of the Armadillos," pp. 162-67, Lesson 48
Comprehension: identifying the main idea of a paragraph; drawing conclusions

What's the Big Idea?

▶ **Choose the main idea of each paragraph.**

paragraph 1
- ● Evolution is accepted by most people today.
- ○ The idea of Creation is an old-fashioned fairy tale.

paragraph 2
- ● Evolutionists try to prove their theories with made-up skeletons.
- ○ Scientists have found many fossils imbedded in rock.

paragraph 3
- ○ The Nebraska man was part man and part ape.
- ● The Nebraska man was a foolish effort to support evolution.

paragraph 4
- ● The Java man is an example of a foolish effort to support evolution.
- ○ The scientist who discovered the Java man finally admitted that the bones were just monkey bones.

paragraph 5
- ○ There are still Cro-Magnon men living today.
- ● Evolutionists have foolishly tried to use the Cro-Magnon man to support their theories.

paragraph 6
- ○ Evolutionists believe that man is the most important being.
- ● People who don't believe in God are fools.

▶ **It is important to examine and look through evidence or "clues" accurately. At the end of each set of evidence, draw a logical and accurate conclusion.**

Evidence: When I am hot, I drink water.
I am hot.

Conclusion:

I drink water.

Evidence: Robins are birds.
This is a robin.

Conclusion:

This is a bird.

Evidence: Cows have four legs.
Bessie is a cow.

Conclusion:

Bessie has four legs.

Evidence: When it snows, I shovel our driveway.
It is snowing.

Conclusion:

I shovel our driveway.

Reading 5: "The Beginning of the Armadillos," pp. 162-67, Lesson 48
Comprehension: identifying the main idea of a paragraph; drawing conclusions

Classy Characters

▶ Match the characters with statements that could be true about them. Some may have more than one answer.

A. Stickly-Prickly Hedgehog

C. Slow-Solid Tortoise

B. Painted Jaguar

D. Mother Jaguar

Which character(s) would be most likely to . . .

_A, C_ 1. go to an exercise class?

_A, C_ 2. help you out of a dangerous situation?

_D_ 3. be a teacher?

_B_ 4. forget he was supposed to clean his bedroom?

_A, C_ 5. tease you?

_B_ 6. forget where he put his notebook?

_D_ 7. give you your instructions again?

_B_ 8. believe you when you're teasing?

_A, C_ 9. be willing to learn a new skill?

_A, C_ 10. think up a new way to do something?

_C_ 11. give swimming lessons?

▶ Read each colored group of words. Decide what each group has in common. Circle the word below that completes the group.

1. cheetah	leopard	ocelot
(jaguar)	elephant	eagle

3. clear	definite	exact
(precise)	incorrect	uncertain

2. room	house	motel
truck	(lodging)	restaurant

4. muddy	messy	dense
tidy	clear	(turbid)

Reading 5: "The Beginning of the Armadillos," pp. 162-67, Lesson 48
Comprehension: identifying character traits; classifying words

Bond or Free?

▶**Answer each question, look up each Scripture verse, and then mark the verse that backs up your answer.**

Wording may vary.

1. Why was it wrong for Onesimus to take the jewels?

    Stealing is sin.

    ● Exodus 20:15
    ○ Colossians 4:9

2. Onesimus told Marcus that Philemon had sent him to Rome on an urgent mission. What was wrong with Onesimus's explanation?

    It was a lie.

    ○ Exodus 20:8
    ● Proverbs 12:22

3. Even though Marcus was not fooled by Onesimus's claims, how did Marcus treat Onesimus?

    with kindness

    ● Ephesians 4:32
    ○ Hebrews 13:6

4. How were the weights of hatred and guilt removed from Onesimus?

    by salvation / by faith in Jesus

    Christ / by asking forgiveness

    ○ Ecclesiastes 7:1
    ● I John 1:9

5. Why did Onesimus not continue to lie and steal after he truly became a Christian?

    He was a new creature. /

    He had a new master.

    ● II Corinthians 5:17
    ○ Proverbs 15:16

6. What was the correct response for Philemon to his slave Onesimus's wrongdoing?

    He should forgive him.

    ● Colossians 3:13
    ○ Philippians 4:11

▶**Look at the picture. Write one factual statement and one opinion statement.**

Factual statement:

Answers will vary.

_____

_____

Opinion statement:

Answers will vary.

_____

_____

Reading 5: "No Longer a Slave," pp. 168-74, Lesson 51
Comprehension: identifying emotional responses of characters; supporting personal conclusions with biblical truth; discerning between fact and opinion; interpreting a picture
Composition: writing a fact and an opinion

Where and When

▶**Choose the correct answer to each question.**

Corporal Johnston shifted his weight over the pebbles and rocks that made his bed. He pulled the scratchy army blanket closer and started to doze off again. Overhead, a rocket exploded, turning a patch of black sky crimson for a moment. Sleepily, Johnston used the glow to glance at his watch. He pulled his helmet down as bits of metal rained around the trench where he had dug in hours earlier. After a moment the hail of metal stopped, and the darkness became peaceful. If it had not been for the enemy close by, these glorious Korean hills would have made a wonderful campsite.

1. What time of day is it?
   - ○ dawn
   - ○ sunset
   - ● the middle of the night
   - ○ afternoon

2. Where is Corporal Johnston?
   - ● in a battle area in Korea
   - ○ in a Korean city
   - ○ in a Korean home

3. Underline the clues in the story that tell you the time and place. *Answers may vary.*

Mrs. Floss poured her husband's coffee while Jeni brought the plate of toast to the table and set it by the eggs.

As Mr. Floss spooned sugar and cream into his coffee, he said, "Jeni, would you bring the jelly too, please?"

"Yes, sir." She went to the cabinet. "Oh, I can't reach it. Can you get it, Mom?"

But unfortunately Mrs. Floss was barely taller than her daughter. "Dad, we need you. Can you help us?" Jeni asked.

"Well, no, I'm afraid I can't," Mr. Floss answered. Jeni and Mom looked at him in surprise. For an answer, Mr. Floss lifted the tablecloth, revealing Stasha, their ninety-pound husky, asleep on top of Mr. Floss's feet.

1. What time of day do you think it probably is?
   - ● morning
   - ○ afternoon
   - ○ evening
   - ○ the middle of the night

2. Where is the Floss family?
   - ○ in a castle
   - ● in a kitchen
   - ○ in a cabin

3. Underline the clues in the story that tell you the time and place.
   Answers may vary.

Reading 5: "No Longer a Slave," pp. 168-74, Lesson 51
Literature: identifying elements of setting

▶ Label each story as *modern realistic fiction, historical fiction, science fiction,* or *fanciful fiction.*

Roderick kept his hood pulled low over his head as his elephant trudged through the wet woods. It wasn't a good day for lion or beast to be outside.

He commanded the elephant to kneel and swung off in front of a clump of oaks grown tightly together. He slid between these and knocked on a hidden wooden door.

"Roderick, soldier of the king!" he called.

Instantly the door was opened by none other than the lion-king himself, Eiken Stave.

Eiken wore no crown, no royal robes, only the usual gold tunic and cape common to lions.

"Come in," he said. "Any news?"

"The forest is quiet as rain, sire," Roderick said, shaking his damp mane. "Not a sneakin' jaguar or laughin' hyena in sight!" He sighed with satisfaction.

Eiken drew Roderick closer to the fireplace. Eiken bellowed a loud roar, and the fire blazed up and crackled merrily.

"Thank you, sire." Roderick spread his hands and smiled at Eiken.

fanciful fiction
_____

"All hands on deck!"

The cry pierced through the clouds of sleep in John's head. He swung out of his hammock and clambered up the ladder.

"Dear Lord, protect us," he prayed as he took his place by one of the cannons. A tall Spanish ship was bearing down on them. Although supposedly at peace on land, England and Spain had been waging a battle at sea for years.

John knew that if he were captured, he would become a slave on the Spanish ship and then face the dreadful Spanish Inquisition. A man in the grasp of the Inquisition had to choose either to become a Roman Catholic or to be executed.

He swung a heavy cannonball into the mouth of the cannon and shoved it into place. Other men were doing the same.

"Fire!" the captain bellowed. Thirteen cannons roared at once.

The Spanish ship suddenly veered away.

"Hah!" John laughed. "They didn't want English cannonballs for breakfast!" He wiped the sweat off his face and breathed a prayer of thankfulness.

historical fiction
_____

▶**Label each story as *modern realistic fiction, historical fiction, science fiction,* or *fanciful fiction.***

In the empty lot behind the car wash, Pedro gently tapped the scarred and cracked wooden bat in the dust, swung it experimentally a few times, and nodded at José, the pitcher. José lobbed a slow, crazy knuckleball at him, but Pedro was ready for it this time. He stayed relaxed as the slow ball approached on a lopsided course.

Then suddenly he let fly. There was a *craack!* and the ball, trailing part of its canvas covering, whistled out of the lot. One of the outfielders ran to get it, but the other players didn't even notice.

The bat—their precious bat—had finally hit its last home run. It had broken on Pedro's grand slam.

"Now what?" Juan asked.

"Maybe Pastor Alvarez will get us a new one," Pedro suggested. They were all residents of Pastor Alvarez's orphanage, and they depended on him for everything, from lessons in school and church to baseball rules.

"We can't bother Papa Alvarez," Sugi said. "He has enough worries."

"Maybe we could earn some money," Tony said thoughtfully.

modern realistic fiction
_____

Joe Spears, Detective Spence, and Bob Owens, the foreman, were huddled around some of the equipment at LASER-OPT LASERS, INC. The foreman looked uncomfortable as Spence examined a circuit with a micromagnifier.

"Someone has damaged it."

Owens mumbled about getting to work on the argon laser. He stepped through the doorway and pushed a button. The floor moved him down the hallway.

"Owens seems worried," Spears said.

"I'll talk to him," Spence replied. "He seems eager to avoid me." He left the room and rode the hallway down to the lab.

When Spence entered the lab, a sudden bolt of light energy knocked a chunk out of the doorway. Owens had shot at him with the powerful argon laser!

Detective Spence rolled away and pulled a mirror out of his pocket. He thrust it in front of him as the ray swept toward him.

The laser beam bounced back into the laser gun.

"Youch!" Owens jumped clear as the laser gun exploded.

"It's a good thing laser is light—and light reflects," Spence said as Spears ran in and tackled Owens. "That mirror saved my life!"

science fiction
_____

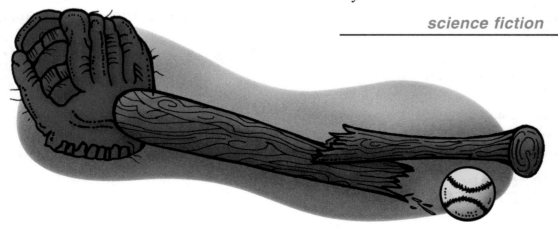

Ma and Muffin

▶ **Match each factual sentence with a sentence that shows imagery and creates a picture in your mind.**

___E___ 1. The pup was a brown color.

___C___ 2. Micah looked at the dead blackbird.

___D___ 3. Ma smelled like home.

___F___ 4. Micah saw a pair of eyes, a tail, a tongue, and a nose.

___H___ 5. Little dogs grow into big dogs.

___G___ 6. Miss Cates had brown hair and walked lightly.

___B___ 7. The pup's body was wiggling.

___A___ 8. Ma walked heavily.

A. Ma moved like a loaded river barge in her heavy shoes.

B. The pup's whole body was wagging in time with his tail.

C. Micah stopped to examine a dead blackbird whose legs stuck straight up in the air.

D. Ma smelled mostly like cornbread and ammonia.

E. The pup was exactly the color of Ma's sweet muffins.

F. Micah saw a pair of the shiniest molasses brown eyes, a little brush of yellow tail whipping back and forth, and a rosy, grainy tongue hanging out underneath a little wet raisin of a nose.

G. Miss Cates had soft brown hair and stepped daintily like a little wren.

H. Cute little pups grow into horsesized hound dogs that could eat more than you and me put together.

> **Imagery** is the use of words to help create a mental picture. An author's choice of words makes a clear, colorful picture in the reader's mind.

▶ **Change some words or add some creative words to make the following sentences show imagery. Write your new sentences.**

Answers will vary.

1. The toddler played with her wagon.

_____

2. The storm blew down the tree.

_____

3. The boy hit the baseball.

_____

Reading 5: "Ma and Muffin," pp. 180-83, Lesson 55
Literature: recognizing imagery
Composition: writing to show imagery

67

A **dialect** is the way language is spoken by a certain group of people. An author may use dialect to help portray the characters and the setting of the story.

▶Choose the correct meaning of the word in color from its context in "Ma and Muffin."

1. Micah lived right in the heart of the delta.
   ○ the organ that pumps blood through the body
   ● the central or main part
   ○ the center of a person's feelings

2. Ma would think of Muffin as nothing but a pack of foolishness.
   ● a small package
   ○ a complete set of similar items
   ○ to fill up with items

3. Ma didn't tolerate a lick of nonsense.
   ○ a movement of the tongue over something
   ○ a natural deposit of salt that animals lick
   ● a little bit

4. Ma's mood was nothing to trifle with.
   ○ a small amount
   ○ a cakelike dessert
   ● to treat something as if it didn't matter

5. "The apple will tide you over till supper time."
   ○ the ebb and flow of ocean waters
   ● to support through a difficult period
   ○ something that changes like the waters of the tide

6. Her broad frame began to rock back on her heels.
   ● to sway violently, as from a blow or shock
   ○ to sway so as to lull to sleep
   ○ to disturb the emotions or mind of

7. Ma was as stout as an oak stump, and she had a will to match.
   ○ the document telling how a person wants his possessions to be given out after his death
   ○ self-control
   ● the power to decide and do things

8. Put the notion out of your mind.
   ● an idea
   ○ thread used in sewing
   ○ to have knowledge

9. Micah sopped the chunk of cornbread in his glass of buttermilk.
   ○ to throw
   ● a piece
   ○ wood

10. Micah's eyes were swimming in tears.
    ○ to move oneself through the water
    ● to be filled or flooded
    ○ to feel shaky or lightheaded

More Imagery

▶ Identify each sentence as a simile (*S*) or a metaphor (*M*). Circle the two things being compared.

> A **metaphor** is figurative language that compares two things without using *like* or *as*.
>
> A **simile** is figurative language that compares two things using ***like*** or ***as***.

___S___ 1. The (delta) was as gummy black as (licorice.)

___M___ 2. Micah saw a pair of the shiniest (molasses) brown (eyes.)

___M___ 3. There was a little (brush) of yellow (tail) whipping back and forth.

___S___ 4. The (land) was as flat as a giant (johnnycake.)

___M___ 5. Its tongue hung out underneath a little wet (raisin) of a (nose.)

___S___ 6. (Ma) moved like a loaded river (barge.)

___M___ 7. "You (pup,)" Ma chided, picking up the little (ball) of fur.

___S___ 8. (Ma) was as stout as an oak (stump.)

> The **setting** of a story can help shape what the story characters do and how they feel.

▶ Answer the questions.

1. Did Micah live in the city or the country? ___*country*___

2. What state did he live in? ___*Mississippi*___

3. How did Micah get to school? ___*walked*___

4. What job did Micah's father have before he died? ___*cotton farmer*___

5. What kinds of things did Micah eat? ___*apples, cornbread, buttermilk, blackberries*___

6. What kind of work did Ma do? ___*gardening and housework for other people*___

Reading 5: "Ma and Muffin," pp. 184-88, Lesson 56
Literature: identifying similes and metaphors; identifying elements of setting; recognizing the relationship between setting and plot

69

A Change of Order

▶Number the events in story order.

___1___ Micah tucked a cute little pup under his arm and started for home.

___3___ Micah promised to feed and to take care of Muffin if he could keep the pup.

___6___ Muffin sneaked out of the Deals' yard and returned to see Ma.

___2___ When he found Ma scrubbing the floor, Micah realized she would not consent to the pup easily.

___5___ Muffin went to live with the Deals.

___7___ Ma gave in and let Muffin come back to live with them.

___4___ Muffin could stay one night out back of the house.

▶1. Find the names of the two main characters in the story. Write each name in the correct oval.

2. Use the phrases to complete the chart, showing how the character acted at the beginning and end of the story. A phrase may be used more than once.

| wanted | changed | did not want | did not change |

Micah

When he brought Muffin home, he _wanted_ to keep the pup.

When he found Ma playing with Muffin, he _wanted_ to keep the pup.

This character _did not change_.

Ma

When Muffin represented another mouth to feed, she _did not want_ to keep him.

When Muffin won her heart, she _wanted_ to keep the pup.

This character _changed_.

Reading 5: "Ma and Muffin," pp. 184-88, Lesson 56
Comprehension: sequencing events; determining character change

Micah's Mississippi

Name_____

▶Use the map and map scale to find the distances.

1. distance from the capital city, Jackson, to Biloxi

   _____160 miles_____

> A **scale** shows the relationship of a distance on a map to the actual distance.

2. approximate distance from Vicksburg to Meridian

   _____about 140 miles_____

3. width of the state of Mississippi at its widest point _____about 200 miles_____

4. approximate length of Mississippi's coastline _____about 80 miles_____

5. approximate length of the Mississippi and Alabama border

   _____about 380 miles_____

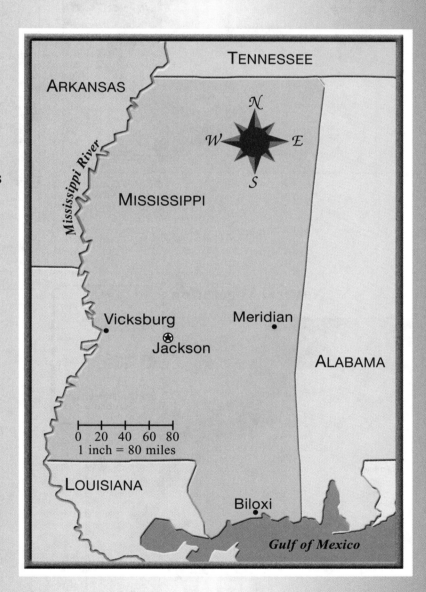

Reading 5: "Skill Lesson: Map Scales," pp. 189-91, Lesson 58
Study skills: reading a map and a map scale; determining distance using a map scale

71

Average July Temperature

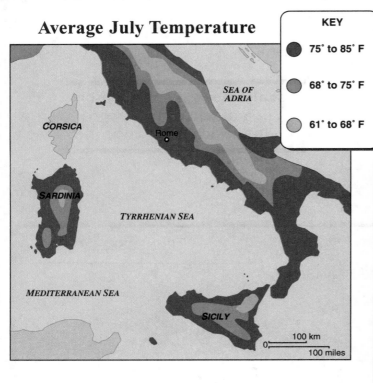

KEY
- 75° to 85° F
- 68° to 75° F
- 61° to 68° F

SEA OF ADRIA

CORSICA

Rome

SARDINIA

TYRRHENIAN SEA

MEDITERRANEAN SEA

SICILY

100 km

0 100 miles

An **atlas** contains a collection of maps.

The Terrain of Italy

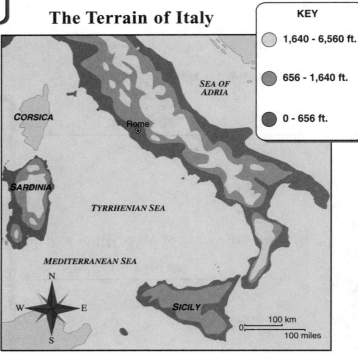

KEY
- 1,640 - 6,560 ft.
- 656 - 1,640 ft.
- 0 - 656 ft.

SEA OF ADRIA

CORSICA

Rome

SARDINIA

TYRRHENIAN SEA

MEDITERRANEAN SEA

N
W   E
S

SICILY

100 km

0 100 miles

Natural Vegetation

KEY
- Deciduous Forest
- Mixed Forest
- Mediterranean Scrubland

SEA OF ADRIA

CORSICA

Rome

SARDINIA

TYRRHENIAN SEA

MEDITERRANEAN SEA

SICILY

100 km

0 100 miles

Paul's Journey to Rome as a Prisoner

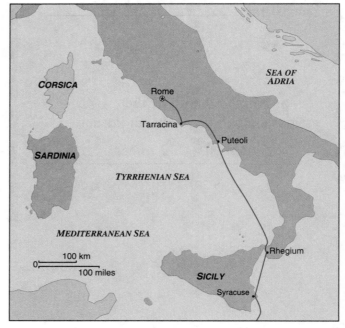

CORSICA

Rome

Tarracina

Puteoli

SEA OF ADRIA

SARDINIA

TYRRHENIAN SEA

MEDITERRANEAN SEA

Rhegium

SICILY

Syracuse

100 km

0 100 miles

Reading 5: "Skill Lesson: Map Scales," pp. 189-91, Lesson 58
Study skills: using an atlas; reading maps; using map keys; determining direction using a compass rose

▶**Choose the correct answer using maps from an atlas on page 72.**

1. Onesimus traveled to the city of Rome. In what country is Rome located?
   - ○ Sardinia
   - ● Italy

2. What kind of vegetation surrounds Rome?
   - ● Deciduous Forest
   - ○ Mediterranean Scrubland

3. What kind of vegetation can be found on the island of Sicily?
   - ● Mixed Forest and Mediterranean Scrubland
   - ○ Mixed Forest and Deciduous Forest

4. What sea is located nearest the city of Puteoli?
   - ○ Sea of Adria
   - ● Tyrrhenian Sea

5. What is the temperature range in July for the city of Rome?
   - ○ 68° to 75° F
   - ● 75° to 85° F

6. What terrain can be found to the east of Rome?
   - ● 1,640-6,560 ft.
   - ○ 0-656 ft.

7. What city in Italy did Paul travel through on his trip to Rome as a prisoner?
   - ○ Syracuse
   - ● Tarracina

8. What landmasses did Paul's ship sail past?
   - ○ Corsica and Sardinia
   - ● Sicily and Italy

Reading 5: "Skill Lesson: Map Scales," pp. 189-91, Lesson 58
Study skills: using an atlas; reading maps; using map keys; determining direction
using a compass rose

▶1. Underline the topic sentence in each paragraph.
2. Match each main-idea sentence with one of the paragraphs.
   Write the correct letter in the Roman column.

In Paul's day Rome was the greatest city of the world. In 1941 an inscription discovered in the seaport of Ostia states the population of Rome as 4,100,000. Most of the people lived in large public houses that were multistoried. The wealthy people lived in dwellings which had rooms that opened on an inner court.

The city of Rome was famous for its roads. Rome was built on seven hills. Its many roads wound among the scenic hills and along the Tiber River. Some of the roads were fifteen to twenty feet wide.

In the Rome of Paul's day, people enjoyed times of pleasure. They celebrated 159 holidays a year. The government paid for over half of these holidays. There were many famous circuses such as Circus Maximus. Pompey's Theater and the Theater of Marcellus were important theaters.

The Palatine Hill was decorated with beautiful temples and emperors' palaces. The palace of Augustus's wife Livia had grand murals. The palace of Nero was one of the wonders of the Roman Empire. Many temples of the Roman gods, such as Jupiter, Apollo, and Saturn, could be found in the city.

Rome was filled with numerous gardens and public parks throughout the city. The estates of Nero's aunt, Domitia, were spectacular. They became known as Nero's Gardens. Public baths were also common.

Main-Idea Sentences

A. Rome had many gardens and public parks.
B. Rome was the greatest city in the world.
C. Rome was famous for its roads.
D. Beautiful temples and palaces could be found in Rome.
E. The Roman people enjoyed times of pleasure.

Reading 5: "Skill Lesson: Map Scales," pp. 189-91, Lesson 58
Comprehension: identifying topic sentences; determining the main idea of a paragraph

Travel Talk

▶ **Write the name of the speaker for each quotation.**

 Blower   Soldier 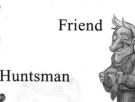 Friend    Runner

Huntsman

Strong man

_____*Runner*_____ 1. "And good day to you, sir! If I were to unbuckle my other leg, I would move so fast that my friend here would soon be left in the dust."

_____*Huntsman*_____ 2. "My dear fellow, two miles from here is a fly sitting on a flower petal, and I wish to shoot out its right eye."

_____*Blower*_____ 3. "Did you not pass three windmills turning, a mile down the road? There is no wind today, so I came out to blow and make them turn."

_____*Friend*_____ 4. "When I place my hat upright on my head, such a terrible frost comes that trees will fall right over from the ice that forms on them."

_____*Soldier*_____ 5. "The merchant has storehouses full of gold to the ceiling. But to me, who risked life and limb for him, he grants only three farthings."

_____*Strong man*_____ 6. "Let me first take this firewood to my mother, and I will join you."

▶ **Select three of the travelers and write a line of dialogue that each might have said as they traveled along.** *Answers will vary.*

_____*Blower*_____ *We shouldn't have to walk around this big lake. Stand back while I blow it away.*

_____ _____

_____ _____

_____ _____

Reading 5: "The Six Travelers," pp. 192-98, Lesson 59
Comprehension: matching characters and dialogue; projecting characters beyond the plot
Composition: writing dialogue

75

Tell It Again

▶ 1. **Read the main ideas from "The Six Travelers."**
2. **Write the supporting details under the appropriate main heading.**

The race to win the daughter's hand
Friend holding hat in his hand (frost)
The merchant's plan to roast the travelers
The guard's attempt to reclaim the treasure
Huntsman aiming at a distant fly
The merchant's offer of riches
Runner hopping on one foot
Strong man uprooting trees
Blower turning windmills

A storyteller doesn't always memorize an entire story. He lists the main ideas and a few supporting details that he needs to remember.

Order may vary under each heading.

Travelers on the journey to the unjust merchant's castle

Strong man uprooting trees

Huntsman aiming at a distant fly

Blower turning windmills

Runner hopping on one foot

Friend holding hat in his hand (frost)

Events at the unjust merchant's castle

The race to win the daughter's hand

The merchant's plan to roast the travelers

The merchant's offer of riches

The guard's attempt to reclaim the treasure

Reading 5: "The Six Travelers," pp. 199-206, Lesson 60
Study skills: organizing facts and details with main ideas

Dramatic Drama

encyclopedia   dictionary

sense of sight   sense of smell

sense of taste   sense of hearing

sense of touch

▶1. **Read each sentence. Circle *F* if it is a fact and *O* if it is an opinion.**
2. **If it is a fact, choose a source from above that would help to determine that it is true. Write the source in the space provided.**
3. **If it is an opinion, leave the space blank.**

1. Drama tells a story through the speech and actions of characters. **F** O _encyclopedia / dictionary_

2. No one knows when or how drama began. **F** O _encyclopedia_

3. Comedy and tragedy are both kinds of drama. **F** O _encyclopedia_

4. Tragedy usually uses the oldest actors. F **O** _____

5. "The Six Travelers" is the best drama to watch. F **O** _____

6. The class performed the play for the parents. **F** O _sense of sight / sense of hearing_

7. The stage props were colorful. **F** O _sense of sight_

8. The audience could feel the wind from the windmills. **F** O _sense of touch_

9. The character of the merchant was the cruelest. F **O** _____

10. The banquet scene was too long. F **O** _____

How Did They Say It?

▶Choose the word that tells the right way to say each line from the play "The Six Travelers."

Soldier: Three farthings! I shall have to see what I can do to make my way in the world with so little.
- ○ excitedly
- ● doubtfully

Strong man: He overcharges us till we haven't a cent, just so he can fill his own coffers to the brim with gold.
- ● sympathetically
- ○ impatiently

Soldier: Surely! Do come with us.
- ○ proudly
- ● excitedly

Huntsman: What is this? Not a breath of wind, but three windmills all turning!
- ● puzzled
- ○ scornfully

Strong man: Now we are off to make our way in the world and seek an audience from an unjust merchant!
- ○ doubtfully
- ● triumphantly

Blower: There is no wind today, so I came out to blow and make them turn. If I had gotten any closer, there is a chance I would have blown them over completely.
- ● boastfully
- ○ puzzled

Friend: And so as not to disappoint you by any means, I will reveal that I have a talent too.
- ○ impatiently
- ● happily

Runner: Oh, I will gladly race for you, if you do indeed want to win the hand of such a girl.
- ● eagerly
- ○ harshly

Merchant: Ha! You are merely a soldier! Better men than you have tried and have not lived to tell the tale.
- ○ briskly
- ● mockingly

Daughter: How now? What is this? My challenger—asleep!
- ● startled
- ○ impatiently

Narrator: The merchant turned a little paler at that, but he ordered more gold to be brought.
- ● thoughtfully
- ○ hastily

Guard: You are under arrest for stealing all these riches!
- ● forcefully
- ○ meekly

Daughter: Father, I still refuse to marry that common soldier!
- ● arrogantly
- ○ excitedly

Narrator: And what of the merchant and his daughter? Well, they discovered that they did indeed have three farthings left.
- ● finally
- ○ meekly

Reading 5: "The Six Travelers," pp. 192-206, Lesson 61
Comprehension: identifying emotional responses of characters; identifying voice expressions

▶**Answer the questions in complete sentences. You may refer to the article "Common Salt."**

Wording may vary.

1. Why is common salt important for good health? _____ *A strong steady heartbeat depends partly on the sodium from common salt.*

2. Why are Christians called "the salt of the earth"? _____ *Christians' presence in the world holds back corruption.*

3. When making ice cream, why do you add salt to the ice around the churning container?

   Salty water has a lower freezing temperature,

   so it allows the mixture to be very cold.

   _____

   _____

   _____

4. Why are the seas getting saltier? _____ *Streams and rivers bring salts to them, and salt is left behind when water evaporates.*

5. Why did evolutionists give up attempting to judge the earth's age by the accumulation of salt in the seas? _____ *Their calculations led them to believe the earth was only a few million years old instead of billions.*

6. What are examples of natural brines? _____ *The Dead Sea and the Great Salt Lake are examples.*

7. How do Creationists believe the salt beds were made? _____ *They believe that God made the salt beds when He made the land.*

8. What is the difference between the evolutionist and the Creationist? _____ *The difference is what he puts his faith in—man's ideas or God's truth.*

A Salt Dome

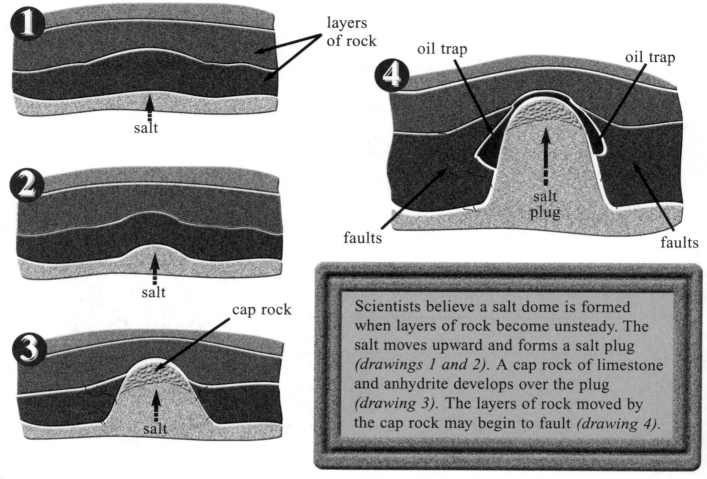

Scientists believe a salt dome is formed when layers of rock become unsteady. The salt moves upward and forms a salt plug *(drawings 1 and 2)*. A cap rock of limestone and anhydrite develops over the plug *(drawing 3)*. The layers of rock moved by the cap rock may begin to fault *(drawing 4)*.

▶ **Use the diagrams and captions of the salt dome to answer the questions.**

1. In what direction does the salt move when the layers of rock become unsteady?

    upward

2. What develops over the salt plug? *a cap rock*

3. What is a cap rock made of? *limestone and anhydrite*

4. Which drawings show the cap rock? *drawings 3 and 4*

5. Which drawings show the layers of rock? *all of them*

6. What may be trapped next to the salt and cap rock? *oil*

7. Which drawing shows the oil traps? *drawing 4*

8. What can happen to the layers of rock being moved? *They may begin to fault.*

Reading 5: "Common Salt," pp. 207-9, Lesson 63
Study skills: reading a diagram and a caption

Why?

▶ **Answer the questions in complete sentences.**

Wording may vary.

1. Why did Hector go to see his rich brother, Pierre? ___ *Hector had no food*

_____ *and thought he was going to have to eat his mule.*

2. Why did Hector go to the Land of Nowhere? ___ *The woodchopper told him to*

_____ *trade his bacon for the hand grain grinder to help his wife.*

3. Why did the people of Nowhere trade the grain grinder for the bacon? ___ *They*

_____ *loved bacon more than any other food.*

4. Why was Pierre jealous of Hector? ___ *Hector had the hand mill which*

_____ *would grind out anything that he wanted.*

5. Why did the sea captain want the grain grinder? ___ *He would never*

_____ *have to search for salt again.*

6. Why do you think the sea captain went far out to sea after he got the grain grinder?

_____ *Answers will vary. Perhaps he feared that Hector would try to get it*

_____ *back, and he wanted to get away from him.*

▶ **Choose the correct definition for each colored word.**

1. Hector's resolve would not budge.
   - ○ uncertainty
   - ● determination

2. Hector dismounted and patted Ferdy on the nose.
   - ○ climbed upon
   - ● got off

3. The woodchopper beckoned Hector to follow him.
   - ● signaled someone with the hand or head
   - ○ bowed

4. Pierre heard tidings of the hand mill.
   - ○ the soap
   - ● news or information

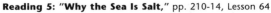

Reading 5: "Why the Sea Is Salt," pp. 210-14, Lesson 64
Comprehension: recalling facts and details; inferring facts and details; drawing conclusions
Vocabulary: matching words and definitions

81

Salty Creatures

Saltwater Fish

Type	Length	Weight	Habitat	Features
Pacific Cod	2-3 ft.	3-20 lb.	North Pacific Ocean	3 fins on back; 2 fins on underside near tail
Sole (Flounder)	0.83-2 ft.	1 lb.	Atlantic Ocean along the North American coast	flat oval-shaped body with both eyes on one side of the head
Wolf Fish (Mackerel)	5 ft.	40 lb.	North Atlantic and North Pacific Oceans	large, fanglike front teeth
Pilchard (European Sardine)	0.75-1 ft.	0.25 lb.	near the coasts of western Europe and northern Africa	upper bluish-gray body; a silvery lower body
White Shark	21 ft.	31,360 lb.	cool waters to tropical waters	two rows of razor-sharp teeth; body covered with tiny toothlike scales

▶**Use the information on the chart to answer the questions.**

1. Which saltwater fish has the shortest length? ___*Pilchard*___

2. What fish can weigh twice as much as an African elephant? ___*White Shark*___

3. Which two fish live in the Pacific Ocean? ___*Pacific Cod and Wolf Fish*___

4. What unusual feature does the Sole have? ___*both eyes on one side*___
___*of the head*___

5. Which fish weighs the least? ___*Pilchard*___

6. What fish has three fins on its back and two on the underside near its tail? ___*Pacific Cod*___

GENESIS 1:21
And God created great whales, and every living creature that moveth, which the waters brought forth abundantly.

2002 BJU Press. Reproduction prohibited.

© 2002 BJU Press. Reproduction prohibited.

Reading 5: "Why the Sea Is Salt," pp. 210-14, Lesson 64
Study skills: getting information from a chart; perceiving size relationships
Comprehension: inferring facts and details

A Friend Indeed

Name_____

▶ **Answer each question. Look up each Scripture verse and write the verse that backs up your answer.**

1. King Dionysius was a strong and cruel tyrant. What character traits should a ruler use to govern his people?

   ● A ruler should be just with a fear of God.

   ○ A ruler should be strong and cruel.

   Verse: _____*II Samuel 23:3*_____

   II Samuel 23:3   Psalm 118:14

2. What characteristics was Pythias showing by speaking against King Dionysius?

   ● Pythias showed disrespect and a lack of honor.

   ○ Pythias showed honor and courage by speaking up.

   Verse: _____*I Peter 2:17-18*_____

   I Peter 2:17-18   I Corinthians 10:31

3. What character trait did Pythias demonstrate by making a request to King Dionysius?

   ○ Pythias showed meekness.

   ● Pythias showed boldness.

   Verse: _____*Proverbs 28:1*_____

   Jeremiah 33:3   Proverbs 28:1

4. Why was Damon willing to take Pythias's place and face possible death?

   ○ Damon wanted the king to think he was noble.

   ● Damon trusted his friend.

   Verse: _____*Proverbs 27:10*_____

   Isaiah 50:4   Proverbs 27:10

5. Why did King Dionysius not believe that Pythias would return to take his punishment and free Damon?

   ○ King Dionysius didn't care which one would die.

   ● King Dionysius didn't think a person would die for a friend.

   Verse: _____*John 15:13*_____

   Psalm 145:18   John 15:13

6. When Pythias returned, what did this tell you about him?

   ● Pythias was truthful and loyal.

   ○ Pythias was almost too late.

   Verse: _____*Proverbs 17:17*_____

   Proverbs 17:17   Hebrews 13:15

7. Why was the expression of a loyal friendship so unbelievable for King Dionysius?

   ○ King Dionysius has wealthy friends.

   ● King Dionysius had never experienced true friendship.

   Verse: _____*Proverbs 18:24*_____

   Nehemiah 8:10   Proverbs 18:24

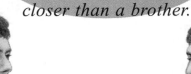

PROVERBS 18:24

A man that hath friends must shew himself friendly: and there is a friend that sticketh closer than a brother.

Reading 5: "Damon and Pythias," pp. 215-17, Lesson 66
Study skills: locating Bible verses
Comprehension: identifying character traits; supporting personal conclusions with biblical truth

Jonathan and David

The news of David's fight with Goliath spread rapidly. King Saul even commanded that David stay at the palace. Saul's son Jonathan respected David as a hero. At the palace they became close friends. Jonathan gave David the shepherd boy gifts to show his promise that he would always be David's friend. King Saul made David captain of his army. David's accomplishments for the nation of Israel were great.

However, proud Saul became angry and jealous when he heard the people praising David's accomplishments more than his own accomplishments. Saul determined to kill David, Jonathan's friend.

Did Jonathan keep his promise and remain loyal to his friend? Jonathan felt terrible when he heard that his father wanted to kill David. Jonathan told David to hide until he could talk with his father. Saul was ashamed of his jealousy. But as David continued defeating the enemy, Saul grew more jealous than ever. He sent messengers to kill David at his house. But David escaped and fled to the prophet Samuel. God continued to protect David as Saul pursued him.

Saul knew of Jonathan and David's friendship. The friends made a plan to save David's life. While Jonathan was trying to defend David, Saul became so enraged that he threw his spear at his own son. Jonathan knew then that David's life was in great danger.

As planned, Jonathan sent a little boy to gather his arrows in a field where David was hiding. The directions that Jonathan gave for gathering the arrows were a signal to David. The friendship of Jonathan and David is indeed a classic. In order to protect his friend, Jonathan parted with David, but their bond of friendship remained steadfast.

▶ **Write the letter of each of the following in the appropriate section of the Venn diagram.**

A. warned his friend of danger
B. trusted his friend completely
C. was angry and proud
D. had great accomplishments for the nation of Israel
E. was a jealous king
F. gave of his own wealth to his friend
G. went to his father on behalf of his friend
H. sent his friend away
I. protected by God

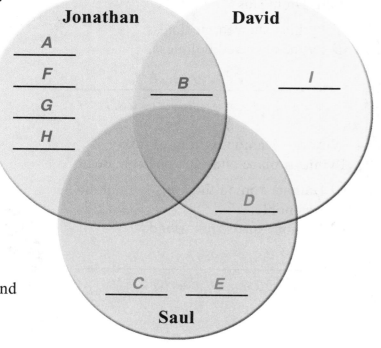

Reading 5: "Damon and Pythias," pp. 215-17, Lesson 66
Study skills: ompleting a Venn diagram
Comprehension: identifying character traits

Blowing Rock

In North Carolina, high in the Blue Ridge Mountains, is an unusual rock formation that forms the background for a fascinating legend. Blowing Rock, as it is called, is long, bare, and flat. But it tilts at a precarious angle of forty-five degrees.

Stories say that the wind there is so strong that over thousands of years ago it tilted this huge rock, which used to lie parallel with the sea of treetops.

The legend goes that a Cherokee brave was in love with a beautiful Cherokee maiden, but their parents would not let them marry. They often met secretly at a huge rock. One day, in sadness and despair, the brave jumped from the peak of the rock in an effort to kill himself. But instead of falling to his death, the brave was caught by the strong wind and blown back to his maiden.

Today at Blowing Rock, if you throw something lightweight over the edge, the wind will bring it back to you. But do not try jumping.

Stories that contain some truth and are passed down from generation to generation are called **legends.**

▶**Write _T_ for probably true and _E_ for probably exaggerated.**

____T____ 1. The rock lies at a forty-five-degree angle.

____E____ 2. The wind blowing against the rock may have caused this formation.

____T____ 3. A Cherokee brave and a maiden were in love.

____E____ 4. The wind caught the Cherokee brave and blew him back up.

____T____ 5. If you throw something light over the edge of Blowing Rock, the wind will blow it back.

Summary Legends

▶ 1. Underline the main idea in each paragraph.
2. Circle three supporting details for the main idea in each paragraph.
3. Write a summary sentence or two for each paragraph.

John Chapman was a pioneer who believed in what he did, and he became the legend of Johnny Appleseed. He used his herbs and medicinal plants to heal people. He also carried apple seeds to distribute because he believed in the saying "An apple a day keeps the doctor away." He sold his apple seeds for anything a farmer or homesteader had to exchange for them. It is said that he even planted some as he walked along the Ohio River.

Summary sentences:

Answers will vary.

John Chapman became the legend of Johnny Appleseed.

He healed people with herbs and medicinal plants,

he distributed apple seeds, and he sold apple seeds.

Legend says that the courageous Pocahontas, an Indian princess, saved John Smith. He was caught and brought before Indian Chief Powhatan. The medicine man talked the chief into beheading Smith. When Smith's head was on the stone, Pocahontas threw herself over him. Chief Powhatan was proud of his daughter's courage and released Smith, who later became the leader of Jamestown.

Summary sentences:

Legend says that Pocahontas saved John Smith.

Chief Powhatan was pleased with his daughter's

courage to save John Smith from beheading.

Reading 5: "Literature Lesson: Legends," pp. 218-19, Lesson 67
Study skills: identifying the main idea of a paragraph; determining supporting details; summarizing a paragraph

Be a Sharp Arrowhead

▶ **Complete the crossword puzzle, using a synonym for the colored word or words in each sentence.**

concentrate	flint	harrow
insistent	relic	hefted
summon	vicious	

Across

5. Jesse tried to focus his attention on his chores.
6. Did the fierce coon harm the dog?
7. Jesse lifted a rock to drop on the coon.

Down

1. Lifting the heavy rock required Jesse to call upon his last bit of strength.
2. Jesse will treasure the historical object he found along the bank of the river.
3. Jesse hunted for a piece of quartz as well as an arrowhead.
4. Mom was not flexible when she woke up Jesse in the mornings.
7. Dad will break up the field before he plants the corn.

Crossword puzzle answers:

1 Down: SUMMON
2 Down: RELIC
3 Down: FLINT
4 Down: INSISTENT
5 Across: CONCENTRATE
6 Across: VICIOUS
7 Across: HEFTED
7 Down: HARROW

▶ **Write a note to a friend telling about Jesse and his dog Rusty. Use some of the vocabulary words from above in your note.**

Dear _____ *Answers will vary.* _____ ,

_____

_____

_____

_____

Sincerely,

_____

Reading 5: "Some Special Day," pp. 220-25, Lesson 69
Vocabulary: matching words and definitions
Composition: writing sentences to convey word meaning

Jesse's Graphs

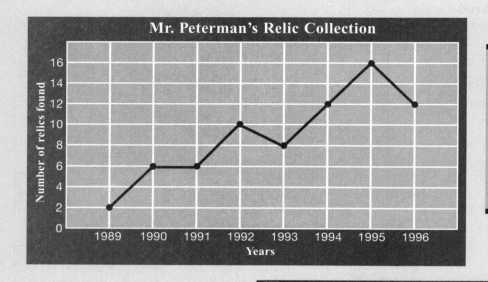

Mr. Peterman's Relic Collection

Number of relics found: 16, 14, 12, 10, 8, 6, 4, 2, 0

Years: 1989, 1990, 1991, 1992, 1993, 1994, 1995, 1996

Graphs are pictures of information. They provide an easy way to look at a lot of information quickly.

A **line graph** makes changes easier to see.

A **bar graph** compares similar information.

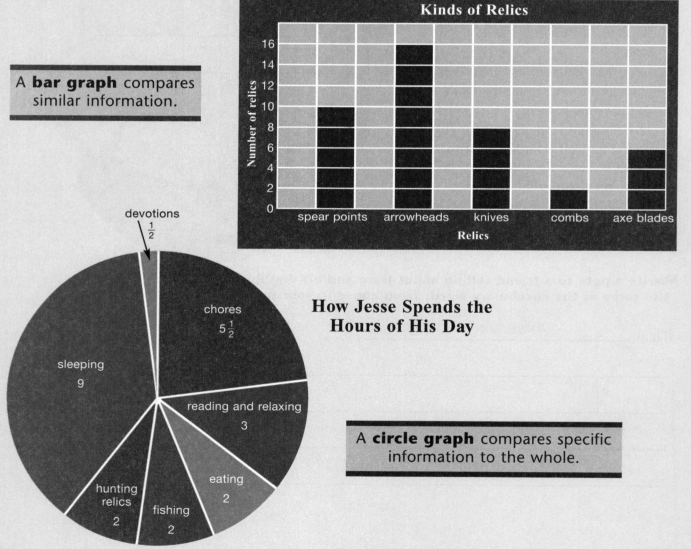

Kinds of Relics

Number of relics: 16, 14, 12, 10, 8, 6, 4, 2, 0

Relics: spear points, arrowheads, knives, combs, axe blades

devotions $\frac{1}{2}$

chores $5\frac{1}{2}$

sleeping 9

How Jesse Spends the Hours of His Day

reading and relaxing 3

hunting relics 2

fishing 2

eating 2

A **circle graph** compares specific information to the whole.

© 2002 BJU Press. Reproduction prohibited.

88

Reading 5: "Some Special Day," pp. 220-25, Lesson 69
Study skills: determining and comparing information from a bar graph, a circle graph, and a line graph

Reading Graphs

Name_____

▶**Use the graphs on page 88 to answer each question.**

1. What activity does Jesse do most of the hours of each day? _____ *sleep* _____

2. In which year did Mr. Peterman find the most relics? _____ *1995* _____

3. How many more arrowheads than spear points are there in the relic collection? __ *6* __

4. How many hours a day does Jesse spend having fun? _____ *7* _____

5. What kind of relic is most common where Jesse lives? _____ *arrowheads* _____

6. How long does Jesse spend on his devotions? _____ $\frac{1}{2}$ *hour* _____

7. In which year did Mr. Peterman find the fewest relics? _____ *1989* _____

8. Which relic is rarest in the relic collection? _____ *combs* _____

9. Does Jesse spend more time hunting relics or reading and relaxing? _____
_____ *reading and relaxing* _____

10. In which year did Mr. Peterman find more relics: 1992 or 1993? _____ *1992* _____

11. How many hours a day does Jesse spend doing chores? _____ $5\frac{1}{2}$ _____

12. How many axe blades are in the collection? _____ *6* _____

13. How long does Jesse spend eating each day? _____ *2 hours* _____

14. Are there more spear points or knives in the collection? _____ *spear points* _____

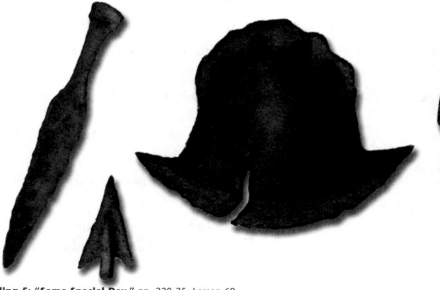

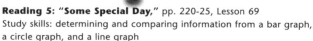

Reading 5: "Some Special Day," pp. 220-25, Lesson 69
Study skills: determining and comparing information from a bar graph,
a circle graph, and a line graph

89

▶**Choose two answers for each question.**

1. Which of Jesse's actions showed his persistence?

   ● He kept pounding on the coon.
   ● He had been digging for arrowheads all morning.
   ○ He was afraid the coon would drown Rusty.

2. How did Jesse show that he loved his dog?

   ○ He couldn't drive the tractor.
   ● He tried to pull Rusty away from the coon.
   ● He drove the tractor even though it scared him.

3. How did Jesse show that he was brave?

   ● He fought the coon to rescue Rusty.
   ○ He was afraid the coon would drown Rusty.
   ● He jumped into the water after the dog and the coon.

4. How did Dad show that he was a caring person?

   ● He was concerned about Rusty's injury.
   ○ He knew that Jesse could handle the tractor.
   ● He reminded Jesse of his chores and responsibilities.

▶**Choose one answer for each question.**

1. What did Mom do to show she was a caring person?

   ● She ran out to meet the tractor when it returned early.
   ○ She knew where Jesse had been by his muddy pants.

2. How do you know that Dad loved the Lord?

   ○ He understood how Jesse felt about the arrowheads.
   ● He told Jesse to ask the Lord for help.

3. How did Dad show that he was wise?

   ● He knew Jesse could handle the tractor.
   ○ He was concerned about Rusty's injuries.

4. What did Jesse do to show that he was impulsive?

   ○ He tried to pull Rusty away from the coon.
   ● He jumped into the water after the dog and the coon.

5. How did Mom show she was good-natured?

   ● She didn't scold Jesse for coming home all dirty.
   ○ She predicted that Rusty would get well.

6. How did Dad show he was a cautious man?

   ○ He led family devotions.
   ● He wouldn't let Jesse drive the tractor yet.

Reading 5: "Some Special Day," pp. 226-29, Lesson 70
Comprehension: identifying character traits

The Snowflake Man

W. A. Bentley, a farmer from Jericho, Vermont, fascinated the world with his photography of snow crystals. He became the first person to photograph a single snow crystal.

Mr. Bentley was like Sherlock Holmes in a blizzard. He would hold a black board into the swirling snowflakes. Back in his shed he would examine the board with a hand lens. He carefully picked up a bit of snow from the board with a wooden splint. He gently placed it on a glass slide. Then he brushed it lightly with a small feather to force it to stick in place. He put the slide under the microscope. Many times the snow crystal was broken or damaged. Mr. Bentley would begin the process again. Finally, a snowflake unbroken and symmetrical was found.

The slide with the symmetrical snowflake was then placed on a different microscope attached to a bellows camera. The camera and microscope lenses were carefully adjusted to produce a sharp image. The farmer had to keep the warmth of his breath and body away from the slide with its frozen crystal. A photographic plate was placed over the snow crystal slide. The exposure for the photograph began and then the plate was removed. Using this procedure, Mr. Bentley captured numerous photos of the snowflakes.

Wilson "Snowflake" Bentley said, "Under the microscope, I found that snowflakes were miracles of beauty; and it seemed a shame that this beauty should not be seen and appreciated by others. Every crystal was a masterpiece of design and no one design was ever repeated. When a snowflake melted, that design was forever lost. Just that much beauty was gone, without leaving any record behind."

▶**Number the photo-taking steps in the correct order.**

__4__ Feather used to hold snow crystal in place

__1__ Black board placed into snow

__6__ Slide placed in microscope attached to a camera

__2__ Snow examined with a hand lens

__5__ Slide observed under the microscope

__7__ Camera image adjusted

__8__ Picture of snowflake taken

__3__ Snowflake placed on slide with a wooden splint

Reading 5: "Snowflakes," pp. 230-31, Lesson 71
Comprehension: sequencing events

▶Greek (G) and Latin (L) root words form the basis of many of our English words. Study the root words on the tree. Write the letter of the correct definition for each word.

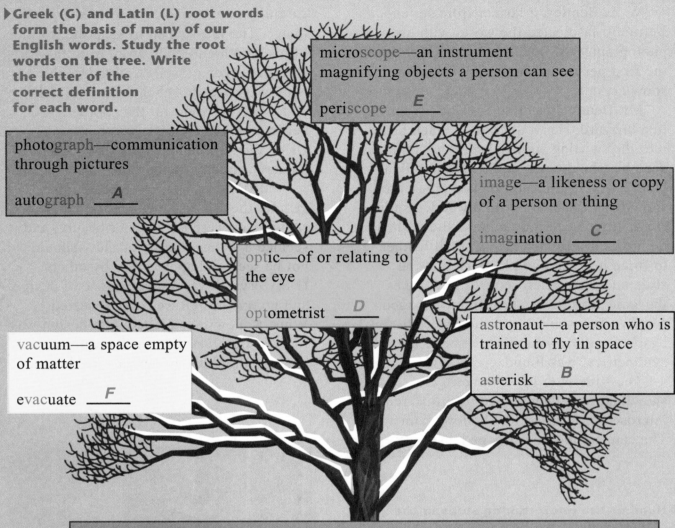

microscope—an instrument magnifying objects a person can see

periscope ___E___

photograph—communication through pictures

autograph ___A___

image—a likeness or copy of a person or thing

imagination ___C___

optic—of or relating to the eye

optometrist ___D___

astronaut—a person who is trained to fly in space

asterisk ___B___

vacuum—a space empty of matter

evacuate ___F___

A. a written name or signature
B. a star-shaped figure used in print
C. the ability of the mind to form pictures or likeness of things not there

D. a person who examines the eyes
E. an instrument that allows one to see an object indirectly
F. to empty the contents of

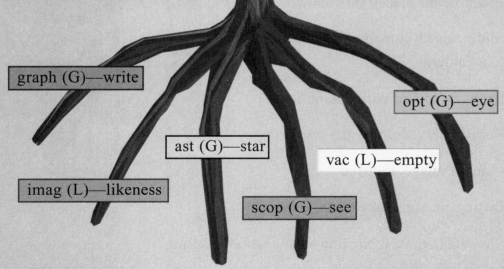

graph (G)—write

opt (G)—eye

ast (G)—star

vac (L)—empty

imag (L)—likeness

scop (G)—see

Reading 5: "Snowflakes," pp. 230-31, Lesson 71
Vocabulary: determining word meaning from Greek and Latin roots

Relevant information is important to a particular subject. **Irrelevant** information has no connection or importance to a subject.

▶ 1. Circle the topic sentence in each paragraph.
2. Cross out the irrelevant sentence in each paragraph.

(The Eskimos are a people who live in and near the Arctic.) Their native land reaches from the northeastern tip of Russia across Alaska and northern Canada to the island of Greenland. ~~Animals of the north include Arctic foxes, seals, caribou, and polar bears.~~ The name *Eskimo* comes from an American Indian word meaning "eaters of raw meat." The Eskimo people call themselves words that mean "people." In Canada they use the word *Inuit,* in Alaska the words *Inupiat* and *Yupik,* and in Siberia they use the word *Yuit.*

(For Eskimos wintertime means more time inside and lots of indoor recreation.) Eskimos use their creativity to liven up the extra hours of darkness and storms of the Arctic that keep them inside. ~~The igloo was used only during the winter and was made of packed snow.~~ Eskimo men play games that test their strength, like wrestling and tug of war. They also perform trapeze acts on a rope of skin stretched across the inside of a house. And you can imagine how the children enjoy games, singing, and listening to stories about legendary heroes.

▶ **Use the information from the paragraphs to answer the questions below. Write the letter of the correct answer.**

___d___ 1. Under what topic do you think that you might find relevant information about the games Eskimos play?

    a. hunting   c. igloos
    b. religion   d. recreation

___a___ 2. Which specific recreation would be irrelevant in your search?

    a. rodeos   c. tug of war
    b. wrestling   d. indoor games

___b___ 3. Which location do you think would ***not*** provide relevant information about Eskimos?

    a. Arctic   c. Alaska
    b. Africa   d. Greenland

___c___ 4. Under which other topic would you ***not*** find relevant information about Eskimos?

    a. Inupiat   c. Hawaii
    b. Siberia   d. Yupik

Reading 5: "Venture to Mierow Lake," pp. 232-37, Lesson 73
Study skills: identifying relevant and irrelevant information; identifying topic sentences

For God So Loved

▶ Write the solution to each of the problems Steve and Liz Bailey faced as missionaries.

Wording may vary.

1. Steve did not know the Eskimo language. _*Victor translated for him. /*_

   *Steve kept a notebook of Eskimo words.*

2. The Baileys needed to travel from village to village to spread the gospel. _____

   *They used a sled and sled dogs.*

3. The Baileys didn't want the Eskimos to think that their trip to Mierow Lake was a hunting

   trip. _*They talked to each person, telling him*_

   *where they were going and why.*

4. Steve needed to know what things to pack for the trip and hazardous weather. _____

   *He asked Gus, the owner of the trading post, for advice.*

5. When the Baileys stopped for the night on the way to Mierow Lake, there were no

   sheltering rocks to keep out the wind. _*Victor cut snow blocks and piled*_

   *them around the base of each tent.*

6. Liz had a windburned face. _*She put on seal oil that Victor gave her.*_

7. Why did Steve think the story of David as a young boy would be strange for the people of

   Mierow Lake? _*The people in the pictures had white faces with brightly*_

   *colored clothes. / They probably had never seen a lion.*

Imâk Gûdib sillaksoarmuit nagligivait, Ernetuane tunnilugo, illûnatik okpertut tâpsomunga assiokonnagit, nungusuitomigle inôgutekarkovlugit. —John 3:16 in Eskimo (Labrador dialect)

Reading 5: "Venture to Mierow Lake," pp. 238-41, Lesson 74
Comprehension: identifying solutions to problems; recalling facts and details

Moods of Vasko

▶**Choose the mood of each selection. Then write the words or phrases that help create the mood in each.**

If it had not been December, Vasko might have given up hope. He huddled in a corner where two old buildings met and tried to think of something warm. He had not eaten since the morning before—a piece of dark bread no bigger than his hand—but today he was sure that something would happen. It was nearly Christmas, and Christmas was hope.

A shiver ran over him. *That's good,* he thought. *If I am shivering, I'm still warm*

inside. His grandmother had told him stories about his father, a sailor, and his father's father, a ship's captain. They braved many winter storms at sea, where icy waves ripped over the decks, drenching every sailor. His grandmother had made her voice deep and repeated his grandfather's words: "We were all of us chilled to the marrow, but if we could shiver, we knew we were still alive."

> The **mood** of a story is the emotion that the reader shares with the character.

Mood:
- ● uncertain but hopeful
- ○ hopeful and happy

Words or Phrases: _____ *possible answers: might have given up hope,*

_____ *something would happen, still warm inside*

"Here." Someone had handed him a bowl of broth. The bowl was rough and warm in his hands. He put the rim to his lips and the taste of fish was real this time, not the fleeting memory of a taste brought on by the smell of the barrel.

He could not stop drinking it. He knew that he slurped, and he knew that

somehow he knew better than that, but he could no more slow down than he could disappear. He tipped the bowl all the way up, drained it, and licked the rim.

The heat of the fire seeped in from the outside and the warmth of the broth filled him from the inside. And when the two met, he felt suddenly overwhelmingly sleepy.

He lowered himself to the hearthstones—knees, hands, a shoulder—and he was asleep.

Mood:
- ○ carefree and tense
- ● content and satisfied

Words or Phrases: _____ *possible answers: could not stop drinking,*

_____ *licked the rim, filled him from the inside, was asleep*

Reading 5: "Vasko's Christmas Rescue," pp. 242-46, Lesson 75
Literature: determining the mood of a story; identifying details that create the mood

Vocabulary Rescue

▶**Complete the crossword puzzle.**

Across
4. stared angrily
6. struggled; moved with difficulty
9. a species of fish
10. cowardly person; a dog considered lowly
11. skipped, glided, or moved rapidly along a surface

Down
1. the soft material inside bones
2. faced danger courageously
3. people who are superior in position, wealth, or intelligence
5. produced a loud sound
7. made a sudden, forceful attack
8. wetting completely; soaking

betters	braved
cur	drenching
floundered	glowered
lunged	marrow
menhaden	skittered
thundered	

Across:
4. GLOWERED
6. FLOUNDERED
9. MENHADEN
10. CUR
11. SKITTERED

Down:
1. MARROW
2. BRAVED
3. BETTES → BETTERS
5. THUNDERED
7. LUNGED
8. DRENCHING

Reading 5: "Vasko's Christmas Rescue," pp. 242-46, Lesson 75
Vocabulary: matching words and definitions

Name _____

▶**Write the correct letter in the blanks on the plot frame to put the events in story order.**

A. Vasko finds an empty fish barrel to make a home.

B. Vasko sits in a corner of two buildings hungry and cold.

C. Cappy feeds Vasko a bowl of broth and gives him a warm place to sleep.

D. A man shouts, "This is my property. Get out of here."

E. Vasko realizes that he has been rescued just as his grandfather rescued Cappy years ago.

F. Vasko finds himself again in search of warmth, food, and a place to stay.

G. Cappy pulls Vasko from his barrel home.

H. Vasko tells the captain about his grandfather's ship and his death.

I. Vasko will always have a home.

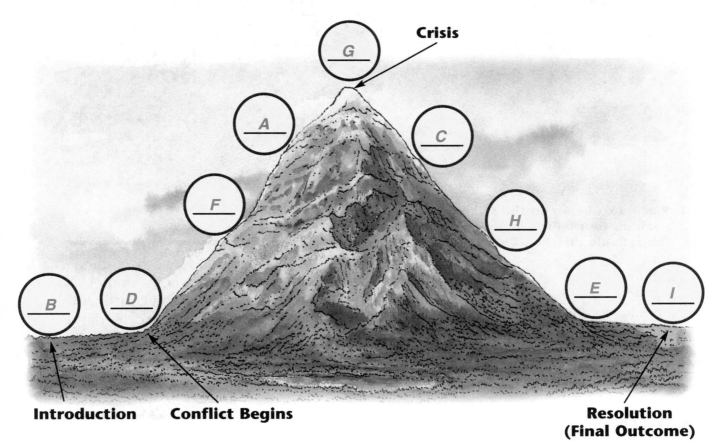

Reading 5: "Vasko's Christmas Rescue," pp. 247-48, Lesson 76
Comprehension: sequencing events
Literature: identifying story plot

97

Which Theme?

▶ Match each story with its theme.

___D___ 1. "Ma and Muffin"

___B___ 2. "Common Salt"

___F___ 3. "Damon and Pythias"

___E___ 4. "Some Special Day"

___C___ 5. "Venture to Mierow Lake"

___A___ 6. "Vasko's Christmas Rescue"

A. The person you rescue today may be the person who rescues you tomorrow.

B. The salty sea was in God's plan of creation.

C. Presenting the gospel to the unsaved can be difficult but rewarding.

D. Continuous love can soften the heart and how you feel.

E. In the time of difficulty God can help you to be responsible and to have courage.

F. A true friend is a loyal friend.

The author's purpose or message is called the **theme** of the story.

▶ 1. Place dots between the syllables.
  2. Look up four words in your glossary to check the syllable division. Circle the four words.

a m•b l e   j i g•g l e   s t a•p l e

c o b•b l e•s t o n e   k i n•d l e   s u b•t l e

c r i n•k l e   n e e•d l e   t r e s•t l e

g a r•b l e   p r i c k•l e   w h e e•d l e

g u r•g l e   s h u t•t l e•c o c k   w h i t•t l e

Divide words ending with a consonant + *le* before the consonant + *le*. In words ending with the consonant digraph *ck* before the *le,* divide the word after the *ck.*

Reading 5: "Vasko's Christmas Rescue," pp. 247-48, Lesson 76
Literature: identifying the theme of a story
Structural analysis: applying Syllable Division Rule 3—words ending with a consonant + *le* and words ending with *ck* + *le*
Study skills: using a glossary

Word Partners

Name_____

▶ **Choose the synonym for each bold word. You may use your glossary.**

1. left it **jutting** in spiky ribbons
   - ○ sleeping
   - ● extending

2. the creature to **emerge** from this sack
   - ● appear
   - ○ join

3. returned to the **Consulate** General
   - ● an office
   - ○ a sympathizer

4. was simply **aloof** and indifferent
   - ○ sensitive
   - ● distant

5. was simply aloof and **indifferent**
   - ● uncaring
   - ○ opposite

6. a **keen** interest in his surroundings
   - ● sharp
   - ○ hold

7. around the bend of the **corridor**
   - ○ doorway
   - ● hallway

8. fumbling at the **chromium** taps
   - ○ songs
   - ● metal

9. play in their **holts**
   - ● dens
   - ○ stops

10. a **query** used at closer quarters
    - ○ hole
    - ● question

▶ **Choose the evidence that supports each conclusion.**

1. Mijbil was neither friendly nor unfriendly.
   - ● He chose to sleep on the floor as far from Mr. Maxwell's bed as possible.
   - ○ He always ate with five crunches on alternating sides of the jaw.

2. Mijbil looked like a very small dragon.
   - ○ An otter could be found in the Tigris marshes, for there otters were as common as mosquitoes.
   - ● From the head to the tail he was coated with pointed scales of mud armor.

3. Mijbil was playful.
   - ● He loved to lie on his back and dribble a rubber ball.
   - ○ He ate small reddish fish from the Tigris River.

4. Mijbil seemed to be fond of Mr. Maxwell, the author of the story.
   - ○ He always overturned any container that was holding water.
   - ● He often rubbed Mr. Maxwell's back and slept in the crook of Mr. Maxwell's knees.

Reading 5: "Mijbil—Iraq to London," pp. 250-55, Lesson 78
Comprehension: identifying evidence that supports a conclusion
Vocabulary: identifying synonyms to develop word meaning

Koonta and Luk-Luk

Dr. Remus adjusted his binoculars and swept the Arctic valley with his eyes. Koonta, leader of the wolf pack that he had been trailing, was fighting it out with Luk-Luk, a member of the same pack.

For the first two weeks of Dr. Remus's study, Luk-Luk had been like the other five members of the pack under Koonta—obedient and diligent in tracking down moose. But he had been aggressive lately, defying Koonta and seeming to show rebellion in every action of his body. And now that the pack had finally eaten after a week of hunting, Luk-Luk seemed to be trying for leadership of the pack.

Horrible fangs bared, both wolves wrestled and tumbled in the snow. But Koonta was the better fighter. In another minute Luk-Luk rolled onto his back, showing that he was beaten. Koonta walked around him, stiff-legged and snarling. Then he let the beaten wolf get up.

Every now and then for the next few hours Koonta nipped at Luk-Luk to remind him who was boss, but when the time came to hunt, Luk-Luk fell in with the others.

Later, Dr. Remus sat directly in the path of Koonta. The big wolf avoided him at first, but when Dr. Remus rolled onto his back, Koonta came up and sniffed his boot, looking more like a giant German shepherd than anything else.

▶ **In each pair of statements below, write the letter of the one that you know is true from reading the story.**

_b_ 1. a. Wolves run in packs and kill any animal they find.
   b. Wolves run in packs and eat meat.

_b_ 2. a. Wolves usually avoid men but kill them when necessary.
   b. Wolves usually avoid men but may come close to a man if they are not frightened.

_b_ 3. a. Wolves in the same pack often kill each other.
   b. Wolves in the same pack may fight but seldom kill each other.

_a_ 4. a. If an animal rolls over on its back, the wolf takes that as a sign of peace.
   b. If an animal rolls over on its back, the wolf believes that the animal is dead.

Reading 5: "Mijbil—Iraq to London," pp. 250-55, Lesson 78
Comprehension: drawing conclusions

Before or After

▸**Underline the correct word in the parentheses.**

1. Mr. Maxwell, the author, planned to get an otter (<u>before</u>, after) his trip home to London.

2. The otter was in a sack on the floor (<u>before</u>, after) Mr. Maxwell cleaned off Mijbil's mud armor.

3. Mijbil took a car trip through the streets of Basra (<u>before</u>, after) he became friends with Mr. Maxwell.

4. Mijbil was aboard the airplane (before, <u>after</u>) he learned to turn the chromium taps.

5. Mijbil disappeared at high speed down the aircraft (before, <u>after</u>) Mr. Maxwell had unlocked the padlock of the box.

6. The stewardess told Mr. Maxwell she would find the otter (before, <u>after</u>) Mr. Maxwell covered his face in curry.

7. Mijbil yanked out magazines from the neighbor's TWA travel bag (<u>before</u>, after) the plane arrived in Paris.

8. Mijbil traveled in the freight portion of the Air France airplane (before, <u>after</u>) he traveled in the passenger section of the TWA airplane.

9. One of the plane's crew nailed Mijbil's box shut (<u>before</u>, after) Mijbil traveled in the freight section of the plane.

10. Mijbil greeted Mr. Maxwell with a frenzy of affection (before, <u>after</u>) the lid was pried open at Mr. Maxwell's studio.

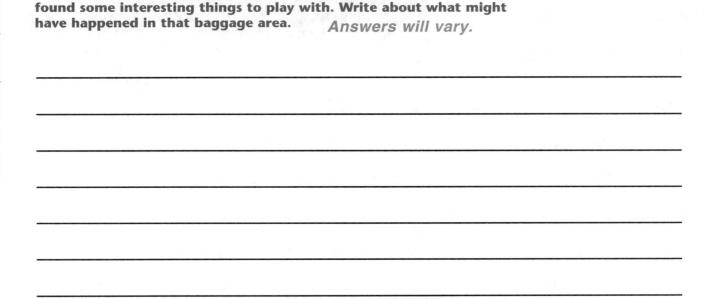

▸**Mijbil slept in the baggage area during the second part of his plane journey. If he had been able to escape from his box, he might have found some interesting things to play with. Write about what might have happened in that baggage area.** *Answers will vary.*

_____

_____

_____

_____

_____

_____

Reading 5: "Mijbil—Iraq to London," pp. 256-60, Lesson 79
Comprehension: sequencing events; predicting outcomes
Composition: writing creatively

101

▶Write the letter of the correct definition for each bold word.

b 1. The plane was **taxiing** out to take off.
   a. taking a taxi
   b. moving slowly over the ground

b 2. I was rushed through the customs by **infuriated** officials.
   a. hit by a storm
   b. extremely angry

a 3. I had the **bulkhead** before me instead of another seat.
   a. a partition that divides a plane into compartments
   b. the head of a bull

b 4. The **port** engines roared, and then the starboard, and the aircraft trembled.
   a. fat or stout in a dignified way
   b. the left side of a plane

a 5. The port engines roared, and then the **starboard,** and the aircraft trembled.
   a. the right side of a plane
   b. a board with stars

b 6. With these scant resources I prepared myself to withstand a **siege.**
   a. a flood
   b. an attack

b 7. Halfway down the **fuselage** a woman stood up on her seat.
   a. the place to set off fuses
   b. the main body of an airplane

b 8. My face was **inexplicably** covered in curry.
   a. inexpensively
   b. without explanation

▶Complete the similes from "Mijbil—Iraq to London."

mole	soccer player
street	bullet
stone	mosquitoes

starboard wing

fuselage

bulkhead

Taxiing down the runway

port wing

1. Otters were as common as _____ *mosquitoes* _____.

2. Between the layers of mud was a soft velvet fur like that of a chocolate-brown _____ *mole* .

3. Mij shuffled a rubber ball like a four-footed _____ *soccer player* _____.

4. Otters' teeth crunch into pulp fish heads that seem as hard as _____ *stone* _____.

5. The Arab driver tore through the streets of Basra like a _____ *bullet* _____.

6. The place looked like a _____ *street* _____ upon which royalty has been given a tickertape welcome.

Reading 5: "Mijbil—Iraq to London," pp. 256-60, Lesson 79
Vocabulary: matching words and definitions
Comprehension: completing similes

In Other Words

Name_____

▶ **Match each statement with another way to say the same thing.**

Paraphrasing is putting the author's words into your own words but keeping the same meaning.

___E___ 1. Otters were as common as mosquitoes in the Tigris marshes.

___H___ 2. I managed to remove the last of the mud and see him, so to speak, in his true colors.

___A___ 3. Mijbil went wild with joy in the water, plunging and rolling in it, shooting up and down the length of the bath underwater.

___C___ 4. The aircraft trembled and teetered against the tug of her propellers, and then we were taxiing out to take off.

___I___ 5. I prepared myself to withstand a siege.

___G___ 6. I staggered up babbling apology, and the Indian gave me a long, silent stare.

___J___ 7. In that first return to me was sown the seed of the absolute trust he gave me for the rest of his life.

___B___ 8. There is, I am convinced, something positively provoking to otters about order and tidiness in any form; and the greater the untidiness that they can make, the more contented they feel.

___D___ 9. The box was zinc lined, and it seemed to me as nearly ideal as could be.

___F___ 10. Then began a journey the like of which I hope I shall never know again.

A. Mijbil enjoyed playing in the water.

B. The messier a room is the happier the otter is.

C. The airplane shook and then moved down the runway.

D. The box seemed nearly perfect with its zinc lining.

E. There were many otters in the Tigris marshes.

F. I don't want to ever take a trip like that again.

G. The Indian just stared at me as I made an excuse.

H. I was able to see the otter without any mud on him.

I. I prepared for an attack.

J. After coming back to me, he trusted me forever.

▶**Paraphrase or write in your own words each of these sentences from "Mijbil—Iraq to London."**

Answers will vary.

1. Otters spend much of their time in play that does not even need a partner. _____

    Possible answer: Otters can spend a lot of time playing by themselves.

2. The Arab driver tore through the streets of Basra like a bullet. _____

    Possible answer: The Arab driver drove fast through the city.

3. Mij cried in the box, and both of us were hurled to and fro and up and down. _____

    Possible answer: Mij cried in his box, and we were both thrown in every direction.

4. My face was inexplicably covered in curry. _____

    Possible answer: There was no explanation for the curry all over my face.

5. Mijbil attacked the newspapers spread carefully around my feet, and in a minute or two the place looked like a street upon which royalty has been given a tickertape welcome.

    Possible answer: Mijbil made a mess by tearing up the newspapers.

    _____

6. I heard the ripple of flight and pursuit passing up and down the body of the aircraft

    behind me. _____ _Possible answer:_

    I could hear Mijbil being chased up and down the aisle of the plane.

Reading 5: "Mijbil—Iraq to London," pp. 250-60, Lesson 80
Study skills: paraphrasing sentences

Is That So?

▶**Write _yes_ in the blank if you can deduce the statement from the story. Write _no_ if you cannot.**

_no_ 1. Otters and dachshunds are good friends.

_no_ 2. Since otters make such great pets, many people will soon be buying them.

_no_ 3. The mother otter usually gives birth to five otter pups.

_no_ 4. Otters are found in forest lakes in eastern regions.

yes 5. If the door to the otter den were not hidden, other animals might eat the pups.

_no_ 6. A young otter's favorite game is "piggy-back riding."

_no_ 7. Otters eat chipmunks and other small animals.

yes 8. Otters are born with a fear of water.

_no_ 9. Baby otters soon learn to swim even better and more gracefully than their parents.

_no_ 10. Otters love swimming in streams along football fields.

_no_ 11. One-year-old otters are reluctant to leave the safety of their homes.

yes 12. An otter would probably be a fun pet to have.

yes 13. Otters usually do not live far from water.

yes 14. Mother and father otters are deeply loyal to each other.

yes 15. Otters are some of the most playful animals in the world.

yes 16. Otters seem to enjoy swimming and diving just for fun.

yes 17. An otter appears to grieve for its dead mate.

_no_ 18. Because otters like water so much, just about every pond or lake in America is likely to have one or two otter families living in it.

_no_ 19. Otters use their elbows to trap their prey in water.

yes 20. Otters catch their food while they play.

Reading 5: "Man's Next-Best Friend," pp. 261-65, Lesson 81
Comprehension: recalling facts and details; drawing conclusions

105

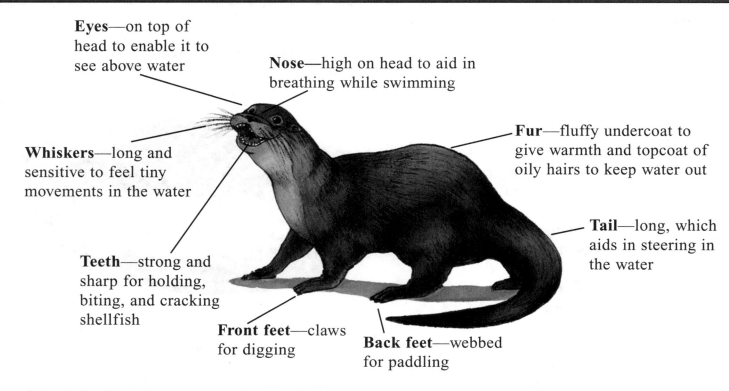

Eyes—on top of head to enable it to see above water

Nose—high on head to aid in breathing while swimming

Whiskers—long and sensitive to feel tiny movements in the water

Fur—fluffy undercoat to give warmth and topcoat of oily hairs to keep water out

Tail—long, which aids in steering in the water

Teeth—strong and sharp for holding, biting, and cracking shellfish

Front feet—claws for digging

Back feet—webbed for paddling

▶**Read the diagram to answer the questions.**

1. How does the otter keep dry? _____ *a topcoat of oily hairs* _____

2. What aids the otter in swimming? _____ *back feet and tail* _____

3. How can the otter see above the water? _____ *because its eyes are on top of its head* _____

4. Compare the functions of the otter's front and back feet. _____ *Front feet are used for digging; back feet are used for paddling.* _____

5. How do the otter's whiskers help him? _____ *help to feel tiny movements in the water* _____

6. What helps guide the otter in the water? _____ *long tail* _____

7. How many layers of fur does the otter have? _____ *two* _____

8. What kind of teeth does the otter have? _____ *strong and sharp* _____

▶**On your own paper draw a picture of what you think an otter holt looks like.**

The otter holt is made of a large pile of logs and tree branches. The entrance is a secret underwater tunnel that opens on the side of the lake. It is like a cave that is lined with plant life and divided into five different rooms for the otters to use.

Reading 5: "Man's Next-Best Friend," pp. 261-65, Lesson 81
Study skills: reading a diagram
Comprehension: recalling facts and details

▶**Complete the steps of the research and writing process using the acronym CROWN.**

C ___*hoose*___ a topic.

R ___*esearch*___ the topic.

O ___*rganize*___ an outline.

W___*rite*___ a rough draft.

N ___*ail down*___ the final presentation.

Spiders can be very helpful to humans. They eat insects like mosquitoes and flies that both annoy man and spread disease. Spiders also eat grasshoppers and locusts, which destroy crops and also sometimes bother people.

Tarantulas are the typical spider that people think of when they think of poisonous spiders. However, most tarantula bites are no more serious than a bee sting. Tarantulas can grow up to five inches long and are extremely hairy. So they fit the popular ideal of the "horrid" spider.

Enemies of the spider include toads, snakes, frogs, lizards, fish, birds, and some insects. Wasps are especially hazardous to the tarantula.

Spiders live every place imaginable: if food is available, spiders will be there. Some spiders live only in burrows, others only underwater. They also live in fields, woods, swamps, caves, deserts, mountains, and in every kind of building.

▶**Take notes on part of the research Robert found about spiders, using the following guide.**

Order may vary.

How spiders are helpful to man

1. ___*They eat mosquitoes*___
   ___*and flies.*___

2. ___*They eat grasshoppers*___
   ___*and locusts.*___

3. ___*fields*___

4. ___*woods*___

5. ___*swamps*___

6. ___*caves*___

7. ___*deserts*___

Where spiders live

1. ___*burrows*___

2. ___*underwater*___

8. ___*mountains*___

9. ___*buildings*___

Reading 5: "Skill Lesson: Research and Writing," pp. 266-69, Lesson 82
Study skills: taking notes

Body parts of a spider differ from those of insects. Most spiders have eight eyes, though some have only two. They have no teeth, just some small structures that form a straw for sucking the body juices from their victims. Chelicera, located between the spider's eyes and mouth, are small extensions that end in curved, fanglike projections. These curve inward and inject poison into the spider's prey; sometimes they are used to crush food. The pedipalp are larger, leglike projections that form the sides of its mouth. Spiders have eight legs—a major difference from insects, which have six. Each leg is made up of seven segments. The spinnerets are small projections on the spider's abdomen. Most types of spiders have six spinnerets, but each type has at least two. They funnel the silken liquid into the air, where it hardens into thread form.

Different types of spiders use different methods for catching food. The most common spiders spin large webs that catch flying insects. The spider then injects the insect with poison that paralyzes or kills it. Some spiders spin a length of web with a sticky portion at the end. When an insect flies by, the spider flings out the line and snares it. Other types stalk and pounce on prey with a jumping motion. These jumping spiders are able to jump more than forty times the length of their bodies. They can move quite a bit faster that way than their cousins who walk on eight legs! Some spiders are also capable of *ballooning.* They raise their spinnerets to the wind, allowing silk to escape. The wind lifts the webbing and carries the spider through the air. Spiders have been known to travel hundreds of miles in this way.

▶**Continue taking notes on Robert's research, using the following guide.**

Order may vary.

Body parts of a spider

1. _____ eyes _____
2. _____ mouth _____
3. _____ chelicera _____
4. _____ pedipalp _____
5. _____ legs _____
6. _____ spinnerets _____

How spiders capture food

1. _____ by spinning webs _____
2. _____ by flinging a sticky thread _____
3. _____ by pouncing _____

How spiders travel

1. _____ jumping _____
2. _____ walking _____
3. _____ ballooning _____

Name_____

	Tuna	Jellyfish	Redfish	Snapping Turtle	Lake Trout	Lobster
Saltwater	X	X	X			X
Freshwater				X	X	
Gills	X		X		X	X
Backbone	X		X	X	X	
Fins	X		X		X	
Swim	X	X	X	X	X	
Carnivore	X	X	X	X	X	X
Food for people	X		X	X	X	X
Lay eggs	X	X	X	X	X	X

▶ **Put each creature from the chart under the heading that describes it. Some creatures will go under more than one heading.**

Saltwater, Fins

tuna

redfish

Saltwater, Lay eggs

tuna

jellyfish

redfish

lobster

Freshwater, Lay eggs

snapping turtle

lake trout

Gills, Backbone, Fins

tuna

redfish

lake trout

Saltwater, Swim, Carnivore

tuna

jellyfish

redfish

Carnivore, Food for people, Lay eggs

tuna

redfish

snapping turtle

lake trout

lobster

Reading 5: "The Silent Witness," pp. 270-74, Lesson 83
Study skills: classifying by multiple attributes

Action and Settings

▶ Fill in the blanks to show the time and the place of the setting.   *Responses will vary.*

The fisherman paddles a slender canoe across the still, clear water of a lake. Beside him lies a fishing line that ends in a bone hook. Its polished bone lure is decorated with hairs from a deer's tail. Nearby a spear with sharp stone tips on its three prongs is ready to use as soon as the fish is hauled close to the boat.

1. **Time** (general) _____ *long ago* _____

2. **Place** _____ *in a canoe on a lake* _____

Late in the year 1875, the Chinese fisherman stood at the front of his houseboat, anchored in a broad muddy-yellow river. His eyes never left the large black birds diving into the water. The birds wore metal bands around their long, thin necks to keep them from swallowing the fish they caught. On the deck beside the fisherman, big bamboo baskets were empty and waiting.

3. **Time** (year) _____ *1875* _____

4. **Place** _____ *on a houseboat on a river* _____

The tall, lanky fisherman sets a plastic tackle box of feathered flies down on the rocky bank. Still holding on to his long, thick fiberglass pole, he crouches at the edge of the stream to look for a deep pool that might be hiding a rainbow trout.

5. **Time** (general) _____ *the present* _____

6. **Place** _____ *beside a stream* _____

The fisherman hunches deep into his fur-lined parka for protection against the icy wind that sweeps across the snowy fields. His feet are warm inside his heavy boots, even though he is standing on ice. Quietly he waits beside a round air hole in the ice, gripping his bone-tipped harpoon.

7. **Time** (season) _____ *winter* _____

8. **Place** _____ *an ice-covered lake or stream* _____

Reading 5: "The Silent Witness," pp. 270-74, Lesson 83
Literature: identifying setting; recognizing the relationship between setting and plot

Going Home

Name_____

▶ **Use complete sentences to answer the questions.**   *Wording may vary.*

1. Why did the smile leave Mera's eyes when Cato went fishing instead of going to church with her? _____ *She wanted Cato to hear the gospel being preached.* _____

2. Why did Mera whisper, "I'm going home"? _____
   _____ *She knew she was dying and going home to heaven.* _____

3. Why did Cato avoid Tali, Belee, Mr. Sam, and even Punik? _____ *He was angry and* _____
   hurt because of Mera's death. He had no faith he would see her again.
   _____

4. Why did Punik continue to go to church with Tali and Belee? _____
   _____ *He showed loyalty to Mera. / He was in the habit of going.* _____

5. Why did Cato follow Punik? _____
   _____ *Cato was curious about where Punik was going.* _____

6. Why did Mr. Sam invite Cato to eat lunch with him? _____
   _____ *Mr. Sam could take as much time as needed to help Cato.* _____

7. Why did Cato have questions for Mr. Sam? _____ *He had things he did not* _____
   understand. / He did not understand what Mera meant about going home.
   _____

8. Why did Cato leave the missionary's house "a new creature in Christ"? _____
   _____ *He asked Jesus to save him. / He had new life in Christ.* _____

Reading 5: "The Silent Witness," pp. 275-78, Lesson 84
Comprehension: inferring cause-and-effect relationships; inferring unstated supporting details

Personality Plus

Personification is giving animals or objects the actions or qualities of people.

▶Look at the words in color. Do the words show the actions or qualities of people? Circle the number of each sentence that shows personification.

(1.) The dry earth drank the refreshing rain.

(2.) The pink bud's face peeked through the green leaves.

3. The sun shone in the sky.

(4.) The rising sun painted the mountaintops red.

(5.) The snow crept over the sleeping town.

▶ Replace the word in color with a word that will show personification.

leaped	blushed	danced	smiled

1. The moon shined in the night. _____ *possible answers: smiled, blushed*

2. The leaves blew in the wind. _____ *possible answers: leaped, danced*

▶If the sentence from "The Silent Witness" shows personification, write the letter *P*.

P ____ 1. Cato listened to the whisper of early morning waves on the beach.

____ 2. By the time the fire burned hot, others in the village would be awakening.

P ____ 3. The waves crashed on the sand, spinning the shining foam almost to Cato's feet, then breathing the foam back into the water.

P ____ 4. By the time the two men returned, shadows had crept into the hut.

P ____ 5. The pale light touched her face.

____ 6. Punik wagged his tail when Tali and Belee stopped by for Mera.

Reading 5: "The Silent Witness," pp. 275-78, Lesson 84
Literature: identifying personification

Name_____

Falconry is a sport that uses trained birds to hunt small animals and birds. The best birds for falconry are birds of prey like falcons, hawks, and eagles, because their natural instinct is to kill small animals. With their excellent eyesight and sharp beaks and talons, they are well-equipped to be successful hunters.

These birds of prey are naturally very wild, so training them is a slow process. At first, the bird has leather jesses tied to its legs with a leash attached to them. While it is on the leash, the bird must first learn to fly a short way back to the heavy leather glove on its master's hand for a tidbit of food. Then it is allowed off the leash and taught to catch wild game.

The bird may be taught to fly back to a lure, which looks like a small dead animal and reminds it of food. When the trainer swings the lure in circles over his head, a good bird will return from surprisingly long distances. It is taught to fly longer and longer distances.

In the United States today, there are hundreds of falconers and falconry clubs, and they fly a total of more than ten thousand trained birds. Teaching birds of prey to hunt takes many months and a good supply of patience, but it can be a rewarding hobby.

▶**Write the letter of the main idea of each paragraph.**

___*b*___ paragraph one
    a. the instincts of birds
    b. the sport of falconry

___*b*___ paragraph two
    a. strapping jesses on the birds
    b. training the birds

___*a*___ paragraph three
    a. falconry as a hobby
    b. patience in training birds

▶**Decide whether you would like to try your hand at being a falconer. Write a short paragraph telling why or why not.**

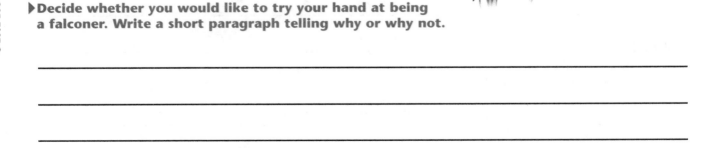

Reading 5: "Eagle on a Leash," pp. 279-83, Lesson 86
Comprehension: identifying the main idea of a paragraph
Composition: writing creatively

Birds of Prey

	Wingspan	Kind of Nest	Food	Voice
Black Vulture	54 in.	none; lays eggs on ground	dead animals, young birds	hisses
Red-tailed Hawk	56 in.	platform of sticks	rats, mice, small animals, insects	piercing scream
Broad-winged Hawk	36 in.	bowl of sticks lined with cedar bark and deer hair	frogs, mice, rats, snakes, insects	thin whistle
Osprey	72 in.	reeds, weeds, sticks; lined with moss	fish	soft *kree*-ing
Sparrow Hawk	21 in.	cavity in a tree	insects, mice, small birds	sharp *killy killy killy*
Golden Eagle	84 in.	platform of sticks lined with leaves and grass	rabbits, small animals	high-pitched squeal

▶ **Use the chart to answer the questions.**

1. What is the title of the column that tells you the distance from one wing tip to another?

   Wingspan

2. Which is the smallest bird of prey? *Sparrow Hawk*

3. What do golden eagles eat? *rabbits, small animals*

4. What kind of nest does a black vulture have? *None; it lays eggs on the ground.*

5. If you heard *killy killy killy,* what kind of bird would you be hearing?

   Sparrow Hawk

6. Which birds eat mice? *Red-tailed Hawk, Broad-winged Hawk, Sparrow Hawk*

7. Which bird's nest do you think would be the hardest to make?

   Answers may vary; Broad-winged Hawk / Red-tailed Hawk

8. Which bird has the longest wingspan? *Golden Eagle*

Reading 5: "Eagle on a Leash," pp. 284–87, Lesson 87
Study skills: reading a chart
Comprehension: perceiving size relationships

▶ **Choose the best character trait for each character in bold print.**

1. **Mr. Culpepper**'s cold eyes turned on Brent, and the boy felt a shiver run down his spine. "Perhaps your boy here let her out."

   ● hostile
   ○ friendly

2. **Jasper** stood half behind his father, scuffing the toe of his boot in the dirt.

   ○ bold
   ● shy

3. **Jasper** followed him slowly. Suddenly he stopped, took off his hat and began turning it around and around in his hands. He swung around and faced Brent. "I'm sorry."

   ○ brave
   ● responsible

4. Brent protested, "I told Rama this morning she could fly today!" "Not today, Son." **Mr. Thompson** shook his head. "Let's let things simmer down a little."

   ● insightful
   ○ impatient

5. "Hot as a firecracker and it's only July." **Brent** carefully pulled out a chocolate drink, dropped his money into the coin box, and pried the cap off the drink. He looked at Jasper. "Aren't you hot?"

   ● friendly
   ○ timid

6. "But I've read lots of books about eagles. We can use Dad's bow net and lure. It won't hurt to try, anyway," **Brent** replied.

   ● creative
   ○ tolerant

7. "Sure," **Brent** said with more confidence than he felt. "It's done all the time. Besides, we've got to do something to prove to your father that Rama isn't a killer."

   ○ fair-minded
   ● impatient

8. **Brent** finished his chores and made sure Rama had water and food.

   ○ cleanliness
   ● responsible

9. The eagle's wings spread, beating the air fiercely. With a wild shriek, it rose into the air. "It missed the squirrel, too." **Jasper** shrunk back against Brent. "And it's mad!"

   ○ bold
   ● fearful

10. Barlow lowered the rifle. "Pop," Jasper ran to his father. "You didn't shoot." **Mr. Culpepper** shook his head. "They were right. There are two eagles and I can't be sure which one did the killing."

   ● fair-minded
   ○ hostile

    COLOSSIANS 3:23
    And whatsoever ye do, do it heartily, as to the Lord.

Reading 5: "Eagle on a Leash," pp. 288-92, Lesson 88
Comprehension: perceiving a character's perspective; identifying character traits

115

As a Result

▶ **Choose the correct effect.**

1. **Cause:** Brent started a friendly conversation with Jasper.

   Effect:
   - ○ Jasper continued to be silent.
   - ● Jasper began to talk.

2. **Cause:** Mr. Culpepper rattled the cage door.

   Effect:
   - ○ Rama, tired from flying, lay down and closed her eyes.
   - ● Rama threw herself against the cage wall.

3. **Cause:** Brent lured the wild eagle into the canyon.

   Effect:
   - ● Rama rose to defend her territory and broke her leash.
   - ○ Rama remained asleep in her cage.

4. **Cause:** Mr. Culpepper threatened to shoot Rama.

   Effect:
   - ● Jasper agreed to help Brent prove there was another eagle.
   - ○ Brent decided to prove there was another eagle by himself.

▶ **Choose the correct cause.**

1. **Cause:**
   - ● One of Mr. Culpepper's lambs was killed.
   - ○ Brent set a trap for the wild eagle.

   Effect: Mr. Culpepper was angry and felt Rama was responsible.

2. **Cause:**
   - ○ Rama broke free of her leash.
   - ● The wild eagle was seen fighting with Rama.

   Effect: Mr. Culpepper changed his mind about Rama.

▶ **Write a word that matches each definition.**
The shaded letters spell something Rama enjoyed doing in the canyon.

glinted	fledgling	unwieldy	lure	menacingly

1. flashed briefly
2. not easily managed
3. in a threatening manner
4. a young bird just learning to fly
5. something that attracts

1. G L I N T E D
2. U N W I E L D Y
3. M E N A C I N G L Y
4. F L E D G L I N G
5. L U R E

© 2002 BJU Press. Reproduction prohibited.

Reading 5: "Eagle on a Leash," pp. 288-92, Lesson 88
Comprehension: identifying cause-and-effect relationships
Vocabulary: matching words and definitions

▶ **Suppose you were asked to write a report on eagles. You have read "Eagle on a Leash" and "Eagle: King of Birds." Use the information from those selections to answer the questions.**

> When researching, you must determine whether information is **relevant** or **irrelevant** to your topic.

1. Under what topic might you find relevant information about eagles?

   ● birds
   ○ fireflies
   ○ canyons

2. Under which other topic might you find relevant information about eagles?

   ○ sheep ranches
   ● falconry
   ○ rifles

3. Which topic would be irrelevant in your search?

   ● reptiles
   ○ carnivores
   ○ United States symbols

4. Which sentence would be irrelevant in an advertisement for saving the eagles from extinction?

   ○ Protect these magnificent birds.
   ● The razor-sharp talons may be two to three inches long.
   ○ It is against the law to kill an eagle.

5. Which **two** sentences are relevant in a paragraph about an eagle as a hunter?

   ● The eagle's weapons are his beak and talons.
   ○ The golden eagle is kept on a leash.
   ● The eagle is a predator because it kills its own food.

6. What **two** sentences would be relevant in a paragraph describing the nests of eagles?

   ○ Eaglets exercise by flapping their wings, jumping up and down, and stamping about.
   ● Leaves, grass, feathers, moss, and other soft materials line the nest.
   ● Bald eagles build their nests in tall trees.

7. Which sentence is irrelevant in a paragraph explaining the responsibility of an eaglet's parents?

   ● Eagles can live thirty to fifty years.
   ○ Parents show the eaglets how to tear the food into pieces.
   ○ The parents take turns sitting in the nest.

8. Which sentence would be irrelevant in a paragraph about eaglets growing up?

   ○ Eaglets learn to grasp objects with their talons.
   ● Eagles are swift, powerful, and faithful.
   ○ Eaglets take their first flight from the edge of the nest.

© 2002 BJU Press. Reproduction prohibited.

Reading 5: "Eagle: King of Birds," pp. 293-97, Lesson 89
Study skills: identifying relevant and irrelevant information

117

ISAIAH 40:31

But they that wait upon the Lord shall renew their strength; they shall mount up with wings as eagles; they shall run, and not be weary; and they shall walk, and not faint.

The best known eagles in the United States are the golden eagle and the bald eagle. The bald eagle was named years ago by early settlers, who used *bald* to mean "white." A bald eagle is distinguished by the white feathers covering its head, while the golden eagle displays golden brown feathers at the back of the neck. Because of its strength and splendor, the bald eagle was chosen to be the symbol of our country.

Bald eagles build their nests in tall trees; golden eagles prefer high cliffs. The nests, called *aeries,* are built mainly of sticks. They are lined with leaves, grass, feathers, moss, and other soft materials. Eagles use the same nesting site year after year. They build each new nest on top of the others. Since these birds can live from thirty to fifty years, the nests become enormous.

The female eagle lays two or three white eggs each year. The eggs are not much bigger than chicken eggs. Over the next thirty-five to forty days, the parents take turns sitting in the nest until the eaglets hatch. At birth the eaglets are covered with fuzzy, grayish-white down until the feathers begin to grow.

When the babies are first hatched, the adults put food directly into their mouths. Soon, however, the parents show the youngsters how to tear the food into pieces and feed themselves.

▶ **Take notes on the paragraphs about eagles, using the following guide.** *Order may vary.*

Types of eagles

1. _____ golden eagle _____

2. _____ bald eagle _____

Places to nest

1. _____ tall trees _____

2. _____ cliffs _____

Lining materials for nests

1. _____ leaves _____

2. _____ grass _____

3. _____ feathers _____

4. _____ moss _____

5. _____ other soft materials _____

Parents' responsibilities

1. _take turns sitting in nest_

2. _____ put food directly _____

_____ into eaglets' mouths _____

3. _____ show the youngsters _____

_____ how to tear the food _____

Reading 5: "Eagle: King of Birds," pp. 293-97, Lesson 89
Study skills: taking notes

On Eagle's Wings

▶**Choose the correct paraphrase for the following Bible verses.**

1. **Psalm 103:5**
   - ● God gives us strength that we need.
   - ○ God gives children energy.

DEUTERONOMY 32:11-12
As an eagle stirreth up her nest, fluttereth over her young, spreadeth abroad her wings, taketh them, beareth them on her wings: So the Lord alone did lead him.

2. **Obadiah 4**
   - ○ God made the eagle to soar with the stars.
   - ● God will bring down those who think that they are great and mighty.

3. **Deuteronomy 32:11-12a**
   - ● God takes care of us as an eagle cares for her young.
   - ○ God will gather His children together as a hen gathers her children under her wings.

4. **Jeremiah 49:16**
   - ○ God's Word tells us how to live.
   - ● God will bring down the wicked who think that they are above Him.

5. **Job 9:25-26**
   - ● Life is short. The days fly by as swiftly as an eagle hunting an animal.
   - ○ Life gives us many days to enjoy.

6. **Isaiah 40:31**
   - ○ Christians need to look to Jesus as they go through life.
   - ● If you wait on God, He will give you special strength.

▶**Write a paraphrase for each statement. Be sure to keep the original meaning.**

Wording will vary.

1. The boy ran as swift as an eagle down the hill.

   The boy ran quickly down the hill.

2. My eagle-eyed math teacher found the error in the word problem.

   My math teacher sees everything and

   found the error in the word problem.

Reading 5: "The Eagle," pp. 298-99, Lesson 90
Study skills: locating Bible verses; paraphrasing Bible verses and sentences

119

Eagle Eyes

▶ **Read the steps to learn how to complete an analogy.**

1. Analogy: hen is to chick as eagle is to _____

2. An **analogy** compares or relates the two statements or facts. The key is to figure out the relationship of the first words. The second set of words will have the same relationship.

3. What is the relationship between the hen and the chick? The hen is the mother of the chick. What is the eagle the mother of?

> *hen* is to *chick* as *eagle* is to *eaglet*

4. An analogy may be expressed using an arrow to represent *is to* and a colon in place of the word *as*. Read the symbols as if they were these words.

> hen *is to* chick *as* eagle *is to* eaglet
> hen → chick : eagle → eaglet

An **analogy** is a comparison that shows the relationship between words.

▶ **Use the words to complete the analogies.**

soar	fish	jesses	nest

1. fish is to swim as eagle is to _____ *soar*

2. horse is to bridle as eagle is to _____ *jesses*

3. bear is to den as eagle is to _____ *nest*

4. koala is to leaves as eagle is to _____ *fish*

carnivore	feet	stubbornness	aerie	freedom

5. dove → peace : eagle → _____ *freedom*

6. eagle → courage : donkey → _____ *stubbornness*

7. cow → herbivore : eagle → _____ *carnivore*

8. beak → head : talons → _____ *feet*

9. undigested food → casting : nest → _____ *aerie*

▶Label each event from the story "One in a Million" as
  B (before the game began) or **A** (after the game began).

___B___ 1. Coach Wilson had an outrageous idea.

___B___ 2. The football players went on strike.

___A___ 3. The gazelle made a leaping catch.

___B___ 4. Mr. Libscomb determined not to pay his players a million dollars each.

___A___ 5. The stadium was named in honor of Coach Wilson.

___A___ 6. The Gators' quarterback dropped the ball.

___B___ 7. The animals sat quietly in their custom-made jerseys.

___B___ 8. Flex Bulk threatened to injure anyone who signed up for the new team.

___A___ 9. The rhino dragged five players into the end zone.

___B___ 10. Coach Wilson watched a news story about the zoo.

___A___ 11. The ostrich ran around the top of the stadium with the football.

___A___ 12. The old Mobsters booed the new team.

▶Match each player with his actions.

___F___ 1. The orangutan

___B___ 2. The ostrich

___A___ 3. The rhinoceros

___C___ 4. The giraffe

___E___ 5. The gazelle

___G___ 6. The hippo

___D___ 7. The monkeys

A. enjoyed charging.

B. ran into the stands instead of the end zone.

C. was offside with his neck.

D. were agile.

E. made a terrific receiver.

F. had a good arm.

G. let out a tremendous roar.

Reading 5: "One in a Million," pp. 300-307, Lesson 93
Comprehension: sequencing events; matching characters and actions; recalling facts and details

121

Football Comparisons

▶ **Put an X on the word that does *not* belong in each group.**

Example:	hot dogs	popcorn	~~stadium~~ French fries

1. San Francisco	Boston	Pittsburgh	~~Mexico~~
2. referee	linebacker	~~golf~~	quarterback
3. running	~~swimming~~	blocking	passing
4. ostrich	~~huddle~~	hippo	giraffe
5. screaming	~~clapping~~	yelling	shouting
6. Mobsters	Gators	Mustangs	~~American~~
7. ~~skiing~~	football	basketball	tennis
8. ~~cheerleader~~	kickoff	touchdown	huddle
9. stands	bleachers	~~bedroom~~	benches
10. teams	~~governor~~	cheerleaders	crowd

▶ **Put the accent mark on the correct syllable.**

mus´ • tangs   dis • like´   ros´ • ter

hud´ • dle   in • vest´   tal´ • on

bench´ • es   pon • toon´

a • loof´   can´ • yon

In words with prefixes and suffixes, the base word is usually accented.

In a two-syllable word, the accent usually falls on the first syllable. If the second syllable has two vowels, the second syllable usually receives the accent.

Reading 5: "One in a Million," pp. 300-307, Lesson 93
Vocabulary: classifying words
Structural analysis: applying Accent Rule 2—words with affixes;
applying Accent Rule 3—two-syllable words without affixes

Fitly Spoken

▶ **Complete the crossword puzzle.**

Across

1. a boat made by hollowing out a log
4. to smile in a knowing, superior manner
5. having sharp projections
7. underwater fishing using a wooden shaft with a metal point
10. to stare at something with one's mouth open
11. to float without moving much
12. something used temporarily
17. mild or pleasant
19. to move or swirl vigorously
20. a sudden increase

Down

2. a long, flowing garment worn mostly in Muslim countries
3. pulled back quickly in pain; flinched
6. jutting out

8. to light an area
9. a ridge of rocks or coral that reaches to the surface of the water
13. a wooden or metal beam that runs down the center of the bottom of a boat
14. to place or go beneath the surface of water
15. overconfident
16. sudden, strong breezes
18. muddy; stirred up

PROVERBS 25:11
A word fitly spoken is like apples of gold in pictures of silver.

balmy
churn
cocky
dugout
galabia
gape
gusts
hover
illuminate
jagged
keel
makeshift
murky
protruding
reef
smirk
spearfishing
submerge
surge
winced

Reading 5: "A Spear for Omar," pp. 308-14, Lesson 94
Vocabulary: matching words and definitions

123

A Family Chart

▶Find the character from the story who fits the words. Write the name in the box.

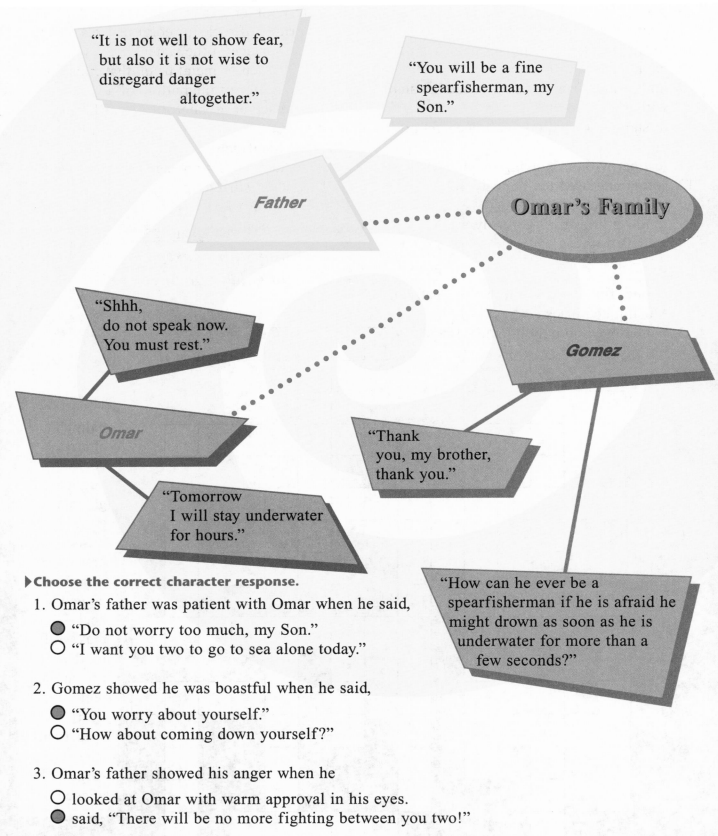

"It is not well to show fear, but also it is not wise to disregard danger altogether."

"You will be a fine spearfisherman, my Son."

Father

Omar's Family

"Shhh, do not speak now. You must rest."

Gomez

Omar

"Thank you, my brother, thank you."

"Tomorrow I will stay underwater for hours."

"How can he ever be a spearfisherman if he is afraid he might drown as soon as he is underwater for more than a few seconds?"

▶Choose the correct character response.

1. Omar's father was patient with Omar when he said,
   - ● "Do not worry too much, my Son."
   - ○ "I want you two to go to sea alone today."

2. Gomez showed he was boastful when he said,
   - ● "You worry about yourself."
   - ○ "How about coming down yourself?"

3. Omar's father showed his anger when he
   - ○ looked at Omar with warm approval in his eyes.
   - ● said, "There will be no more fighting between you two!"

124

Reading 5: "A Spear for Omar," pp. 308-14, Lesson 94
Comprehension: matching characters and dialogue; evaluating character responses

▶**Answer the questions in complete sentences.**

1. What did 'Vumbe enjoy doing near the Jungle Hospital, besides spending his time in mischief?

   He enjoyed rummaging in the

   rubbish-heap.

2. What treasure did 'Vumbe find that alarmed Twiga?

   'Vumbe found a pot of

   red paint.

3. Why did Twiga want 'Vumbe to look in the mirror at the

   hospital? _____

   He wanted him to see the red paint on his face.

4. Why did 'Vumbe feel satisfied when the jackal, the lion, and his friends looked at him

   with the mirror? _____*They were impressed with his mirror.*_____

5. How is the Bible like a mirror? _____*When you read the Bible, you see yourself*

   exactly as God sees you.

▶**Write the correct character for each description.**

'Vumbe (monkey)	Twiga (giraffe)	Mbisi (hyaena)
Nyani ('Vumbe's uncle)	Lwa-lwa (tortoise)	Daudi (missionary)

_____*Twiga*_____ 1. said the mirror is a thing of true wisdom

_____*'Vumbe*_____ 2. impressed friends and relatives

_____*Lwa-lwa*_____ 3. had a flying bob of light flashed in his beady eyes

_____*Mbisi*_____ 4. said to wrap the mirror in a banana leaf and hide it

_____*Nyani*_____ 5. splattered banana on 'Vumbe's face

_____*Daudi*_____ 6. told a parable of a monkey, a mirror, and red paint

Reading 5: "The Monkey, the Mirror, and the Red Paint," pp. 315-19, Lesson 95
Comprehension: comparing and contrasting story elements; matching characters and actions

125

▶ **Write the letter of the lesson for each parable.**

A. We should help those in need, whether we know them or not.
B. The Lord rewards all His workers as He sees fit.
C. Our own spiritual houses should be founded on the Rock of Christ.
D. It pays to count the cost of entering the kingdom of God.
E. We should lay up our treasures in heaven rather than on earth.

> A **parable** is a story or an object lesson that teaches a spiritual truth.

"Therefore whosoever heareth these sayings of mine, and doeth them, I will liken him unto a wise man, which built his house upon a rock: and the rain descended, and the floods came, and the winds blew, and beat upon that house; and it fell not: for it was founded upon a rock. And every one that heareth these sayings of mine, and doeth them not, shall be likened unto a foolish man, which built his house upon the sand: and the rain descended, and the floods came, and the winds blew, and beat upon that house; and it fell: and great was the fall of it." (Matthew 7:24-27)

Lesson: _____ *C* _____

"And he spake a parable unto them, saying, The ground of a certain rich man brought forth plentifully: and he thought within himself, saying, What shall I do, because I have no room where to bestow my fruits? And he said, This will I do: I will pull down my barns, and build greater; and there will I bestow all my fruits and my goods. And I will say to my soul, Soul, thou hast much goods laid up for many years; take thine ease, eat, drink, and be merry. But God said unto him, Thou fool, this night thy soul shall be required of thee: then whose shall those things be, which thou hast provided?" (Luke 12:16-20)

Lesson: _____ *E* _____

"A certain man went down from Jerusalem to Jericho, and fell among thieves, which stripped him of his raiment, and wounded him, and departed, leaving him half dead. And by chance there came down a certain priest that way: and when he saw him, he passed by on the other side. And likewise a Levite, when he was at the place, came and looked on him, and passed by on the other side. But a certain Samaritan, as he journeyed, came where he was: and when he saw him, he had compassion on him. And went to him, and bound up his wounds, pouring in oil and wine, and set him on his own beast, and brought him to an inn, and took care of him. And on the morrow when he departed, he took out two pence, and gave them to the host, and said unto him, Take care of him; and whatsoever thou spendest more, when I come again, I will repay thee." (Luke 10:30-35)

Lesson: _____ *A* _____

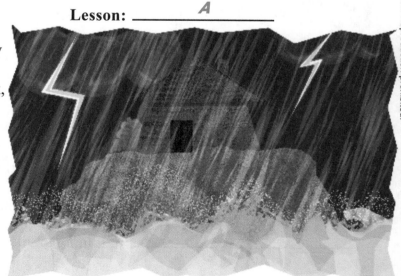

Reading 5: "The Monkey, the Mirror, and the Red Paint," pp. 315-19, Lesson 95
Comprehension: determining the lesson of a parable

Conflicting Courses

Name_____

Struggles in stories are called conflicts. **Internal conflict** shows the character having a struggle inside himself. **External conflict** shows the character having a struggle with people or things outside the character.

Accept any answer with a reasonable explanation.

▶**Identify the type of conflict by writing *internal* or *external* in the blank.**

Derrick befriends a wounded coyote and raises it as a pet. When several spring lambs are found slaughtered by a wild animal, the ranchers accuse the coyote. Derrick attempts to protect his pet while trying to prove its innocence.

external
_____

For weeks, Gary hasn't wanted to go to chapel or to church. He avoids any talk of the Lord in his Christian school. He mopes around the house unhappily. Finally, one day in chapel, he can't stand it any longer. When the chapel speaker gives the invitation, Gary goes forward and is saved.

internal
_____

Miriam wants to try for editor of the school paper in April, but her lack of responsibility disturbs her parents. They talk with her about improving her work at home before taking on additional responsibility at school. Miriam tries to solve her problem by keeping charts of her jobs—their beginning and their completion. By April, Miriam has improved so much that her parents let her try for the editor's job.

internal
_____

Emanuel spends the summer studying survival skills at a special camp. The following autumn, he goes on a wilderness hunt with his father. When his father is injured in a freak accident, Emanuel has to get him back to civilization where he can be treated.

external
_____

Michelle capsizes her boat in rough seas and is marooned on a small island. She must survive by living off the island until she is rescued.

external
_____

Preston lives beside a lake. Though all his friends and his family are excellent swimmers, Preston is afraid of the water. His friends laugh at him, leaving him out of the summer activities. Preston works diligently and overcomes his fear. Now he enjoys swimming with his friends.

internal
_____

Reading 5: "Literature Lesson: Conflict in Stories," pp. 320-22, Lesson 96
Literature: identifying types of conflict

127

Conflict and Resolution

> Each story or narrative must have **conflict** or a struggle.

▶**Mark the conflict of each story.**

1. "Mijbil—Iraq to London"

   ○ Mijbil played with the chromium bathroom taps.

   ● A playful otter did not like to be transported in a cage from Iraq to London.

2. "The Silent Witness"

   ● Cato refused to go to church with Mera.

   ○ Cato had a great knowledge of the sea.

3. "Eagle on a Leash"

   ● Mr. Culpepper thought the golden eagle Rama was killing his sheep.

   ○ Rama was on a leash and could not be a troublemaker.

4. "One in a Million"

   ○ The Mobsters had two undefeated seasons in a row.

   ● The football players decided to strike in order to get more pay.

▶**Mark the resolution of each story.**

> The ending of a story is the **resolution,** the final outcome.

1. "Mijbil—Iraq to London"

   ● Mijbil was home and free from the box that kept him from his play.

   ○ Mijbil looked like a very small dragon.

2. "The Silent Witness"

   ● Cato became a new creature in Christ.

   ○ Cato fished without Tali on Sundays.

3. "Eagle on a Leash"

   ○ Mr. Culpepper accused Rama of killing a lamb.

   ● Mr. Culpepper could understand eagles as pets.

4. "One in a Million"

   ○ Coach Wilson arranged to train animals to play football.

   ● The Boston Mobsters become a winning, unforgettable team.

Reading 5: "Literature Lesson: Conflict in Stories," pp. 320-22, Lesson 96
Literature: identifying the conflict of a story; identifying the resolution of a story

▶**Underline the phrase that makes each statement correct.**

1. Everyone wanted to be in the fifth- and sixth-
   grade play because
   a. Mrs. Morrison gave extra credit.
   b. <u>Mrs. Morrison was the best play director.</u>
   c. there were so many lines to memorize.

2. Mark thought he would get the main part because
   a. he had worked hard to learn the part.
   b. Mrs. Morrison heard him saying his lines.
   c. <u>he was one of the best speakers.</u>

3. Mark learned all the lines for the part of Joshua
   because
   a. he needed to know all of the lines for
      the tryout.
   b. he wanted to impress his family.
   c. <u>he thought he would get the part.</u>

4. Mark was starting to get nervous during his
   tryout because
   a. he had rehearsed for so many days.
   b. <u>Mrs. Morrison was frowning and whispering
      to the principal.</u>
   c. he had to leave early.

5. Mrs. Morrison had lost sleep because
   a. <u>she had been worrying and praying.</u>
   b. she had no concern for Mark.
   c. the principal had said that Mark must be Moses.

6. Mark didn't want to help Randy because
   a. he liked Randy very much.
   b. he did not see Mrs. Morrison.
   c. <u>he felt as if Randy had taken his part away from him.</u>

7. Mark felt smug that Randy was having trouble with his part because
   a. <u>he had tried to warn Mrs. Morrison.</u>
   b. Mrs. Morrison didn't seem to understand his feelings.
   c. the part of an Israelite was so much easier to learn.

8. Mrs. Morrison wanted the students to honor the Lord through the play because
   a. there were many parts to learn.
   b. <u>unsaved parents would be coming to see the students.</u>
   c. the principal wanted a bigger boy to play Joshua.

Reading 5: "Moses and Joshua," pp. 324-29, Lesson 99
Comprehension: inferring facts and details; identifying cause-and-effect relationships

Opposite Viewpoints

▶**Label each sentence as fact (F) or opinion (O).**

_O_ 1. Mrs. Morrison did the best job putting on plays of all the teachers at Riverside Christian School.

_O_ 2. Mark thought he was the best for the part of Joshua.

_F_ 3. The Lord can give you the strength to help Randy.

_F_ 4. The principal and Mrs. Morrison attended the tryouts.

_O_ 5. Mark made a better Joshua than Randy.

_F_ 6. Mark studied all the lines for the part of Joshua.

_O_ 7. Mark was the most nervous student waiting to tryout.

▶**Write the antonym for each colored word.**

disallow close in	insignificant roomiest	vacate occupied

insignificant 1. I figured I would probably get the main part.

occupied 2. I worked on my lines every spare minute for days.

vacate 3. Tell us what sort of people inhabit this land.

close in 4. The waters shall part and stand up in a heap.

roomiest 5. The reading circle was the most cramped it had ever been.

disallow 6. "Mark, I won't tolerate that kind of spirit."

Reading 5: "Moses and Joshua," pp. 324-29, Lesson 99
Comprehension: distinguishing between fact and opinion
Vocabulary: using context clues to determine meaning; matching antonyms

Plot in Sequence

▶ **Write the correct letter in the blanks on the plot frame to put the events in story order.**

A. Randy's mother attends the play.

B. Without Mark coaching him, Randy stumbles through his lines at the first rehearsal.

C. The fifth- and sixth-graders at Riverside Christian School receive scripts for the play.

D. Instead of applause, Mark's change of attitude matters most to him and the Lord.

E. Mark is diligent to learn all the lines for the part of Joshua.

F. Mark helps Randy learn his part and a friendship begins.

G. After reading Deuteronomy 3:23-28, Mark knows that God wants him to follow Moses' example and help Randy.

H. Mark is asked to be Randy's coach instead of getting the part of Joshua.

> ## DEUTERONOMY 3:24
> *O Lord God, thou hast begun to shew thy servant thy greatness.*

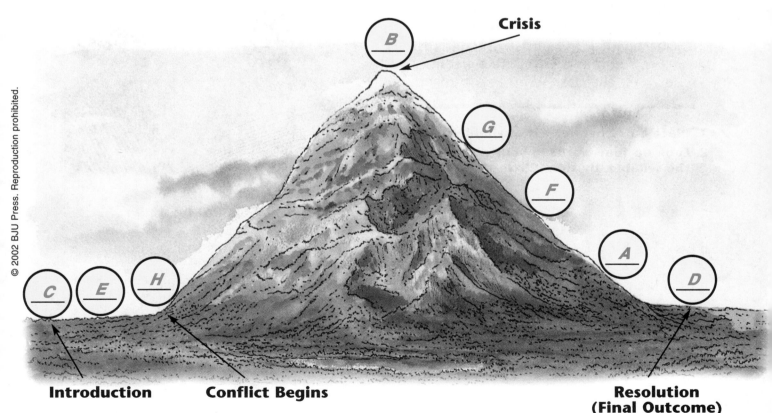

Crisis — B

G

F

A

D

C   E   H

Introduction

Conflict Begins

Resolution (Final Outcome)

Reading 5: "Moses and Joshua," pp. 330-35, Lesson 100
Literature: sequencing events of a story; identifying story plot

131

Compose It

▶ Choose four words from the box and write an original sentence for each. Make sure that your sentence makes the meaning of each word clear. You may use your glossary.

Answers will vary.

understudy	suffice	superstitious
besought	congratulate	script

1. _____

_____

2. _____

_____

3. _____

_____

4. _____

_____

In words with prefixes, divide into syllables between the prefix and the base word. In words with suffixes, sometimes divide into syllables between the base word and the suffix.

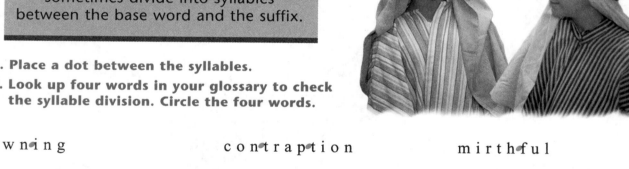

▶ 1. Place a dot between the syllables.

2. Look up four words in your glossary to check the syllable division. Circle the four words.

awn•ing	con•trap•tion	mirth•ful
be•sought	dis•card	ob•struc•tion
break•er	dis•tinct•ly	re•morse
ci•pher•ing	in•dif•fer•ent	re•spect
com•mo•tion	lodg•ing	sus•pense•ful

Reading 5: "Moses and Joshua," pp. 330-35, Lesson 100
Composition: composing sentences to convey word meaning
Structural analysis: applying Syllable Division Rule 4—words with affixes
Study skills: using a glossary

132

▶ **Choose the person, persons, or things to which the colored pronoun refers. You may use your reader.**

___*a*___ 1. verse 1—"Now the Philistines gathered together their armies"

  a. Philistines
  b. Israelites

___*b*___ 2. verses 4 and 5—"named Goliath, of Gath, whose height was six cubits and a span. And he had an helmet of brass"

  a. Gath
  b. Goliath

___*b*___ 3. verse 11—"When Saul and all Israel heard those words of the Philistine, they were dismayed"

  a. Philistine
  b. Saul and all Israel

___*a*___ 4. verse 12—"Now David was the son of that Ephrathite of Bethlehem-judah, whose name was Jesse; and he had eight sons"

  a. Jesse
  b. Bethlehem-judah

___*b*___ 5. verse 20—"And David rose up early in the morning, and left the sheep with a keeper, and took, and went, as Jesse had commanded him"

  a. Jesse
  b. David

___*b*___ 6. verse 23—"the Philistine of Gath, Goliath by name, out of the armies of the Philistines, and spake according to the same words: and David heard them"

  a. Philistine
  b. Goliath's words

David probably had only the first five or six books of the Bible—the Pentateuch and maybe Joshua. How fortunate we are to have the entire Bible to read and study! But David was thankful to have the first part to read again and again and to memorize. Later in his life he wrote in Psalm 119:11: "Thy word have I hid in mine heart." David may have memorized promises like the one in Exodus.

▶ **Answer the questions.**

1. Read Exodus 14:13-14. What command does it give us? _____

"Fear ye not, stand still, and see the salvation of the Lord."

2. What promise do these verses give us? _____

The Lord shall fight for you.

3. Do you think that David trusted the Lord to fight for him against Goliath? ___*yes*___

Reading 5: "David's Endeavor," pp. 336-41, Lesson 101
Comprehension: identifying pronoun references; comparing and contrasting personal opinion with biblical truth

133

Word Use

▶Write the correct synonym for each colored word. You may
use your glossary to find the definitions of the synonyms.

| parched | prevailed | target |
| greaves | array | host |

_____*prevailed*_____ 1. After I had triumphed in the contest, I tried to make my
opponent feel better.

_____*target*_____ 2. Goliath picked up his special shield and got ready for the fight.

_____*parched*_____ 3. The dried corn made good food for the birds.

_____*host*_____ 4. Did you see a multitude of students at the youth rally?

_____*array*_____ 5. The marching band made a beautiful display of red, white, and
blue.

_____*greaves*_____ 6. The soldier was wounded even though he wore leg armor.

▶Choose the correct definition for each bold word. You may
use your glossary.

1. whose height was six **cubits**
   - ● units of measure
   - ○ devices for cleaning nails

2. and he **assayed** to go
   - ○ lay down and rested
   - ● tried

3. And the Philistine said, I **defy**
   - ● resist or challenge
   - ○ go along with

4. five thousand **shekels** of brass
   - ○ heavy chains
   - ● Hebrew coins

5. six cubits and a **span**
   - ● about nine inches
   - ○ bridge

6. taketh away the **reproach** of Israel
   - ○ respect
   - ● dishonor

Reading 5: "David's Endeavor," pp. 336-41, Lesson 101
Vocabulary: identifying synonyms to develop word meaning; matching words and definitions
Study skills: using a glossary

FRIEND

Exod. 33:11	as a man speaketh unto his *f.*	Matt. 11:19	a *f.* of publicans and sinners
II Chron. 20:7	Abraham thy *f.* forever	26:50	*F.,* wherefore art thou come?
Prov. 17:17	A *f.* loveth at all times	John 11:11	Our *f.* Lazarus sleepeth
18:24	A man that hath *f.* must shew	15:13	lay down his life for his *f.*
	There is a *f.* that sticketh closer	15:14	Ye are my *f.* if ye do
		15:15	I have called you *f.*
27:10	own *f.* and thy father's *f.*	James 2:23	he was called the *F.* of God
Isa. 41:8	the seed of Abraham my *f.*		

> The **concordance** is a tool to study the Bible. **Keywords** are listed alphabetically, but the references are in Bible order. Most concordances show the keyword only as an initial in the phrases.

▶ **Use the concordance entry and your Bible to answer the questions.**

1. What is the keyword for these verses? _____ *friend* _____

2. How many times is the word *friend* mentioned in Proverbs 27:10? _____ *2* _____

3. Who said "Our friend Lazarus sleepeth"? _____ *Jesus* _____

4. What verse tells you Christ was called a friend of publicans and sinners?
   _____ *Matthew 11:19* _____

5. What must we do to be a friend of Christ? _____ *do what He commands us* _____

6. What verse tells you a friend loveth at all times? _____ *Proverbs 17:17* _____

7. Who was called the Friend of God? _____ *Abraham* _____

8. Give the references for three verses in which Abraham is mentioned as a friend.
   _____ *II Chronicles 20:7; Isaiah 41:8; James 2:23* _____

9. If a man is to have friends, how must he show himself? _____ *friendly* _____

10. There is a friend that sticketh closer than _____ *a brother* _____.

Reading 5: "Skill Lesson: Bible Study," pp. 342-45, Lesson 103
Study skills: reading a concordance; locating Bible verses

135

| 17:9 | PROVERBS | 17:18 |

9 He that covereth a transgression seeketh love; but *a*he that repeateth a matter separateth very friends.

10 A reproof entereth more into a wise man than an hundred stripes into a fool.

11 An evil man seeketh only rebellion: therefore a cruel messenger shall be sent against him.

12 Let a bear robbed of her whelps meet a man, rather than a fool in his folly.

13 Whoso rewardeth evil for good, evil shall not depart from his house.

14 The beginning of strife is as when one letteth out water: therefore

*a*Prov. 16:28

*b*Prov. 27:10

leave off contention, before it be meddled with.

15 He that justifieth the wicked, and he that condemneth the just, even they both are abomination to the Lord.

16 Wherefore is there a price in the hand of a fool to get wisdom, seeing he hath no heart to it?

17 *b*A friend loveth at all times, and a brother is born for adversity.

18 A man void of understanding striketh hands, and becometh surety in the presence of his friend.

A **cross-reference** directs you from some word or phrase on that page to another place in the Bible that can help explain the passage you are reading.

▶**Answer the questions.**

1. Read Proverbs 17:9 above. What phrase in verse 9 has a cross-reference before it?

   he that repeateth a matter separateth very friends

2. What is the cross-reference Bible verse for this phrase? ___ *Proverbs 16:28*

3. What phrase in Proverbs 16:28 is similar to the phrase in Proverbs 17:9? ___

   a whisperer separateth chief friends

4. What does a friend do at all times according to Proverbs 17:17? ___ *loves*

5. What is the cross-reference listed for Proverbs 17:17? ___ *Proverbs 27:10*

6. What is the other verse in the passage above that has the word *friend* in it? ___ *verse 18*

7. Since this verse does not have a cross-reference, what other tool could you use to study

   friendship? ___ *a concordance*

Reading 5: "Skill Lesson: Bible Study," pp. 342-45, Lesson 103
Study skills: using cross-references to aid in Bible study; locating Bible verses

Sword Play

▶**Write the correct word for each definition.**

thrust	lunge	parry
corps-à-corps	foil	riposte

_____*foil*_____ 1. the fencing sword

_____*parry*_____ 2. to block an attack

_____*thrust*_____ 3. to push the sword forward

_____*riposte*_____ 4. to counterattack

_____*lunge*_____ 5. to leap forward with the front foot

_____*corps-à-corps*_____ 6. literally, in a "body-to-body" position

▶**Choose the correct term to describe each picture.**

1. ○ lunge
   ● thrust

2. ○ riposte
   ● corps-à-corps

3. ● lunge
   ○ parry

4. ○ riposte
   ● parry

Reading 5: "Today's Swordsmen," pp. 346-52, Lesson 104
Comprehension: recalling facts and details
Vocabulary: matching words and definitions

Gladiators were trained warriors who fought bloody battles to amuse the ancient Romans. Gladiators used a variety of weapons, like the oblong shield, a visored helmet, and a stabbing sword. A three-pronged spear called a *trident* was the weapon of some warriors. The battle between the gladiators usually continued until one opponent was defeated. If the spectators waved their handkerchiefs, the life of the loser was spared.

[See also: Colosseum; Rome]

Sword, a sharp-edged metal weapon, is used in hand-to-hand fighting to bring about cutting or stabbing blows. The blades of swords have one or two cutting edges and a handle called a *hilt*. Handles on some of the swords of the European Vikings and Japanese samurai warriors expose a highly decorative work of art. But the Roman gladius has a more useful hilt.

[See also: Fencing; Dagger; Vikings]

At the end of an encyclopedia entry, you can often find **cross-references,** a list of related articles that have further information on the topic that you are studying.

▶ **Read the encyclopedia entries and answer the questions.**

1. What cross-reference teaches you about the sport of sword fighting? _____*Fencing*_____

2. Which encyclopedia volume would you look in to find out what kind of sword the Vikings may have used? _____*the V volume*_____

3. Under what cross-reference would you look to find out about the building the gladiators fought in? _____*Colosseum*_____

4. Under what city would you look to find out more about the gladiators? _____*Rome*_____

▶ **Match the article subheadings with the questions they will answer.**

___*B*___ 1. How does the fencer protect his head?

___*C*___ 2. What is a fencer doing when he does a glide?

___*D*___ 3. What are the dimensions of a fencing strip?

___*A*___ 4. What are the rules of etiquette while competing?

The Sport of Fencing

A. Competition
B. Uniform
C. Attacking Techniques
D. Fencing Strip

Reading 5: "Today's Swordsmen," pp. 346-52, Lesson 104
Study skills: getting information from the encyclopedia; distinguishing among the subheadings of an article; using cross-references to locate further information

▶**Circle the letter of each picture that could match the setting described in the story.**

the fencing gym

A.

B.

What evidence or details from the story support your choice? _____

Possible answer: Patrick is practicing his fencing using a foil.

the living room of Patrick's house

A.

B.

What evidence or details from the story support your choice? _____

Possible answer: Mom moves the furniture because the living room is small.

▶**Answer the questions.**

1. Did Patrick have any brothers or sisters? _____*no*_____

2. Were there girls in Patrick's fencing class? _____*no*_____

3. Did Patrick live in the middle of the country far from other people, or did he live closer

   to the city? _____*closer to the city*_____

4. Did Patrick have his fencing class in the morning, afternoon, or evening? _____*evening*_____

Reading 5, "Corps-à-Corps," pp. 353-59, Lesson 105
Comprehension: drawing conclusions; identifying evidence that supports a conclusion
Literature: identifying setting

The Dewey Decimal System

900-999 History, Geography, Biography, Travel
Topics within the General Subject
960 History of Africa
970 History of North America
  Subtopics
  970 General information on North America
  971 Canada
  972 Middle America; Mexico
  973 United States, Historical
    973.1 Discovery Period
    973.2 Colonial Period
    973.3 War for Independence

974 Northeastern United States
975 Southeastern United States
976 South Central United States; Gulf Coast
977 North Central United States
978 Western United States
979 Great Basin and Pacific Slope

In the **Dewey decimal system,** books are classified in one of ten subjects. Each subject has a three-digit number to represent it. Within each number, the digits in the hundreds, tens, and ones place identify a more specific topic.

▶ **Use the call numbers to help you decide in which section of the library you would find the book.**

Book	**Section**
1. 973.3 *Give Me Liberty!*	1. *War for Independence*
2. 973.2 *Struggle for a Continent*	2. *Colonial Period*
3. 976 *Gunfighters*	3. *South Central United States; Gulf Coast*
4. 973.1 *America Begins*	4. *Discovery Period*
5. 977 *The Ottawa*	5. *North Central United States*
6. 972 *The Aztecs*	6. *Middle America; Mexico*
7. 974 *About Our States*	7. *Northeastern United States*
8. 970 *The Hidatsa*	8. *General information on North America*

Reading 5: "Corps-à-Corps," pp. 353-59, Lesson 105
Study skills: using the Dewey decimal system

Another Sport

Patrick	Robert	Dad	Mother	LeBlanc

▶ **Write the initial of the person who you think said or would say each quotation.**

__L__ 1. "A champion at heart can never be defeated."

__M__ 2. "Strength alone guarantees nothing."

__R__ 3. "A fencer wins any way he can: he can use strength, fear, even pain to make his opponent give up and lose."

__P__ 4. "I can't let him win the match by frightening me."

__D__ 5. "I have fought defeat all my life. Not just defeat in a fencing match, but the defeat of despair."

__P__ 6. "I must fence my best, even if I can't defeat my opponent."

▶ **Look at the colored words in the paragraph. Find a synonym for each word below and then write it on the blank.**

It was a dramatic moment. The perspiring crowd of people stood silently, watching the strong man as he stepped up to the barbells. The presiding judge told him to begin, and the man obeyed. He grasped the heavy barbells and swung them up against his chest, deliberately holding them there until the judge signaled him. Then he lifted them straight up over his head. The spectators cheered while the other weight lifters looked on wistfully at the masterful strength of the man. His style made it look easy to hoist three hundred fifty pounds.

1. sweating   _perspiring_

2. excellent   _masterful_

3. purposefully   _deliberately_

4. onlookers   _spectators_

5. tense   _dramatic_

6. manner   _style_

7. ruling   _presiding_

8. longingly   _wistfully_

Reading 5: "Corps-à-Corps," pp. 360-67, Lesson 106
Comprehension: matching characters and dialogue; identifying character traits and motives
Vocabulary: determining meaning from context; matching synonyms

Story Sense

Select the phrase that tells what the bold words in each sentence describe. The last two sentences have two answers.

1. She parried with **a clack of foil against foil.**
   - ○ how it looked
   - ● how it sounded
   - ○ how it felt

2. "Perhaps," she said, **puffing,** "a half-hour is enough."
   - ○ how she looked
   - ● how she sounded
   - ○ how she felt

3. The red button **drilled** into my chest as I met it full force.
   - ○ how it looked
   - ○ how it sounded
   - ● how it felt

4. Red-faced, Robert was walking toward the dressing room, **his eyes bitter.**
   - ● how they looked
   - ○ how they sounded
   - ○ how they felt

5. **The bruise glistened** as though it weren't a bruise at all but a puddle of ink somebody had spilled on me.
   - ● how it looked
   - ○ how it sounded
   - ○ how it felt

6. The **clusters of names** around his name grew smaller and smaller.
   - ● how they looked
   - ○ how they sounded
   - ○ how they felt

7. Something savage **surged** through me.
   - ○ how it looked
   - ○ how it sounded
   - ● how it felt

8. When I lifted my eyes to **that faceless mask,** the tears stopped.
   - ● how it looked
   - ○ how it sounded
   - ○ how it felt

9. Dad glanced down at his bad leg a little wistfully but **without pain in his eyes.**
   - ● how he looked
   - ○ how he sounded
   - ○ how he felt

10. That one dramatic part of the game— **the snapping of the foil straight up and then snapping it back down**—he had mastered that.
    - ● how it looked
    - ● how it sounded
    - ○ how it felt

11. He **slapped his foil against mine,** beating the blade.
    - ○ how it looked
    - ● how it sounded
    - ● how it felt

Reading 5: "Corps-à-Corps," pp. 360-67, Lesson 106
Literature: developing awareness of the author's use of descriptive sensory words

Personification Plantation

▶**Choose the statement that uses personification. Then answer the question.**

Wording may vary.

> **Personification** is giving human characteristics to an object.

● I could feel the clock on the wall watching me as I worked.
○ As I worked, I kept watching the clock to see the passing time.

1. What human trait does the clock have? _____ *eyes* _____

○ The leaves on the trees rustled in the wind as the bus sped along the highway.
● As our bus sped along, the trees on the side of the mountain waved at us.

2. What human trait do the trees have? _____ *hands* _____

○ The wind blew the leaf helter-skelter along the top rail of the fence and finally down to the ground.
● The oak leaf tiptoed along the fence and then stumbled and fell to the ground.

3. What human trait does the leaf have? _____ *feet* _____

● I hurried down the lane where the trees on either side were arrayed for battle.
○ I ran between the trees, which were tall and stiff with equal spaces between them.

4. What are the trees being compared to? _____ *soldiers* _____

● After climbing that hill, my feet cried out for relief.
○ I just wanted to lie down because my feet hurt so much after the long climb.

5. What human trait do the feet have? _____ *voices* _____

○ I was overjoyed when the buzzer sounded and our team won by just one point.
● We were only one point ahead when the buzzer shouted the good news that we had won.

6. What human trait does the buzzer have? _____ *voice* _____

○ That's the most wilted plant I've ever seen!
● Boy, that plant looks sad.

7. What does the author say about the plant that can be true only of people? _____ *It is sad.* _____

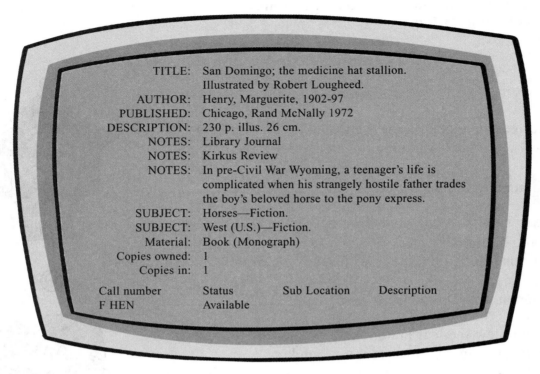

TITLE: San Domingo; the medicine hat stallion.
Illustrated by Robert Lougheed.
AUTHOR: Henry, Marguerite, 1902-97
PUBLISHED: Chicago, Rand McNally 1972
DESCRIPTION: 230 p. illus. 26 cm.
NOTES: Library Journal
NOTES: Kirkus Review
NOTES: In pre-Civil War Wyoming, a teenager's life is complicated when his strangely hostile father trades the boy's beloved horse to the pony express.
SUBJECT: Horses—Fiction.
SUBJECT: West (U.S.)—Fiction.
Material: Book (Monograph)
Copies owned: 1
Copies in: 1

Call number   Status   Sub Location   Description
F HEN   Available

▶**Use the computer screen to answer the questions.**

1. What is the call number for this book?
   - ● F HEN
   - ○ 1972

2. Who is Marguerite Henry?
   - ○ illustrator
   - ● author

3. In which section of the library would you find this book?
   - ○ nonfiction
   - ● fiction

4. What year was the book published?
   - ● 1972
   - ○ 1902

▶**1. Help each person with his book problem. Complete the chart with the type of catalog card needed—*author*, *subject*, or *title*.**

2. Write the information each person would look for to find the answer to his problem.

Problem	Type of Card	Look for
Mike wants to read the book *Nothing Daunted*.	*title*	*Nothing Daunted*
Maria needs a poem by Christina Rossetti.	*author*	*Christina Rossetti*
Rose is making a travel brochure about Paraguay.	*subject*	*Paraguay*

Reading 5: "100-Meter Dash," pp. 368-69, Lesson 108
Study skills: using the card catalog to locate books and information in the library

Rules of the Game

Name_____

▶**Circle the correct basketball.**

1. The YMCA needed a new indoor game because

 the men were tired of playing the same old games.

 soccer and baseball were too rough to play indoors.

2. The men didn't like doing calisthenics and weight lifting because

 they weren't competitive and exciting like games.

 there wasn't enough weight equipment, so they often had to take turns.

3. Dr. Naismith wanted the new game to be played with a big ball because

 a larger ball would be easier for the men to catch.

 then they wouldn't need bats or mallets that might break windows.

4. Dr. Naismith used peach baskets as goals because

 he wanted the goals to be round, not square like soccer goals.

 the janitor couldn't find boxes.

5. Dr. Naismith wanted the game to be based on passing the ball rather than running with it because

 he was afraid a window would be broken.

 he wanted the game to be fair for everyone.

6. It took Dr. Naismith so long to come up with a new game because

 he was so busy he didn't have much time to work on it.

 he wasted time trying to change other games.

7. Dr. Naismith placed the baskets up high so that

 the game would require more skill.

 the men wouldn't break any windows.

8. Baskets were eventually made without bottoms because

they probably felt silly for not having thought of it before.

then the game wouldn't have to be stopped after every basket to get the ball out.

Reading 5, "The All-American Game," pp. 370-73, Lesson 109
Comprehension: recalling facts and details; inferring facts and details

145

Balls and Bats

Baseball has a long and interesting history. The game originated from the English game cricket. In colonial times the game was called townball. Almost one hundred fifty years ago, Alexander Cartwright changed the rules of baseball into its modern form.

The rules of baseball have changed over the years, but they finally have been reduced to a few simple ones. The most basic are that a baseball team has nine players, a game lasts for nine innings, and an inning is over when the batting team has received three outs.

Baseball equipment has also changed over the years. Today, the official baseball is about nine inches around. Bats can be up to three and a half feet long. Gloves are used by fielders, catchers, and pitchers.

Some of the most important baseball players in the field are the first baseman, the catcher, and the

pitcher. A first baseman is often left-handed so that he can more conveniently catch with his right hand. A catcher, squatting behind the plate, signals the plays to the pitcher. Some pitchers can throw balls at speeds of more than ninety miles an hour.

Baseball is the most popular sport in America. Young people play in the Pony and Little Leagues. Professionals play in the National and American Leagues. Baseball has even grown to be a symbol of America, just like apple pie!

▶1. **Complete the main headings.**
2. **Write the supporting details under each main heading.**   *Wording may vary.*

I. The _____*History*_____ of Baseball

   A. _____*It originated from the English game cricket.*_____

   B. _____*It was called townball in colonial times.*_____

   C. _____*Alexander Cartwright changed the rules.*_____

Reading 5: "The All-American Game," pp. 370-73, Lesson 109
Study skills: recognizing main ideas in an outline;
supplying supporting facts and details in an outline

II. The _____*Rules*_____ of Baseball

   A. _____*A team has nine players.*_____

   B. _____*A game has nine innings.*_____

   C. _____*An inning lasts for three outs.*_____

III. The _____*Equipment*_____ of Baseball

   A. _____*A baseball is nine inches around.*_____

   B. _____*Bats are up to three and a half feet long.*_____

   C. _____*Gloves are used by fielders, catchers, and pitchers.*_____

IV. The _____*Players*_____ of Baseball

   A. _____*First basemen are often left-handed.*_____

   B. _____*Catchers signal the plays.*_____

   C. _____*Some pitchers can throw balls at speeds of over ninety miles an hour.*_____

V. The _____*Popularity*_____ of Baseball

   A. _____*Young people play in the Pony and Little Leagues.*_____

   B. _____*Professionals play in the National and American Leagues.*_____

   C. _____*Baseball has grown to be a symbol of America.*_____

Reading 5: "The All-American Game," pp. 370-73, Lesson 109
Study skills: recognizing main ideas in an outline; supplying supporting facts and details
in an outline

147

SOCCER

As early as 400 B.C., the Chinese played a game like soccer, and in A.D. 200 the Romans played a similar game. In the 1100s in London, children played it in the streets. The first set of official rules was drawn up in 1848 in England, and then soccer (originally called football) spread throughout the world. It was the only foot game played in the United States until the game that we now know as football became popular.

Soccer is played in two halves, with a break only at halftime, for a total game time of ninety minutes. A goal is scored when the ball goes by a single goalkeeper and into a net. Only the goalie can pick up the ball, so the game requires much skill with the feet. It also requires a tough head!

FOOTBALL

Football began in the 1800s with the object of just kicking a soccerlike ball across the opponent's goal. The first college game included running with the ball as well as tackling. Later, in the United States, players were allowed to keep the ball while trying for a "first down." Passing and an oval-shaped ball were soon added; the forward pass became a way to score without making the game quite as violent.

The total time played in a game is sixty minutes. There are four ways to score in football: a touchdown (6 points), a conversion (1 point), a field goal (3 points), and a safety (2 points).

> When you **compare** two things, you show ways that they are similar. When you **contrast** them, you show ways that they are different.

▶ **Complete the following sentences to compare and contrast the two games.**

COMPARE

1. Both articles are about games that score using a _____*ball*_____ .

2. In both games the players use their _____*feet*_____ to kick the ball.

CONTRAST

1. In football, playing time is ___*60*___ minutes; in soccer it is ___*90*___ minutes.

2. Running and passing the ball are the methods used in _____*football*_____ . A tough

   head and skill with the feet are necessary in _____*soccer*_____ .

Reading 5: "The All-American Game," pp. 370-73, Lesson 109
Comprehension: comparing and contrasting information

A Lesson for Barry

Barry and Sonia stared at the chessboard in silence. Slowly Sonia reached out, picked up the white knight, and moved it to another square. "Check."

"Ha!" Barry laughed. "I thought you might do something like that. I can get out of that trap easily!" With one finger he scooted the black king over one square. "There. Your knight can't bother me over here."

Sonia didn't reply. She studied the board for a minute and then picked up one of her rooks. "Why do they call this a 'rook'?" she asked. "If I were going to invent chess, I'd call it a 'castle.' After all, that's what it looks like."

"I don't know. Come on," Barry said impatiently. "You're stalling. I'm going to win, and you know it. Let's just play and get it over with."

"Okay, I'll move. But I still might win, you know." She put her rook on a new square and said "Check" again.

"Ha! The day you win, I'll walk you down to the corner and buy you the biggest ice-cream sundae you want. I can still get out of check." Using one finger again, Barry quickly slid his king over one more square.

While Sonia gazed at the board, Barry picked up a magazine and started flipping through it. "'Hmm," Sonia said at last. "This is a hard decision."

Barry tossed down the magazine. "Don't take all day. Just move anywhere."

"I can't help it if I can't think as fast as you. Say, did you really mean it about buying me a sundae?"

"Only if you win, I said. But since I'm not going to let you, I don't have anything to worry about."

"Promise?" Sonia asked.

"Yes, yes. If it'll speed up the game, I promise."

"Good!" Sliding her white queen all the way across the checkered board, Sonia declared, "Checkmate! I win!"

Barry stared at the board in shock as Sonia called, "I'll get my sweater while you get the money. I'm hungry enough to eat the Super-Jumbo Sundae!"

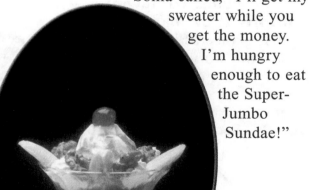

▶**Choose the correct answer.**

1. The moral of this story is

   ○ to learn to get along with others.
   ● it is wrong to brag.

2. The title of the story refers to

   ● the story's moral.
   ○ Sonia's tricky move.

▶Think of the topic—the real history of chess—as you read the paragraphs. Underline all the sentences that do not apply directly to the topic. You should find seven irrelevant sentences.

The Real History of Chess

The first form of chess was played in India as early as 550 B.C., according to Sir William Jones, who wrote an essay on the history of chess in 1790. Sir William had a brother, Thomas, who was a captain in the English army. The game of chess was originally called *chaturanga*. The Indian word *chaturanga* means "four parts of an army." From the name of the game you can see why the four kinds of playing pieces in chaturanga were elephants, horses, chariots, and soldiers.

Around A.D. 500, chess spread to Persia. Today Persia is the country of Iran. The word *chess* came from the Persian word *shah,* which meant "king." Thus *checkmate,* or *shah mat,* literally meant "the king is dead." Both chess and checkers have sixty-four squares on their game boards.

The Arabs learned the game of chess in the 600s, when they conquered Persia. The Arabs are now the people that we usually think of when we think of "oil sheiks." Their little country is the third largest oil producer in the world. They took the game to Spain, where it soon spread through all of Europe. The game took its modern form in the fifteenth or sixteenth century. Some of the early Spanish explorers brought the game of chess to South America. One famous South American explorer was Cortés. In North America chess was popularized by Benjamin Franklin. He also wrote an almanac called *Poor Richard's Almanack.*

Sometimes **irrelevant information** might look at first glance as if it belongs with the story. You must ask yourself the question, "Is this information telling about the main topic of this paragraph?"

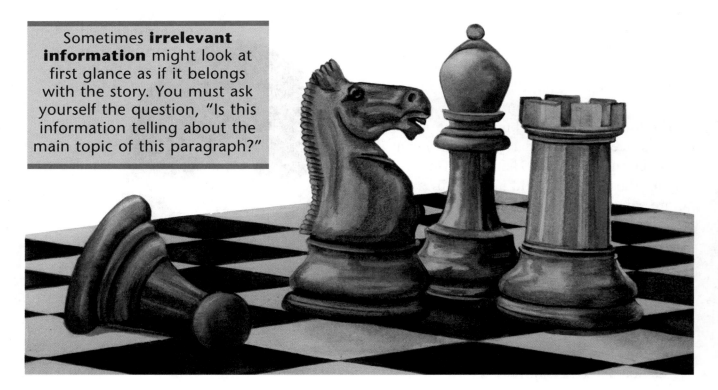

Reading 5: "The Little Things of Sissa," pp. 374-79, Lesson 111
Study skills: identifying irrelevant information

Action-Packed Words

▶Choose the correct answer to replace the bold word.

1. **whacking** out a shrill tune on her instrument
   - ○ swinging
   - ● slapping
   - ○ singing

2. best seats on the **scaffolding**
   - ○ concrete curbs
   - ● wooden platforms
   - ○ quilted blanket

3. gentlemen off to see the **Coronation**
   - ● ceremony
   - ○ flower
   - ○ battle

4. to **cock** his hat at an angle
   - ● tilt
   - ○ dust
   - ○ rooster

5. shirts and **plumed** hats
   - ○ plum-filled
   - ○ fruited
   - ● feathered

6. life of a **spinster**
   - ● unmarried woman
   - ○ single man
   - ○ small child

An **adverb** answers the question *when, where,* or *how* about the verb.

▶Circle the adverb that answers the question about each verb in bold print.

1. **When?** John Bunyan (always) **returned** to the jailhouse of his own free will.

2. **How?** Cissy **ate** (heartily) at breakfast.

3. **Where?** Frank **moved** (ahead) for he had a long walk.

4. **How?** The mudlarks **could** (hardly) **earn** any money.

5. **Where?** Cissy and Frank **scooted** (outside) to bring back the real coins.

6. **When?** The cap (usually) **covered** her head down to her eyebrows.

7. **When?** The Black Pot **would** (frequently) **do** a grand bit of business.

8. **How?** Frank (cautiously) **pinned** the ribbon on himself.

9. **How?** The men (carefully) **slipped** the leather straps off their shoulders.

10. **When?** (Sometimes) Cissy's family **earned** extra British currency by spending counterfeit coins and receiving genuine money as change.

Reading 5: "Coronation Day," pp. 380-84, Lesson 112
Vocabulary: identifying synonyms to develop word meaning; identifying adverbs

151

England's Rulers
(1660-1714)

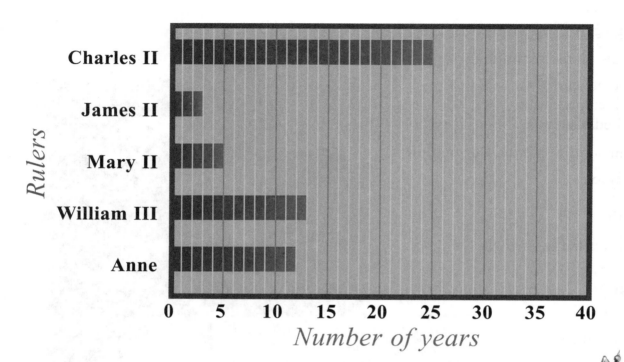

▶**Read the bar graph to answer the questions.**

1. Who had the longest reign? _____*Charles II*_____

2. How many years did Mary II reign? _____*5*_____

3. Which ruler reigned the least number of years? _____*James II*_____

4. Did Anne reign more or fewer years than William III? _____*fewer*_____

5. Who reigned for thirteen years? _____*William III*_____

6. How many years longer did Charles II reign than Mary II? _____*20*_____

7. How many years longer did Mary II reign than James II? _____*2*_____

8. Did Charles II or William III reign longer? _____*Charles II*_____

Reading 5: "Coronation Day," pp. 380-84, Lesson 112
Study skills: determining information from a bar graph

Counterfeit Coins

▶ **Answer the questions in complete sentences.**   *Answers will vary.*

1. Why did Cissy and Frank dress up in suits, shirts, and plumed hats? _____
   They dressed up to be able to spend false coins in the best shops.

2. Why did Cissy feel heavy-hearted about giving the program vendors false coins?
   If the vendors were caught with the false coins, they could be punished.

3. What was Frank's plan for Cissy to be able to see the king? *He and Cissy were*
   to give away free programs to the nobles
   as they climbed to the top of the scaffolding.

4. How did Cissy know the king had been crowned if she couldn't see him? _____
   The bells of all the churches in London rang out.

5. Why do you think Cissy could only whisper instead of joining in the cry "Long live His Majesty, King Charles II"? _____
   She was overcome with joy at the king being crowned.

6. What did Frank steal while he was on the scaffolding watching the ceremony? _____
   He stole two gentlemen's purses.

7. Why didn't Frank want Cissy to buy a Bible as a souvenir? _____
   Frank and Pa thought only Dissenters had Bibles.

8. How did John Bunyan get out of jail to preach and sell Bibles? _____
   Pa left his jail door unlocked.

9. Why did Cissy feel that John Bunyan was looking right into her life? _____
   Cissy felt like he could see that breaking the law
   was causing her to be unhappy on the inside.

10. What two things gave Cissy comfort in returning to Bedford Jail? _____
    She would see John Bunyan again and would be able to read the hidden Bible.

Reading 5: "Coronation Day," pp. 385-91, Lesson 113
Comprehension: drawing conclusions; recalling facts and details
Literature: identifying character traits; projecting characters beyond the plot

Encyclopedia Know-How

▶ Write the keyword and the letter of the volume you would use to find the following information. Some questions have more than one answer.

	Keyword	Volume
1. How long did William III rule England?	England	E
	William III	W
2. How well equipped was the English military during the seventeenth century?	England	E
3. What kind of climate does Chile have?	Chile	Ca-Ch
4. What is the state flower of Idaho?	Idaho	I-J
5. What are the three branches of the United States government?	United States	U
6. Is Yellowstone National Park located in Montana?	Yellowstone National Park	X-Z
	Montana	M

▶ Below are some subheadings that might appear on encyclopedia pages about England. Write the letter of the subheading where you would find the information.

Information

_B_ 1. lakes and animals

_C_ 2. foreign trade

_A_ 3. kinds of religions

_D_ 4. wars and invasions

_A_ 5. languages spoken

_E_ 6. laws and constitution

Subheading

A. People

B. Natural Environment

C. Economy

D. History

E. Government

Reading 5: "Coronation Day," pp. 385-91, Lesson 113
Study skills: determining the keyword for a given idea; matching subheadings with information

Toys, Toys, Toys

Name_____

In John Bunyan's day, there were no toy shops for children. Some peddlers and merchants sold toys in their booths and stores. Tinkers sometimes sold miniature pots, pans, and drums to children as they repaired the mothers' metal utensils. Children made their own toys. Boys made hoops, whistles, popguns, shuttlecocks, and kites. Girls made rag dolls and sewed clothes for them.

Today children do not usually make their own toys, but they do play with many toys that originated in John Bunyan's day. Hobbyhorses have become rocking horses, and popguns have changed to cap guns. And of course, dolls, drums, and kites are still popular too.

▶**Answer the questions.**

1. Why do you think children long ago made their own toys? _____
   Toys were not available, or they cost too much.
   _____

2. How do you think the boys made their toys? *They probably carved them from wood.*
   _____

3. Why do you think most children do not make their own toys today? _____
   They can buy toys.
   _____

▶**Fill in the blanks to answer the clues with words from the paragraphs at the top of the page. Then write the message you find in the box.**

1. This rhymes with *top fun* or *chop one*.
2. Everyone tries to hit this birdie.
3. Hitting this makes a booming sound.
4. Stretch a cloth over a frame to make this fly.
5. This miniature figure is usually modeled after humans.
6. A toy horse's head stuck on the end of a broomstick makes this.
7. Children pushed these huge circular bands down the street with a stick.
8. Everything you just identified is an example of
   ____*old*____   ____*toys*____ .

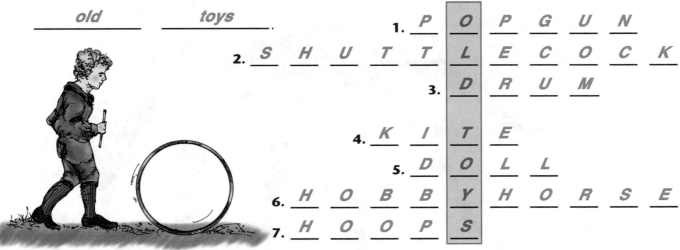

1. P O P G U N
2. S H U T T L E C O C K
3. D R U M
4. K I T E
5. D O L L
6. H O B B Y H O R S E
7. H O O P S

Reading 5: "John Bunyan: Prisoner with a Pen," pp. 392-95, Lesson 114
Comprehension: drawing conclusions
Vocabulary: matching words and definitions

Rootin' It Out

▶Greek (G) and Latin (L) root words form the basis of many of our English words. Study the root words on the tree. Write the letter of the correct definition for each word.

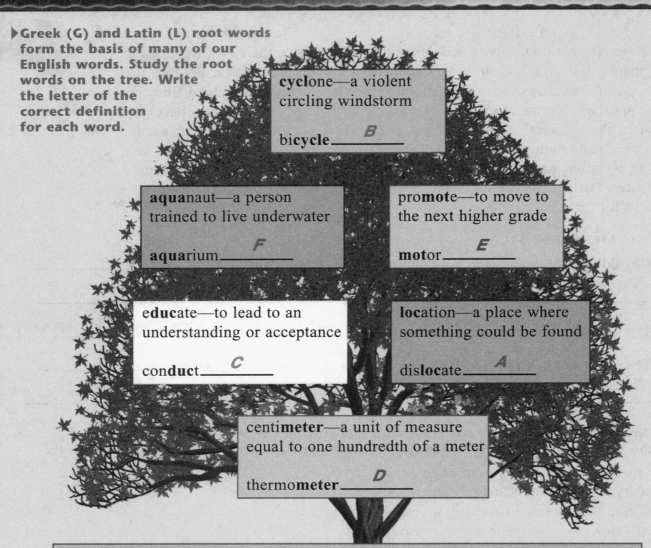

cyclone—a violent circling windstorm

bi**cycle** _____ *B*

aquanaut—a person trained to live underwater

aquarium _____ *F*

pro**mot**e—to move to the next higher grade

motor _____ *E*

educate—to lead to an understanding or acceptance

con**duc**t _____ *C*

location—a place where something could be found

dis**loc**ate _____ *A*

centi**meter**—a unit of measure equal to one hundredth of a meter

thermo**meter** _____ *D*

A. to put in the wrong place
B. a vehicle with two wheels, a seat, pedals, and handlebars
C. to guide or lead
D. a device to measure the temperature
E. an engine that produces motion
F. a water-filled enclosure for living fish

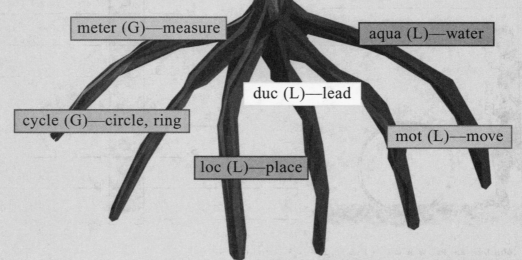

meter (G)—measure

aqua (L)—water

duc (L)—lead

cycle (G)—circle, ring

mot (L)—move

loc (L)—place

Reading 5: "John Bunyan: Prisoner with a Pen," pp. 392-95, Lesson 114
Vocabulary: determining word meaning from Greek and Latin roots

▶**Choose the correct answer.**

1. Why was the Stourbridge Fair the most exciting event of the year?

   ○ It was organized by the people.
   ● Merchants and entertainers from all over England and from other countries came to the fair.

2. How do you know that John Bunyan's family was poor?

   ○ His boyhood was uneventful.
   ● He went to a school for poor farmers' children.

3. How can you tell that John Bunyan's family was religious?

   ○ They were saved.
   ● They read the Bible and were members of a church.

4. Why did Oliver Cromwell exercise such strict discipline?

   ● He wanted his men to be prepared to fight and to be good soldiers.
   ○ He was a cruel commander who expected his men to be in shape at all times.

5. Why was John Bunyan's life spared?

   ● God had a purpose for his life.
   ○ He refused to obey Oliver Cromwell's orders.

6. Why did John Bunyan and his wife read the two Christian books over and over?

   ● They wanted to learn more about God.
   ○ The books were passed down from generation to generation.

7. Why did John Bunyan despair of ever being saved?

   ○ He thought he was too ignorant.
   ● He thought he was a terrible sinner.

8. How did Pastor John Gifford help John Bunyan?

   ○ He told John Bunyan how to be saved.
   ● He told John Bunyan about his experiences, which were similar to Bunyan's.

9. Why did John Bunyan become a leader of the Bedford Church?

   ○ He was eager to write from prison.
   ● He was not afraid to preach in the face of opposition.

10. Why did John Bunyan return to the jail a day early?

    ● God convicted him of the need to return.
    ○ He heard that the jailer was in trouble.

11. What did John Bunyan do to overcome his discouragement?

    ● He read the Bible and prayed.
    ○ He invited friends to visit him in prison.

12. Why was the book *The Pilgrim's Progress* so popular?

    ○ There were few books in those days.
    ● Rich and poor alike could identify with Christian and his journey.

Reading 5: "John Bunyan: Prisoner with a Pen," pp. 396-402, Lesson 115
Comprehension: recalling facts and details; inferring facts and details

157

▶Match the vocabulary word with its definition.

_E_ 1. frivolous

_C_ 2. tinker

_G_ 3. stupor

_D_ 4. mustered

_J_ 5. fervent

_B_ 6. pious

_F_ 7. medieval

_I_ 8. vice

_A_ 9. theology

_H_ 10. thatched

A. the study of the nature of God

B. very religious or holy

C. a traveling salesman

D. gathered or assembled

E. not serious; unimportant

F. of, from, or like the Middle Ages

G. mental confusion; a daze

H. to cover a roof with straw

I. a bad character trait or sin

J. showing enthusiasm

▶**1. Find and shade each vocabulary word from above in the word box. Words can be found horizontally, vertically, backwards, or forwards. The first one is done for you.**

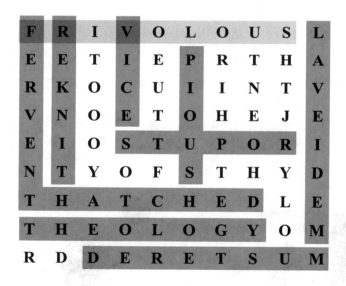

2. Finish the quotation. Write the unused letters in the blanks, keeping them in order from left to right, line by line.

John Bunyan entered the gate to hear the Shining One say,

"E N T E R   T H O U   I N T O   T H E

J O Y   O F   T H Y   L O R D"

Reading 5: "John Bunyan: Prisoner with a Pen," pp. 396–402, Lesson 115
Vocabulary: matching words and definitions

PQ3R—Biography

▶ **Follow the steps in the PQ3R method as you look over reader pages 403-5. Check each box as you complete the step.**

PREVIEW

❑ 1. What will you look at as you preview this article?

   title, subheadings, illustrations, captions,

   italicized or bold words

❑ 2. What do you think the article will be about?

   possible answers: biographies / John Bunyan

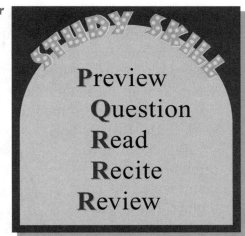

Preview
Question
Read
Recite
Review

QUESTION

❑ 3. Make a question from the title "Literature Lesson: Biography." _____

   possible answer: What does a biography tell?

❑ 4. Look at the caption under the illustration on page 403. Make a question from the caption or illustration. _____ *possible answer:*

   Why did John Bunyan write The Pilgrim's Progress?

❑ 5. Look at the italicized word *biography* on the page. Make a question from the italicized word. _____

   possible answer: What is a biography?

READ

❑ 6. Think about your questions as you read silently page 403.

RECITE

❑ 7. Tell yourself the answer to your questions for numbers 3-5.

QUESTION, READ, RECITE AGAIN

❑ 8. Repeat the three steps again for the next section of the article.

❑ 9. Repeat the three steps again for the last section of the article.

REVIEW

❑ 10. Look back at the title, subheadings, illustrations, captions, and italicized words and remind yourself of the information you learned.

Reading 5: "Literature Lesson: Biography," pp. 403-5, Lesson 116
Study skills: using the PQ3R method of study

Poems to Hymns

Born in 1725, John Newton learned many passages of Scripture as a boy. His mother taught him a catechism and many verses, hymns, and poems. However, he deserted his spiritual teaching. When he was a teenager, he was kidnapped and forced to work in the British navy.

John Newton was often punished for his laziness and his hot temper. His superior skill and experience won him some rank over the common seamen. But he abused these privileges and ran away. He was publicly whipped, which only made his temper worse.

At last he was released from the service, and eventually he found his way to a slave trader. He was later accused of stealing, and for his punishment he was enslaved. The slave trader who became Newton's master often mistreated him just for amusement.

Finally, friends of his father found him and brought him home. After his hard experiences, Newton's heart softened toward the gospel, and he was born again. He continued to go to sea after his salvation and became an officer, a first mate, and then a captain.

The slave trade brought wealth to many men, but as a Christian, John Newton could not endure it for long. The Holy Spirit broke his heart for selling men.

John Newton left the sea trade and became a preacher. Whenever he could, he wrote and spoke against the slave trade. He discovered that he enjoyed writing. He penned many sacred poems. Some of these poems later became hymns: "He Died for Me," "Glorious Things of Thee Are Spoken," and "Amazing Grace."

▶**Answer the questions.**

1. What training did John Newton have when he was young that he deserted? _____

   His mother taught him a catechism, Bible verses, hymns, and poems.

2. How do you think the Lord used the slave trader in John Newton's life? _____

   Because the slave trader mistreated him, John Newton's

   heart was softened toward the gospel.

3. Why did John Newton finally leave the slave trade? _____

   The Holy Spirit convicted him that it was wrong.

Reading 5: "Literature Lesson: Biography," pp. 403-5, Lesson 116
Literature: enjoying biography
Comprehension: identifying facts and details; drawing conclusions

160

Bunyan's Map

▶**Match each item or person from *The Pilgrim's Progress* with the verse that describes it.**

__B__ 1. enemies dressed as shining ones

__F__ 2. the burden

__E__ 3. Faithful

__A__ 4. the King's Highway

__D__ 5. Hopeful

__C__ 6. Apollyon

A. Isaiah 35:8

B. II Corinthians 11:13-14

C. Revelation 9:11

D. Psalm 71:14

E. Psalm 101:6

F. Psalm 38:4

▶**Choose the correct answer using a Bible and the map on reader pages 406-7.**

1. Christian's journey began in the
   ○ Celestial City.
   ● City of Destruction.

2. According to Proverbs 24:2, the inhabitants of this city
   ○ study building up the city.
   ● study destruction.

3. Between the Slough of Despond and Beelzebub's Fort lies
   ● Morality.
   ○ Eternity.

4. According to Proverbs 22:4, it was good for Christian to walk through the Valley of Humiliation to gain
   ○ recognition, popularity, and riches.
   ● riches, honor, and life.

5. The valley mentioned in Psalm 23 is the
   ○ Valley of Salvation.
   ● Valley of the Shadow of Death.

6. The two names that God predicts His people and their land will be called in Isaiah 62:4 are
   ● Hephzibah and Beulah.
   ○ Nebajoth and Bozrah.

7. One of the names in question 6 is on the map. What city is it close to?
   ● Celestial City
   ○ City of Destruction

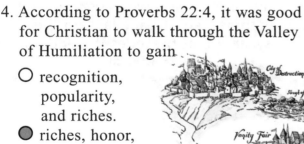

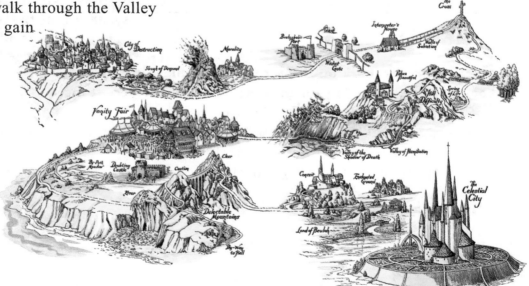

Reading 5: "The Pilgrim's Progress," pp. 406-7, Lesson 118
Study skills: locating Bible verses; reading a map

Word Work

Prefix	Meaning
dis-	not, opposite of, lack of
mid-	middle
re-	again, back
per	thoroughly
pre-	before; prior to

▶ **Write the definition of the bold word.**

1. The traveler was **disrespectful** to his companion. _____ *not respectful*

2. He **recalled** the valleys and mountains that he saw. _____ *to tell again*

3. He wore thick socks and heavy boots as a **precaution** against blisters.

_____ *caution prior to* _____

4. He stopped to sleep at **midnight.** _____ *middle of the night*

5. He **performed** his early morning tasks beside the creek. _____ *thoroughly formed*

6. He ate lunch **midway** between the two cities.

_____ *middle of the way* _____

> In words ending with *-sion* or *-tion*, the accent usually falls on the syllable that precedes the ending.
> va•ca´•tion

▶ **1. Place an accent mark on the accented syllable.**

2. Look up four words in your glossary to check the accent mark. Circle the four words you checked.

com • mo´ • tion	e • va´ • sion	pe • ti´ • tion
con • trap´ • tion	in • ten´ • tion	pro • ces´ • sion
de • ser´ • tion	ob • struc´ • tion	pro • jec´ • tion
en • vi´ • sion	pas´ • sion	ver´ • sion

Reading 5: "The Pilgrim's Progress," pp. 406-7, Lesson 118
Vocabulary: determining word meaning from prefixes
Structural analysis: applying Accent Rule 4—schwa syllables (*-sion* and *-tion*)
Study skills: using a glossary

Events in
John Bunyan's Life

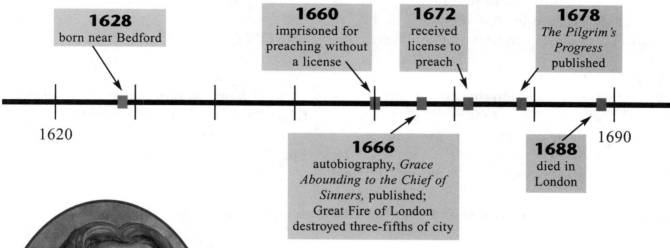

1628
born near Bedford

1660
imprisoned for
preaching without
a license

1672
received
license to
preach

1678
*The Pilgrim's
Progress*
published

1620

1690

1666
autobiography, *Grace
Abounding to the Chief of
Sinners,* published;
Great Fire of London
destroyed three-fifths of city

1688
died in
London

▶**Use the time line to answer the questions.**

1. How many years does the time line show?

70 years

2. In what year was *The Pilgrim's Progress* published?

1678

3. Why was John Bunyan imprisoned in 1660?

He didn't have a license to preach.

4. In what year did John Bunyan receive his license to preach? _____ *1672*

5. How did the Great Fire of London affect the city? _____

Three-fifths of London was destroyed.

6. What event in John Bunyan's life took place in the same year as the Great Fire of London?

His autobiography, **Grace Abounding to the Chief of Sinners,** *was published.*

7. In what year did John Bunyan die? _____ *1688*

8. How many years did John Bunyan live? _____ *60 years*

Reading 5: "Vanity Fair," pp. 408-11, Lesson 119
Study skills: reading a time line; using a time line to relate one event to another

163

Concordance Connections

COMPASSION
Ps. 78:38 he, being full of *c.*
   86:15 a God full of *c.*
   111:4 Lord is gracious and full of *c.*
   145:8 Lord is gracious and full of *c.*
Lam. 3:22 because his *c.* fails not
Matt. 9:36 he was moved with *c.* on them

FAITHFULNESS
Ps. 36:5 *f.* reacheth unto the clouds
   92:2 and thy *f.* every night
Isa. 25:1 counsels of old are *f.* and truth

PRIDE
Prov. 11:2 *p.* cometh, then cometh shame
   16:18 *P.* goeth before destruction
   29:23 man's *p.* shall bring him low
I John 2:16 and the *p.* of life

VANITY
Ps. 39:5 at his best state is altogether *v.*
Prov. 13:11 wealth gotten by *v.* shall be
   22:8 that soweth iniquity shall reap *v.*
Eccles. 1:2 *V.* of vanities, saith the
     Preacher, *v.*
Eph. 4:17 walk, in the *v.* of their mind

▶ **Use the concordance entries and your Bible to answer the questions.**

1. Who is gracious and full of compassion? _____ *the Lord* _____

2. What verse tells you destruction will come upon the proud individual? _____ *Prov. 16:18* _____

3. According to Psalm 36:5, how far does God's faithfulness reach? _____ *to the clouds* _____

4. Who moved Jesus to compassion in Matthew 9:36? _____ *the multitudes* _____

5. In what verse is the word *vanity* mentioned at least two times? _____ *Ecclesiastes 1:2* _____

6. According to Psalm 92:2, what are we to show every morning and every night? _____
_____ *lovingkindness every morning and faithfulness every night* _____

7. What are the two counsels of old? _____ *faithfulness and truth* _____

8. Give the references for four verses in which the phrase *full of compassion* can be found.
_____ *Psalm 78:38; Psalm 86:15; Psalm 111:4; Psalm 145:8* _____

9. What happens to wealth gained through vanity?
_____ *It is diminished.* _____

10. What will a man's pride do?
_____ *bring him low* _____

Reading 5: "Vanity Fair," pp. 408-11, Lesson 119
Study skills: reading a concordance; locating Bible verses

Two Meanings

Name_____

▶**Write the answer that each character or place from *The Pilgrim's Progress* stands for.**

> An **allegory** is a story that has two meanings. The adventures of the characters provide reading pleasure along with the understanding of significant truth.

_**a**_ 1. Christian
  a. any saved person
  b. any preacher
  c. any Christian writer

_**b**_ 2. Faithful
  a. a man who tithes
  b. a Christian martyr
  c. a good steward

_**c**_ 3. Vanity Fair
  a. anything pleasant
  b. any carnival or fair
  c. worldly pleasures

_**b**_ 4. the Celestial City
  a. earthly rewards
  b. heaven
  c. death

_**b**_ 5. Beelzebub
  a. God
  b. Satan
  c. Christian

_**b**_ 6. Lord Hategood
  a. the judge who trusted no one
  b. the judge who hated good works
  c. the judge who ruled justly

_**a**_ 7. Envy
  a. envy of holiness and faith
  b. envy of evil ways
  c. envy of Lord Hategood

_**b**_ 8. Superstition
  a. above average in wisdom
  b. belief in a false religion
  c. belief in the true God

_**a**_ 9. Pickthank
  a. hates to hear the truth about Beelzebub
  b. condemns Beelzebub
  c. thanks Faithful for truthful words

_**c**_ 10. Mr. Blindman
  a. someone without sight
  b. someone who begs
  c. someone blind to the truth

_**c**_ 11. Hopeful
  a. any weak Christian
  b. someone hoping to change a Christian's path
  c. a new Christian who trusts God's promises

_**b**_ 12. the King's highway
  a. the path for the rich
  b. the path of life for the believer
  c. the path for royalty

Reading 5: "Vanity Fair," pp. 412-15, Lesson 120
Literature: interpreting allegory

▶**Write each vocabulary word next to its synonym.**

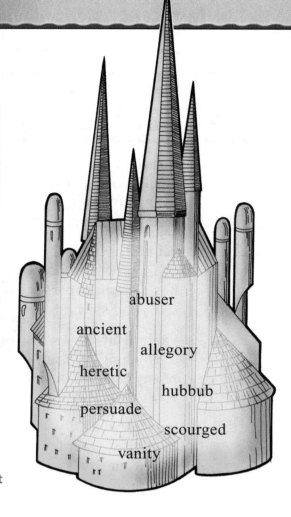

1. uproar _____ *hubbub*

2. pride _____ *vanity*

3. a story with two meanings _____ *allegory*

4. whipped _____ *scourged*

5. wrong user _____ *abuser*

6. convince _____ *persuade*

7. antique _____ *ancient*

8. misbeliever _____ *heretic*

abuser

ancient

allegory

heretic

hubbub

persuade

scourged

vanity

▶**Complete each sentence. Write the Scripture verse that backs up your answer.**

| Ecclesiastes 2:10-11 | Romans 12:12 | Luke 4:3-13 | Ephesians 6:13 |

1. The goods at Vanity Fair were ____.
   ○ valuable
   ● worthless
   Verse: _____ *Ecclesiastes 2:10-11*

2. The Blessed One ____ to the temptation of Beelzebub to cheapen Himself and buy some of the worthless things.
   ● did not give in
   ○ gave in
   Verse: _____ *Luke 4:3-13*

3. Christian and Faithful dressed differently from the people at the fair— they wore the armor that ____.
   ○ Beelzebub had given them.
   ● the Lord had given them.
   Verse: _____ *Ephesians 6:13*

4. The Pilgrims ____ and did not give back evil for evil.
   ○ were not patient
   ● were patient
   Verse: _____ *Romans 12:12*

Reading 5: "Vanity Fair," pp. 412-15, Lesson 120
Vocabulary: identifying synonyms to develop word meaning
Comprehension: supporting personal conclusions with biblical truth
Study skills: locating Bible verses

The King's Men

▶**Answer the questions.**

1. The road that Christian and Hopeful were on was rough, and they began to be much discouraged. What did they do?

   ○ They prayed that the Lord would give them strength and lift their spirits.
   ● They left the road and crossed the stile to walk in the meadow.
   ○ They sat and rested for a while.

   Was this a good solution to their problem? _____*no*_____

   If not, what should they have done instead? _____*They should have trusted in God*_____

   _____*to help them stay on the road.*_____

   Choose two scriptural promises that Christian and Hopeful could have claimed for this problem.

   ● Philippians 4:13
   ● Isaiah 40:31
   ○ Psalm 19:1

2. It began to rain and thunder, and lightning flashed around them, and the water in the river rose and rushed against the banks. What did they do?

   ● They found a sheltered spot beside some trees.
   ○ They began to sing to encourage each other.
   ○ They spent the night at a nearby Christian's home.

   Was this a good solution to their problem?

   _____*no*_____

   Why or why not? _____*Answers will vary. They could have been struck by lightning.*_____

   _____*They were not trusting in the Lord to protect and help them.*_____

   _____*They gave in to fear of circumstances.*_____

   Choose two scriptural promises that Christian and Hopeful could have claimed for this problem.

   ○ James 3:17
   ● Psalm 4:8
   ● Proverbs 21:31

Reading 5: "Doubting Castle," pp. 416-20, Lesson 121
Comprehension: recalling facts and details; analyzing solutions to problems;
applying biblical truth to problem situations

167

Sounds and Spellings

Skill introduction

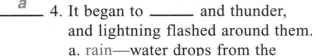

Homonyms are words that sound the same but are usually spelled differently and always have different meanings.

▶Below are six words from the story with their homonyms. Write the letter of the correct word to complete each sentence.

___*b*___ 1. Christian and Hopeful walked along the bank of the river with _____ delight.
    a. grate—a frame of bars; to scrape
    b. great—exceptional; very large

___*a*___ 2. On the left side of the road, there was a meadow and a _____ to go over the wall into it.
    a. stile—a ladder over a fence
    b. style—a specific way to do something

___*b*___ 3. They sang songs in praise of the _____ crystal water and pleasant fruit.
    a. suite—a series of connected rooms
    b. sweet—a pleasant taste

___*a*___ 4. It began to _____ and thunder, and lightning flashed around them.
    a. rain—water drops from the clouds
    b. reign—having authority, power

___*a*___ 5. They lay in the dungeon from Wednesday _____ until Saturday night.
    a. morning—early part of the day
    b. mourning—grief for a person

___*b*___ 6. The path on the other side was very easy on their _____.
    a. feat—a difficult accomplishment
    b. feet—plural of foot

> PSALM 46:4
>
> *There is a river, the streams whereof shall make glad the city of God, the holy place of the tabernacles of the most High.*

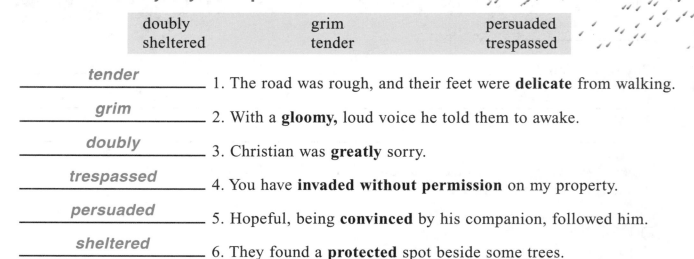

▶Write the correct synonym to replace the bold word or words.

doubly	grim	persuaded
sheltered	tender	trespassed

___*tender*___ 1. The road was rough, and their feet were **delicate** from walking.

___*grim*___ 2. With a **gloomy,** loud voice he told them to awake.

___*doubly*___ 3. Christian was **greatly** sorry.

___*trespassed*___ 4. You have **invaded without permission** on my property.

___*persuaded*___ 5. Hopeful, being **convinced** by his companion, followed him.

___*sheltered*___ 6. They found a **protected** spot beside some trees.

Reading 5: "Doubting Castle," pp. 416-20, Lesson 121
Vocabulary: using homonyms in context; identifying synonyms to develop word meaning

▶ Choose the answer that each character or place from *The Pilgrim's Progress* stands for.

MATTHEW 25:21

His lord said unto him, Well done, thou good and faithful servant: thou hast been faithful over a few things, I will make thee ruler over many things: enter thou into the joy of thy lord.

1. Christian

   ○ any preacher
   ○ any Christian writer
   ● any saved person

2. Hopeful

   ○ any weak Christian
   ● a new Christian who trusts God's promises
   ○ someone hoping to change a Christian's path

3. By-path Meadow

   ○ any restful, grassy place
   ● a path other than the one God wants us to follow
   ○ another path that goes along right next to the path God wants us to follow

4. Doubting Castle

   ● doubts that torment Christians
   ○ a place where bad Christians go
   ○ death

5. Giant Despair

   ○ strong desires to sin
   ○ anger
   ● despair of being loved by God

6. Distrust, the Giant's wife

   ○ distrust of one's own abilities
   ○ selfishness
   ● distrust of God's goodness

7. Christian's key called Promise

   ○ prayer
   ● the promises of God
   ○ courage

8. the King's highway

   ○ the path for the rich
   ● the path of life for the believer
   ○ the path for royalty

9. deep river—last step of the journey

   ○ any temptation
   ● death
   ○ baptism

Unlocking Prison Doors

▶**Answer the questions.**

Christian and Hopeful were locked inside Giant Despair's dungeon, and he was going to kill them. What did they do?

- ⬤ They used the key of promise to escape from Doubting Castle.
- ◯ They set an ambush to snare Giant Despair and killed him.
- ◯ They managed to climb out the dungeon window and got away just in time.

Was this a good solution to their problem? _____*yes*_____

Why or why not? _____*Depending on God is always the best solution to a problem.*_____

_____*They used the tool that God had given them, and He helped them escape.*_____

Choose two scriptural promises that we can use whenever we fall into despair or doubting as Christian and Hopeful did.

- ⬤ Psalm 16:11
- ◯ Genesis 1:31
- ⬤ Proverbs 3:26

II PETER 1:4

Whereby are given unto us exceeding great and precious promises.

▶**Match each promise key with the lock of doubt that it fits.**

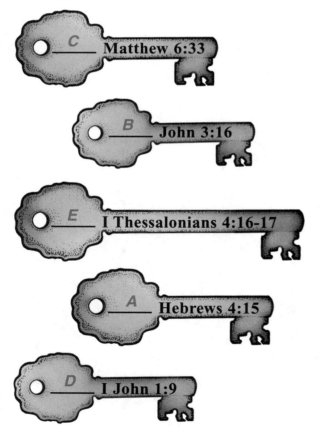

C — Matthew 6:33

B — John 3:16

E — I Thessalonians 4:16-17

A — Hebrews 4:15

D — I John 1:9

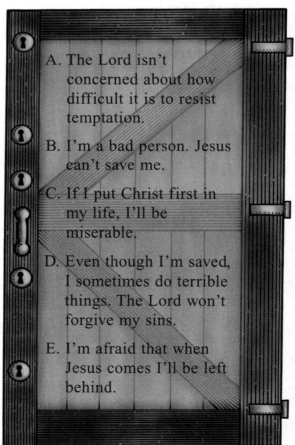

A. The Lord isn't concerned about how difficult it is to resist temptation.

B. I'm a bad person. Jesus can't save me.

C. If I put Christ first in my life, I'll be miserable.

D. Even though I'm saved, I sometimes do terrible things. The Lord won't forgive my sins.

E. I'm afraid that when Jesus comes I'll be left behind.

Reading 5, "Doubting Castle," pp. 421-26, Lesson 122
Comprehension: recalling facts and details; analyzing solutions to problems; applying biblical truth to problem situations and to personal problems
Study skills: locating Bible verses

Batter Up!

> An **analogy** is a comparison that shows the relationship between words.

Example: basketball → net : fishing → rod

▸**Complete the analogies.**

class	fingers	glove
field	game	trap

1. basketball → court : football → ____*field*____

2. soccer → shin guard : baseball → ____*glove*____

3. coach → team : teacher → ____*class*____

4. fish → net : rabbit → ____*trap*____

5. feet → toes : hands → ____*fingers*____

6. judge → trial : referee → ____*game*____

▸**Underline the topic sentence in each paragraph.**

<u>Did you know there are three kinds of baseball gloves?</u> The catcher uses a unique glove called the catcher's mitt. The first baseman wears a special glove called a first baseman's glove. It is usually thinner and more flexible than other players' gloves. Each of the other defensive players wears a fielder's glove.

> The **topic sentence** of a paragraph states in a nutshell what the paragraph is about.

<u>There are rules in baseball about what kind of ball to use.</u> The ball must be between 9 and $9\frac{1}{4}$ inches in circumference. It must weigh not less than 5 or more than $5\frac{1}{4}$ ounces. The center or core is made of cork, rubber, or similar material. This core is wound over with yarn and covered with two strips of white horsehide stitched together. Why do you think a baseball might be called a horsehide?

Reading 5: "The Base Stealer," pp. 428-29, Lesson 124
Comprehension: completing analogies
Study skills: locating the topic sentence

Word Imagery

▶ Rewrite each sentence adding colorful adjectives and vivid verbs to create an image in the reader's mind.

Answers will vary.
Suggestions are given.

1. The batter hit the ball to the outfield. _____

   _____ *The powerful batter slammed the ball into the outfield.* _____

2. Rain filled the village streets. _____

   _____ *Cold, blowing rain flooded the cobbled village streets.* _____

3. Under the chair sat the cat. _____

   _____ *Under the squeaky rocker purred the fat cat.* _____

▶ Write a word that matches the definition. When you are finished, the shaded letters spell the position of a baseball player.

delicate	hover	skitter	teeter
ecstatic	poised	taunt	

1. _P_ _O_ _I_ _S_ _E_ _D_

2. _S_ _K_ _I_ _T_ _T_ _E_ _R_

3. _T_ _A_ _U_ _N_ _T_

4. _E_ _C_ _S_ _T_ _A_ _T_ _I_ _C_

5. _H_ _O_ _V_ _E_ _R_

6. _D_ _E_ _L_ _I_ _C_ _A_ _T_ _E_

7. _T_ _E_ _E_ _T_ _E_ _R_

1. to be balanced
2. skip, glide, or move rapidly along a surface
3. mock or tease
4. marked by a feeling of great happiness
5. stay or wait nearby
6. requiring or needing great skill
7. walk in an unsteady manner

Reading 5: "The Base Stealer," pp. 428-29, Lesson 124
Composition: writing sentences containing imagery
Vocabulary: matching words and definitions

The Big Game

▶ **Complete each sentence.**

assumed	confidence	limbering	offing	vague

1. As soon as spring came, the Frasier Home School League and the Gravely Home

   School League knew that the Big Game was in the _____ *offing* _____.

2. Every year the team members were chosen in strictest _____ *confidence* _____.

3. When either team tried to find out the identities of the players, the other

   team gave them only _____ *vague* _____ replies.

4. Sometimes the players were not the players the other team had

   _____ *assumed* _____ they would be.

5. As the teams were _____ *limbering* _____ up,
   each team inspected the other.

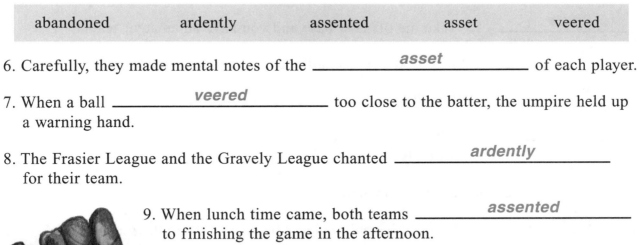

abandoned	ardently	assented	asset	veered

6. Carefully, they made mental notes of the _____ *asset* _____ of each player.

7. When a ball _____ *veered* _____ too close to the batter, the umpire held up
   a warning hand.

8. The Frasier League and the Gravely League chanted _____ *ardently* _____
   for their team.

9. When lunch time came, both teams _____ *assented* _____
   to finishing the game in the afternoon.

10. Each team immediately _____ *abandoned* _____ the
    baseball diamond for hot dogs and punch.

Reading 5: "Rufus and the Fatal Four," pp. 430-34, Lesson 125
Vocabulary: determining word meaning from sentence context

173

Putting Words into Their Mouths

**Hattie
Clara
Rufus
Nancy
Jane**

▶**Write the name of the person who you think would have said each quotation.**

Jane 1. "I'm the catcher, so I ought to be able to catch."

Rufus 2. "I really thought that Fatal Four had something to do with pirates."

Nancy 3. "For a while, Jane and I were the only members."

Nancy 4. "I'll be the captain. Let's take a vote."

Hattie 5. "Take me off first base and you have an amateur team."

Jane 6. "I'm tired of chasing the balls; we need a backstop."

Hattie 7. "I can't be backstop; I have to cover first."

Jane 8. "After all, a backstop is not really part of the team. It's part of the grounds."

Rufus 9. "Sure, I'd be glad to be a backstop!"

Clara 10. "So far, I haven't had any business here in the outfield."

Jane 11. "I don't know what's wrong with my catcher's mitt; it won't catch."

Rufus 12. "I'll hang around in case they decide to have punch and cookies."

Nancy 13. "Rufus is left-handed, so he can catch my curve balls."

Clara 14. "I pick goldenrod in the field except when Rufus is up to bat."

Reading 5: "Rufus and the Fatal Four," pp. 430–34, Lesson 125
Literature: projecting a character beyond the plot

▶**Choose the definition for each bold word.**

1. act in the **capacity** of umpire
   - ● position or role
   - ○ underneath

2. **subdued** and repressed, merely held the bat
   - ○ without any control
   - ● brought under control

3. subdued and **repressed,** merely held the bat
   - ○ leaped forward
   - ● purposely held back

4. **wallop** with the bat
   - ● a severe blow
   - ○ laying down

5. feeling badly at this **desertion**
   - ● leaving a responsibility
   - ○ a sweet-tasting food

6. became even more **animated** with the bat
   - ○ pretended to do
   - ● full of spirit

7. had been **vociferous** at the bat
   - ● noisy
   - ○ silent

8. backed away **apologetically**
   - ● in an excusing, humble manner
   - ○ in a forceful manner

9. never **envisioned** being in a spot like this
   - ○ examined carefully
   - ● imagined

10. **cultivated** her curve balls
    - ● developed by practice
    - ○ tilled the soil

11. **assented** that Rufus chase the balls
    - ● agreed
    - ○ disagreed

12. **accosted** them after school
    - ○ asked the cost of
    - ● approached in an aggressive manner

Who's on First?

▶**Answer the questions.**

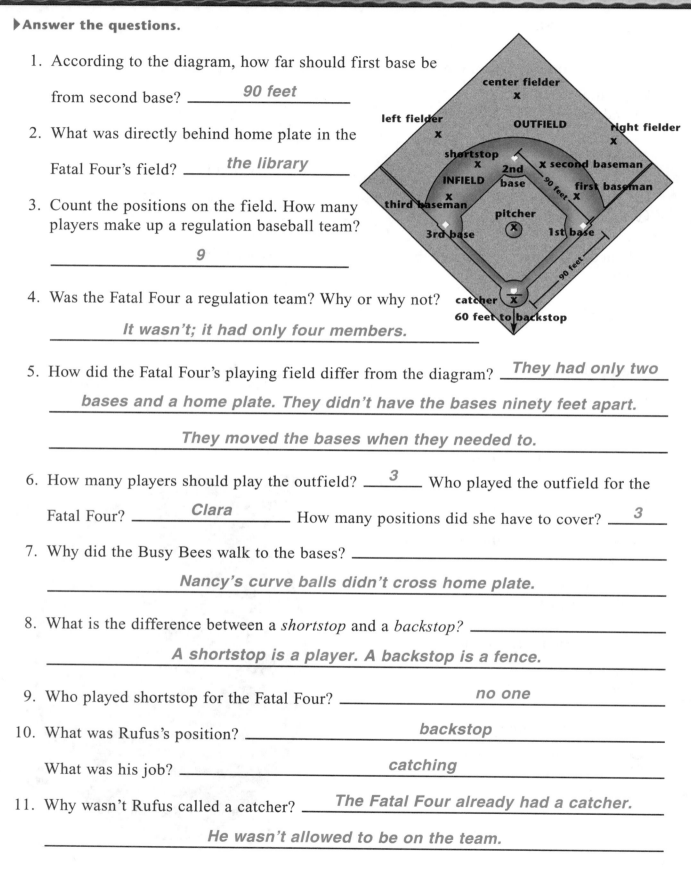

1. According to the diagram, how far should first base be
   from second base? _____ *90 feet* _____

2. What was directly behind home plate in the
   Fatal Four's field? _____ *the library* _____

3. Count the positions on the field. How many
   players make up a regulation baseball team?
   _____ *9* _____

4. Was the Fatal Four a regulation team? Why or why not?
   _____ *It wasn't; it had only four members.* _____

5. How did the Fatal Four's playing field differ from the diagram? _____ *They had only two*
   bases and a home plate. They didn't have the bases ninety feet apart.
   _____ *They moved the bases when they needed to.* _____

6. How many players should play the outfield? _____ *3* _____ Who played the outfield for the
   Fatal Four? _____ *Clara* _____ How many positions did she have to cover? _____ *3*

7. Why did the Busy Bees walk to the bases? _____
   _____ *Nancy's curve balls didn't cross home plate.* _____

8. What is the difference between a *shortstop* and a *backstop?* _____
   _____ *A shortstop is a player. A backstop is a fence.* _____

9. Who played shortstop for the Fatal Four? _____ *no one* _____

10. What was Rufus's position? _____ *backstop* _____
    What was his job? _____ *catching* _____

11. Why wasn't Rufus called a catcher? _____ *The Fatal Four already had a catcher.*
    _____ *He wasn't allowed to be on the team.* _____

Reading 5: "Rufus and the Fatal Four," pp 435-41, Lesson 126
Study skills: reading a diagram
Comprehension: drawing conclusions

The Lady's Torch

The upraised arm of the Statue of Liberty holds a torch that represents the light of freedom streaming out into a darkened world. President Grover Cleveland dedicated the monument in 1886. Inside the torch stood Frederic Bartholdi, the sculptor who had designed it. He had visualized the statue as a symbol of the friendship that developed between France and the United States in their fight for liberty.

On that night, Liberty's torch sent out a mere gleam of light instead of shining fifty miles out to sea as Bartholdi had planned. In disappointment he remarked that it looked like the light of a glowworm.

There have been at least three major renovations to the statue's lighting system. Eventually, a cluster of incandescent and mercury vapor lamps, totaling thirteen thousand watts, was installed. The effect was a flood of light estimated to be 2,500 times as bright as full moonlight.

The restoration that Miss Liberty underwent in preparation for her 100th birthday celebration on July 4, 1986, included a new torch made of hammered copper sheets and a flame that is covered in gold and lighted from the outside. The results would have pleased even Bartholdi.

▶Read the article. Now cover the article with a piece of paper and choose the correct answer to each question.

1. Liberty's torch represents
   ● freedom.
   ○ brotherhood.

2. The statue was finished in the
   ○ 1700s.
   ● 1800s.

3. It was dedicated by President
   ● Cleveland.
   ○ Lincoln.

4. The man who designed the statue, Frederic Bartholdi, was a
   ● sculptor.
   ○ painter.

5. The statue was a symbol of friendship between the United States and
   ○ Mexico.
   ● France.

6. On the first night, the torch shone
   ○ brightly.
   ● faintly.

7. Bartholdi thought the torch's light looked like the light of a
   ● glowworm.
   ○ lantern.

8. The lighting was improved by installing
   ● incandescent and mercury vapor lamps.
   ○ skylights in the torch.

9. New lights made the torch shine more brightly than
   ○ a lighthouse.
   ● full moonlight.

10. Now older than 100 years, Miss Liberty has a flame of
    ○ copper.
    ● gold.

How bright is your light?

10 correct: magnificent

8-9 correct: shiny

6-7 correct: only a glow

5 or fewer correct: needs restoration

Reading 5: "The New Colossus," pp. 442-43, Lesson 127
Comprehension: recalling facts and details

Welcome to the National Mall

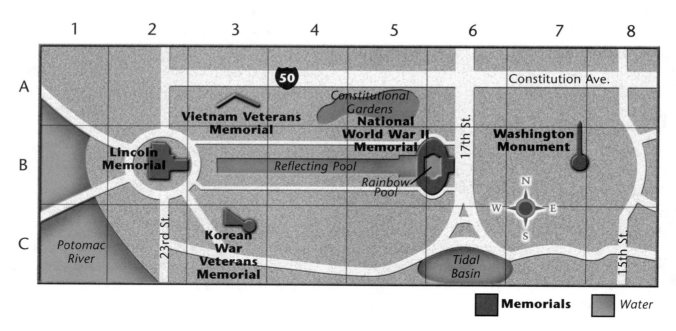

▶ **Use the map to answer the questions.**

1. What memorial is located in Section 3A? _____ *Vietnam Veterans Memorial* _____

2. What memorial is located in 5B and 6B? _____ *National World War II Memorial* _____

3. What two streets go north and south on either side of the Washington Monument?

   _____ *15th St., 17th St.* _____

4. If you went from the Tidal Basin to Constitution Ave., what direction would you travel?

   _____ *north* _____

5. In what sections is the Reflecting Pool located? _____ *3B, 4B, 5B* _____

6. The Reflecting Pool is in what direction from the Washington Monument in 7B? _____ *west* _____

7. In what section do 17th St. and Constitution Ave. cross? _____ *6A* _____

8. Which memorial is nearest the Potomac River? _____ *Lincoln Memorial* _____

9. In what section is the Korean War Veterans Memorial located? _____ *3C* _____

10. Which road is also labeled as Highway 50? _____ *Constitution Ave.* _____

Reading 5: "The New Colossus," pp. 442-43, Lesson 127
Study skills: determining locations on a map using coordinates and a compass rose

Gathering Facts

▶ **Choose the correct evidence from the page given in parentheses to back up each conclusion. You may use your reader.**

1. **Conclusion:** The children were afraid of the Japanese.
   Evidence: (446)

   ○ The children played outside.
   ● The children fled into the buildings.

2. **Conclusion:** The Japanese soldiers spent little time gathering the boys old enough to fight.
   Evidence: (446)

   ○ Calling in Japanese, the soldier yanked up the frightened girl.
   ● The soldiers pounded on the doors, gave harsh orders, and marched the boys out of the orphanage.

3. **Conclusion:** The refugees helped each other.
   Evidence: (448)

   ● Luang helped the mother with her child.
   ○ Seventh Plumblossom pleaded to go away from the orphanage.

4. **Conclusion:** Many girls had the name Plumblossom during the war.
   Evidence: (446)

   ○ Seventh Plumblossom's trembling drew attention to the willow basket.
   ● She was the seventh Plumblossom to come live at the orphanage.

▶ **Write the evidence to back up the conclusion. Use complete sentences.**

Wording may vary.

1. **Conclusion:** The Japanese army was victorious over the Chinese.

   Evidence: (444) _The Japanese invaded China and occupied Chinese cities._

2. **Conclusion:** The Japanese soldier was kind.

   Evidence: (446-47) _He kept the first soldier from hurting Plumblossom. /_
   He spoke gently. / He felt sorrow and pity for Plumblossom.

3. **Conclusion:** Luang was a responsible person.

   Evidence: (448) _He was father and mother to Seventh Plumblossom. /_
   He helped a mother with her child.

4. **Conclusion:** Luang and Seventh Plumblossom had come from a wealthy home.

   Evidence: (445) _Seventh Plumblossom remembered eating shrimp_
   and crystallized fruit.

Reading 5: "May the Plum Tree Always Blossom," pp. 444-48, Lesson 129
Comprehension: gathering evidence to support a conclusion

179

Propaganda is any technique that tries to influence people's opinions, emotions, attitudes, or behavior. The purpose of propaganda is to persuade.

▶ Label the propaganda technique used in each picture: *bandwagon*, *testimonial*, or *name calling*.

Bandwagon is "getting on the bandwagon." Because everyone else has something or does something, so should you.

Testimonial uses personal testimony to win confidence for a person, a product, or a cause.

Name calling uses negative words to create an unfavorable opinion in the viewer's mind.

1. _____ bandwagon

2. _____ testimonial

3. _____ name calling

Reading 5: "May the Plum Tree Always Blossom," pp. 449-54, Lesson 130
Literature: recognizing propaganda—name calling, bandwagon, testimonial; making judgments in reading
Comprehension: drawing conclusions

▶ **Label the propaganda technique used in each picture:**
bandwagon, testimonial, or *name calling.*

Possible answers are shown.
Accept all reasonable answers.

1. _____*testimonial*_____

2. _____*bandwagon*_____

3. _____*bandwagon*_____

4. _____*name calling*_____

Reading 5: "May the Plum Tree Always Blossom," pp. 449-54, Lesson 130
Literature: recognizing propaganda—bandwagon, testimonial, name calling; making judgments in reading
Comprehension: drawing conclusions

▶Write the correct letter in the blanks on the plot frame to put the events in story order.

A. Japanese soldiers pounded on the doors, gave harsh orders, and marched the boys from the orphanage.

B. Luang and Seventh Plumblossom must leave the orphanage.

C. As Seventh Plumblossom watched, old women tottered by the orphanage on their way to market, balancing on tiny feet that had been bound in childhood to prevent growth.

D. The Japanese soldier yanked Plumblossom up.

E. The soldier ripped one of the broken planks away from the cart and exposed Luang and Plumblossom.

F. The soldier wanted Plumblossom to enjoy freedom once again.

G. The soldier brought Ping to guide Luang and Plumblossom to safety.

DEUTERONOMY 31:6
Be strong and of a good courage, fear not, nor be afraid of them: for the Lord thy God, he it is that doth go with thee; he will not fail thee, nor forsake thee.

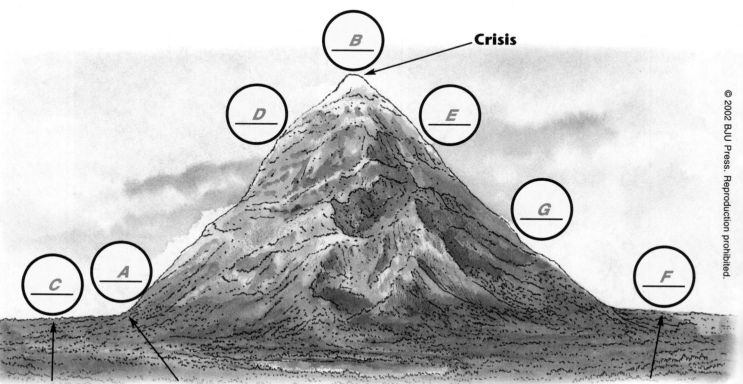

Crisis

Introduction **Conflict Begins** **Resolution (Final Outcome)**

Reading 5: "May the Plum Tree Always Blossom," pp. 449-54, Lesson 130
Comprehension: sequencing events
Literature: identifying the parts of a plot

Skimming is reading quickly to get the general idea. One way to do this is to read carefully the first and last sentences of each paragraph. Quickly read the others.

Leaping Lizards

Long ago people noticed that a certain lizardlike creature had a ruff of scaly skin around its neck. This ruff looked something like a lion's mane, so scientists named it the *Chamaeleonidae,* which means "humble lion of the earth." The name *lion* can still be heard in the name of the creature: the chameleon.

The chameleon is cold-blooded, which means that it cannot produce heat for its own body. At night, when the weather is cool, it grows sluggish. As the temperature drops, all its activity ceases. But the early morning sun warms it until it can move normally.

The chameleon can turn its eyes in different directions at the same time. This comes in handy when it is looking for a quick meal. After breakfast flies into range, the chameleon turns to look at it with both of these cone-shaped eyes.

Zing! Its tongue shoots out, grabs the target with its sticky fluid, and shrivels back up into a little disk. A chameleon's tongue reaches farther than the length of its whole body. Because a chameleon cannot

move fast enough to chase an insect, it has to rely on its lightning tongue.

But even though all these traits are interesting, one characteristic alone gives the chameleon world renown—the strange ability to change color to match whatever surrounds it. Cells in its skin respond to light and cause the lizard to change color. People have joked that if a chameleon crawled across a bright Scottish kilt, it would explode! Even a blindfolded chameleon changes color when the light near it dims or brightens. People who constantly change their minds are sometimes called chameleons.

▶**After skimming the article, answer each question.**

1. What is the article mainly about?
   - ○ a chameleon's ability to catch food
   - ● characteristics of chameleons

2. Which information could be found in this article?
   - ● a chameleon's color-changing ability
   - ○ the ways lizards and snakes look alike

3. Which information would *not* be found in this article?
   - ○ a person being compared to a chameleon
   - ● chameleons as pets

Reading 5: "Literature Lesson: Making Judgments in Reading," pp. 455-58, Lesson 131
Study skills: skimming for main ideas

183

Advertisement Persuasion

▶Label the propaganda technique used in each picture:
bandwagon, testimonial, or *name calling*

1. _____ *name calling* _____

2. _____ *bandwagon* _____

3. _____ *bandwagon* _____

4. _____ *testimonial* _____

Reading 5: "Literature Lesson: Making Judgments in Reading," pp. 455-58, Lesson 131
Literature: making judgments in reading; recognizing propaganda—bandwagon,
testimonial, name calling

Rambling Ram

▶**Choose a synonym for the word in bold print.**

1. the time for the **in-gathering** of the sheep
   - ○ feeding
   - ● gathering together

2. horns for **implements**
   - ● tools
   - ○ noise making

3. the great **rift** that led down to the Plains
   - ● an opening
   - ○ a flat boat

4. something **noble** in the scene
   - ○ familiar
   - ● of high character

5. **hobbled** ponies
   - ○ branded with an iron
   - ● restrained with a rope

6. the wind, **keenly** blowing
   - ● intensely
   - ○ slowly

7. the first **parliament** in the world
   - ● governing body
   - ○ sports team

8. **mutton** stew and boiled potatoes
   - ○ vegetable
   - ● lamb

▶**Paraphrase or write in your own words each of these sentences from "Rounding Up the Sheep."**

Answers will vary.

1. The ponies pressed their noses forward and pricked their ears as if answering the call of the mountains. _____*Possible answer: The ponies were eager to get started.*_____

2. "The fish are certainly in a hurry to be eaten," Finnur shouted. _____
*Possible answer: Finnur thought the fish were easy to catch.*_____

3. "I'm as hungry as a pony," Hans exclaimed. _____
*Possible answer: Hans was very hungry.*_____

4. Blankets were unrolled, and one tired traveler after another rolled up in them. _____
*Possible answer: Each tired person covered up in his blanket.*_____

Reading 5: "Rounding Up the Sheep," pp. 459-63, Lesson 134
Vocabulary: identifying synonyms to determine word meaning
Study skills: paraphrasing sentences

Shepherding the Sheep

▶ Gudrun remembered the Bible story of the lost sheep. The Bible also tells of the shepherd's duties. Answer these questions. Choose the Scripture verse that tells of the shepherd's duty.

1. What animal assists a shepherd in guarding the sheep? _____ *a dog* _____
   Verse:
   ○ Psalm 119:11
   ● Job 30:1

2. What duty of a shepherd was Gudrun ready to perform when she asked Uncle Tomas to take Bruni's place watching the sheep?
   _____ *searching for a lost lamb* _____
   Verse:
   ○ I Corinthians 11:1
   ● Luke 15:4

3. During the night what did Bruni help the shepherd do?
   _____ *watch the sheep in the enclosure* _____
   Verse:
   ● Luke 2:8
   ○ Psalm 66:1-2

4. From what animal did Gudrun protect the little lamb? _____ *an eagle* _____
   Verse:
   ● I Samuel 17:34-35
   ○ John 10:14

5. How did Gudrun speak to and treat the lost lamb? _____ *gently* _____
   Verse:
   ● Isaiah 40:11
   ○ Romans 10:13

6. If you are a Christian, who is your Good Shepherd? _____ *Jesus* _____
   Verse:
   ○ James 4:14
   ● Hebrews 13:20-21

JOHN 10:14
I am the good shepherd, and know my sheep, and am known of mine.

Reading 5: "Rounding Up the Sheep," pp. 464-68, Lesson 135
Study skills: supporting conclusions with biblical truth
Comprehension: recalling facts and details; drawing conclusions

PQ3R—Map Projections

▶ **Follow the steps in the PQ3R method as you look over reader pages 469-71. Check each box as you complete the step.**

STUDY SKILL

Preview
Question
Read
Recite
Review

PREVIEW

❑ 1. What do you think the article will be about?

Possible answers: maps, making maps

QUESTION

❑ 2. Make a question from the title "Skill Lesson: Map Projections."

Possible answer: How are map projections made?

❑ 3. Look at the italicized words, *map projections,* on page 469. Make a question from the italicized words.

Possible answer: What are map projections?

READ

❑ 4. Think about your questions as you read silently page 469.

RECITE

❑ 5. Tell yourself the answer to your questions for numbers 2-3.

QUESTION

❑ 6. Make a question from the subheading "Interrupted projection" on page 470.

Possible answer: What is an interrupted projection?

❑ 7. Look at the caption on page 470. Make a question from the caption.

Possible answer: Why is an interrupted projection accurate?

READ

❑ 8. Think about your questions as you read silently page 470.

RECITE

❑ 9. Tell yourself the answer to your questions for numbers 6-7.

QUESTION, READ, RECITE AGAIN

❑ 10. Repeat the three steps again for the next section of the article.

REVIEW

❑ 11. Look back at the title, subheadings, illustrations, captions, and italicized words and remind yourself of the information you learned.

Reading 5: "Skill Lesson: Map Projections," pp. 469-71, Lesson 136
Study skills: using the PQ3R method of study

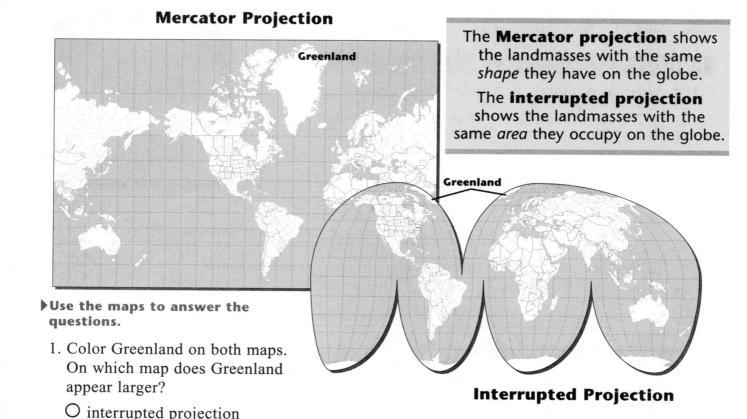

Mercator Projection

Interrupted Projection

The **Mercator projection** shows the landmasses with the same *shape* they have on the globe.

The **interrupted projection** shows the landmasses with the same *area* they occupy on the globe.

▶Use the maps to answer the questions.

1. Color Greenland on both maps. On which map does Greenland appear larger?

   ○ interrupted projection
   ● Mercator projection

2. According to the definitions of the projections, which map shows the correct area that Greenland occupies?

   ● interrupted projection
   ○ Mercator projection

3. Read the definition of each map again. Now compare Greenland on both maps. If a sailor wanted to locate a harbor along the coast of Greenland, which map would be detailed enough to help him?

   ○ interrupted projection
   ● Mercator projection

4. Suppose a surveyor wanted to use a scale to determine the distance across Greenland. Which map would provide the most accurate answer?

   ● interrupted projection
   ○ Mercator projection

5. Look at the islands between Greenland and North America on both maps. Compare the two areas. How do they differ?

   They are larger on

   the Mercator projection.

6. What happens when landmasses near the North or South Pole are drawn using the Mercator projection?

   They look bigger

   than they are.

Reading 5: "Skill Lesson: Map Projections," pp. 469-71, Lesson 136
Study skills: comparing map projections

Sack of Cotton

Name_____

▶**Choose the correct answer.**

1. Merrilee Palmer put her hand on her back as she stood up because
   - ○ it was a signal to her sister to stop picking cotton.
   - ● she was weary from picking cotton.
   - ○ Josie was picking more cotton than she was.

2. Merrilee did not want to walk everywhere, so she
   - ● worked to buy a bike.
   - ○ used her best friend Alice's bike.
   - ○ took the bus.

3. Josie helped Merrilee fill her sack with cotton because
   - ○ she liked being with Merrilee.
   - ○ she wanted to help her catch up.
   - ● she knew how much Merrilee wanted the new bike.

4. When Father saw Mother's pale face, he knew he must take her home because
   - ○ she was not used to working in the fields.
   - ● she had not recovered from the illness enough to be picking cotton.
   - ○ she had been so frightened by the encounter.

5. The boys picked cotton slower when
   - ● the adults were out of sight.
   - ○ Mr. Grant came by.
   - ○ Josie and Merrilee got closer to them.

6. Mr. Palmer gave Josie and Merrilee a ride home in the wagon because
   - ○ Mrs. Palmer needed them to come home quickly.
   - ○ Merrilee did not have her bike yet.
   - ● the first day of picking cotton was always hard.

▶**Paraphrase or write in your own words each of these sentences from "The Store-Bought Dress."**   *Answers will vary.*

1. "I'm half of one mind, half of another about moving up." _____ *Possible answer:*

   Sometimes she wanted to make the change, and sometimes she didn't.

2. Daddy said that Josie was a word spinner, weaving words like Mama wove cloth.

   Possible answer: Talking with people came easy for Josie.

3. She knew that one satisfactory scream could bring on a flock of practical jokes.

   Possible answer: Screaming would be sure to bring on more practical jokes.

4. The four years between them had widened suddenly into a gulf.

   Possible answer: The difference in their ages had become more obvious.

Reading 5: "The Store-Bought Dress," pp. 472-77, Lesson 137
Comprehension: determining cause-and-effect relationships
Study skills: paraphrasing sentences to determine word meaning

The cotton plant is between three and six feet tall. It has fruit called *bolls,* which look something like very large, hard rosebuds. Inside the boll the cotton fibers grow in two stages, first in length, and then in thickness. In autumn the leaves fall off the plants, leaving the bolls exposed to the sunlight. The sunshine ripens the bolls and causes them to open, revealing the fluffy, white fibers. When the bolls are ripe, the stems of the plants and the bolls are dried and hardened. Above the dried stalks, the fibers resemble white clouds.

If workers pick the fibers by hand, they have to pluck them from the scratchy, prickly bolls and put them into long sacks that they drag behind them. The full sacks are emptied into a wagon or truck.

Today almost all cotton is picked mechanically by a specially designed harvester. The fibers are emptied into a truck and taken to a cotton gin. When the truck arrives at the gin, the fibers are sucked through a pipe into the building.

The first step in processing the fibers is to dry and clean them. Any dirt, leaves, or twigs clinging to the fibers are removed. Then the fiber is separated from the seeds by ginning. Circular saws, placed close together, revolve over narrow slits in a grating. As the cotton is pulled over the slits, the teeth of the saws pull the fiber through and leave the seeds behind. The seeds are transported by belt or chutes or are suctioned to the seed house.

The fiber is then sent through a lint flue to be cleaned again. Then it goes to the gin press to be packed into bales. The bales of cotton fiber, sometimes weighing five hundred pounds, are taken to a plant where the fiber is not only spun but also processed into cloth.

▶**Answer the questions.**

Wording will vary.

1. What is the difference between a cotton boll and a rosebud? _The cotton boll is hard._

2. What are the two stages in fiber growth? _length and thickness_

3. How does losing its leaves help the cotton plant? _The sun ripens the bolls._

4. How can you tell if a cotton plant is ready to be picked? _____

   The bolls and stems are dry and hard. The bolls open to expose the fibers.

5. Why do you think most cotton is picked mechanically today instead of by hand? _____

   to help the farmer do the work faster

6. Why is it necessary to clean the cotton? _____

   to remove dirt, twigs, and leaves mixed in with the fiber

Reading 5: "The Store-Bought Dress," pp. 472-77, Lesson 137
Comprehension: identifying facts and details; inferring facts and details; drawing conclusions

Cotton for Money

▶**Answer the questions in complete sentences.**   *Wording may vary.*

1. Why were the Palmers concerned about Mama picking cotton? _____

   They weren't sure that she had fully recovered from her illness.

2. Why wouldn't Josie and Merrilee be riding the same bus to school this year? _____

   They were attending different schools.

3. Why did Josie and Merrilee decide to give their cotton earnings to their father? _____

   To help pay doctor bills since the cotton did not sell for as much this year.

4. Why did the girls agree to put their money together and buy the dress and shoes? _____

   Josie would be able to wear them now;

   later they would be passed down to Merrilee.

▶**Choose the correct word to complete the sentence.**

___*b*___ 1. Do you _____ Mama's going to be able to pick cotton?
   a. reflect
   b. reckon
   c. require

___*c*___ 2. There was a time when some people _____ at the idea of a machine picking cotton.
   a. scuffed
   b. mingled
   c. scoffed

___*a*___ 3. As Keli prepared to jump into the cold water, she _____ herself.
   a. steeled
   b. mimicked
   c. proclaimed

___*b*___ 4. It looked like a colony of ants had _____ around the wet lollipop.
   a. glinted
   b. clustered
   c. manufactured

___*a*___ 5. Tyler _____ when he felt the spider on his arm.
   a. flinched
   b. flickered
   c. reevaluated

___*b*___ 6. Kwanita saw the canary for a _____ second.
   a. scoffing
   b. fleeting
   c. jesting

Reading 5: "The Store-Bought Dress," pp. 472-81, Lesson 138
Comprehension: recalling facts and details; inferring facts and details
Vocabulary: determining word meaning from context

Carlson's Department Store

▶ Carlson's Department Store classifies its merchandise. The bills itemize merchandise by stock number, not by department. Imagine that you have a part-time job at Carlson's. Read the bill and write the name of each item under the correct department.

BILL OF LADING

Stock #	Item	Amount
107621	soccer balls	12
109712	belts	24
112842	lamps	7
117497	ovens	5
117526	plants	24
118324	fishing rods	15
372121	toasters	10
387162	dresses	17
392416	shoes	15 pr.
397112	dolls	8
401775	seeds	70 pkg.
403178	bicycles	5
417213	couches	5
417553	fertilizer	25 lb.

Order may vary.

Clothing Department

belts

dresses

shoes

Lawn and Garden Department

plants

seeds

fertilizer

Appliance Department

ovens

toasters

Sporting Goods Department

soccer balls

fishing rods

Furniture Department

lamps

couches

Toy Department

dolls

bicycles

192

Reading 5: "The Store-Bought Dress," pp. 478-81, Lesson 138
Study skills: classifying

Revealing Speech

▶**Identify the attitude of each speaker.**

angry	doubtful	excited	hopeful	kind	uncaring

1. "It wouldn't bother me a bit if Eli never finishes that contraption. I don't like cotton anyway."

   uncaring

2. "Planting whole plantations in cotton? If you mention that foolish idea one more time, I'm leaving!"

   angry

3. "Oh, it might be profitable if Eli's idea works."

   hopeful

4. "Take as long as you need, Mr. Whitney. You may stay in our home until your work is done."

   kind

5. "Everybody, come quickly! That young fellow from New York is showing how his cotton gin works!"

   excited

6. "That little machine is supposed to solve our problems? I'll believe that when I see it."

   doubtful

cautious	greedy	impatient	jealous	nervous	surprised

7. "I'll think about it and do my best, gentlemen. But I can't make any promises."

   cautious

8. "So what if his cotton gin does work? I could've invented it too if only I'd thought about it first."

   jealous

9. "I wish he would let us in for just a quick peek. I can't stand wondering what he's building in there."

   impatient

10. "I . . . I wonder if it might explode or something."

    nervous

11. "If I could steal that cotton gin, I'd be rich!"

    greedy

12. "I can hardly believe it! That thing really does work! And fast, too!"

    surprised

Reading 5: "Eli Whitney's Big Idea," pp. 482-84, Lesson 139
Literature: identifying the emotional responses of characters

193

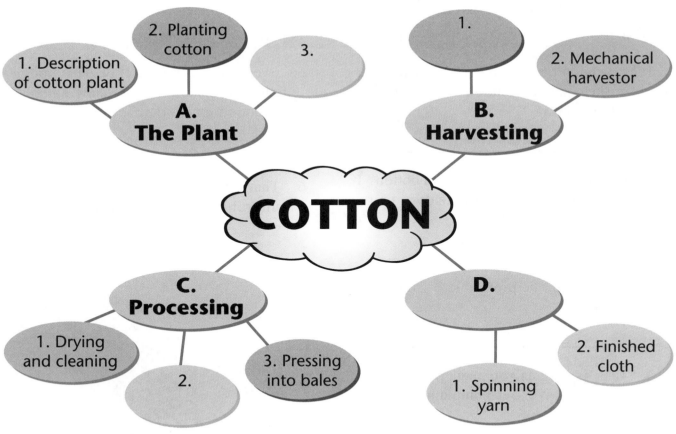

A. The Plant
- 1. Description of cotton plant
- 2. Planting cotton
- 3.

B. Harvesting
- 1.
- 2. Mechanical harvestor

COTTON

C. Processing
- 1. Drying and cleaning
- 2.
- 3. Pressing into bales

D.
- 1. Spinning yarn
- 2. Finished cloth

▶ **Michael made this web to help him organize information about cotton. Use it to help answer the questions.**

1. Which idea belongs in oval 3?
   - ○ Eli Whitney's invention
   - ○ Cotton fabric
   - ◉ Stages of development

2. Which idea belongs in oval 1?
   - ◉ Picking by hand
   - ○ Tilling the soil
   - ○ Uses of cotton

3. Which idea belongs in oval 2?
   - ○ Picking cotton
   - ◉ Separating fiber
   - ○ Growing cotton

4. Which heading belongs in oval D?
   - ○ Types of Machines
   - ◉ Final Product
   - ○ Kinds of Cotton

Reading 5: "Eli Whitney's Big Idea," pp. 482-84, Lesson 139
Study skills: using a web to organize information

Name_____

▶ **Complete the crossword puzzle.**

sump
smolder
mainstay   ventilation   extract
staunch   cardinal
ponderous

grim
saturate

I Corinthians 10:31
Whether therefore ye eat, or drink, or whatsoever ye do, do all to the glory of God.

Across

3. firm; steadfast; true
5. burn with little smoke and no flame
6. gloomy
8. to soak; fill completely
9. a hole in a mine where water collects and is pumped out
10. chief support

Down

1. causing fresh air to enter or move about
2. to pull out with force
4. difficult to handle because of size or weight
7. of greatest or first importance

Reading 5: "The Proving of a Hero," pp. 485-89, Lesson 140
Vocabulary: matching words and definitions

195

▶ **Answer the questions.**

Wording may vary.

1. Why do you think Ethel wanted to join the others at the mine? _____

She was concerned for her father and other family members at the mine.

2. Why did Ethel know she must not go to the mine? ___ *The rule to remain at home with*

Mother assured Father of his family's safety in case of an emergency at the mine.

3. How did the author let you know John Bundy was dead? ___ *Ethel's brother, Herbert,*

turned his eyes away in grief and slowly started home, his head hung low.

4. How might Isaiah 40:31 encourage Mother as she becomes the mainstay of the family?

Our strength is in the Lord.

▶ **These articles describe other recipients of the Carnegie Hero medal. Choose the best headline for each article.**

The Sun-Times Herald

Issue 8

René Javier Cerda saved David English from suffocation. English lay in shock with burns over 75 percent of his body after a flash fire in a hydraulic pump room. Cerda reentered the room twice for English but was turned away by heavy smoke. On a third attempt, Cerda crawled into the room with other men and located English. He removed English with the help of the others. Cerda recovered from smoke inhalation. English later died of his burns.

- ○ English Escapes Smoke
- ● Hero Saves Fire Victim

Furman Brown rescued Herberta Abercrombie from burning. A fire broke out and spread through her one-story dwelling. Noticing the smoke, Brown forced open the kitchen door and crawled through dense smoke into the kitchen. Abercrombie was on the kitchen floor. He dragged her from the dwelling. The front section of the house had collapsed as others arrived to aid Brown in moving Abercrombie.

Abercrombie, extensively burned from the intense heat, died soon after being hospitalized.

- ○ Locked Door Prevents Escape
- ● Heroic Efforts of Brown

James Buchanan Jr. saved Randy Freeman and Stevie Riley from drowning. While trying to cross the Great Pee Dee River, Randy, 12, and Stevie, 11, were swept downstream by a strong current. Buchanan ran 60 feet to the river. Swimming 190 feet diagonally across the current, he overtook Randy and towed him 30 feet to the bank. Buchanan then swam 60 feet to overtake Stevie, who was nearly unconscious and almost completely submerged in water. While towing Stevie, Buchanan, nearly exhausted, was carried 45 feet downstream. He grabbed a fallen tree, lifted Stevie onto it, and then climbed onto it himself. Stevie began to revive as Buchanan forced water from him.

- ● Buchanan Saves Two from Drowning
- ○ Buchanan Swims to Safety

Reading 5: "The Proving of a Hero," pp. 485-89, Lesson 140
Comprehension: evaluating character attitudes; drawing conclusions; determining headlines

What Caused?

Name_____

▶ **Answer the questions.**

___*a*___ 1. What caused Jonas to go to the township of Temple?
   a. He had been promised a piece of land with plenty of water.
   b. He had signed his name in the Town Book.

___*b*___ 2. What caused Jonas to return home without Big Red?
   a. He wanted to own a steer instead.
   b. The army needed horses.

___*b*___ 3. What caused the people of Temple to go without goods?
   a. The people did not have the money to pay for the goods.
   b. The people did not want to pay the high taxes forced upon them by Britain.

___*a*___ 4. What caused Jonas to speak up against the British Crown?
   a. He believed the people had a right to a voice and a vote in the government.
   b. He was a loyal subject of the British Crown.

___*b*___ 5. What caused Jess to remember her motherly duty?
   a. The two little boys helped to plant Indian corn.
   b. Jess heard a small cry coming from the house.

___*a*___ 6. What caused the men of Temple to organize a militia?
   a. The men had heard Samuel Webster address the militia at Groton.
   b. The men met for muster three evenings a week.

___*a*___ 7. What caused Matthew and Mark to sit on the steer instead of riding him?
   a. The steer was too ornery to ride.
   b. The steer needed good grazing.

___*a*___ 8. What caused Matthew and Mark to run for moss and a jug of cold water?
   a. Jonas had a welt on his forehead.
   b. The moss and water were needed for the crops.

___*b*___ 9. What caused the Temple militia to leave for a week?
   a. The militia had heard Mr. Webster's words.
   b. A rider came with news from the Battle at the Bridge.

___*b*___ 10. What caused Jonas to be different after leaving with the militia?
   a. Jonas had been gone a week.
   b. Jonas had seen men killed, houses burned, and fields trampled.

▶ **Choose the correct definition for each bold word. You may use your glossary.**

1. Stone walls served for pasture and **tillage.**
   ● cultivated land
   ○ rivers and creeks

2. the newly **incorporated** township
   ○ core of people
   ● organized as a legal corporation

3. men of Groton at their **muster**
   ● gathering of troops
   ○ spread for sandwiches

4. The steer **balked.**
   ○ ran swiftly
   ● refused to go on

5. News came by **courier.**
   ● messenger
   ○ horse

6. His words were **deliberate.**
   ● said on purpose
   ○ discussed

Reading 5: "We, the People," pp. 490-96, Lesson 141
Comprehension: identifying cause-and-effect relationships
Vocabulary: matching words and definitions

Who?

A. Captain Allen	C. Jess	E. Priest Trowbridge
B. Courier	D. Jonas	F. Mr. Webster

▶**Match the name of the person that you think said or would say each quotation.**

___D___ 1. "No need to wear yourself out. We can finish it next year."

___E___ 2. "I will take care of the women and children whose men are away."

___D___ 3. "I want to be able to drink our own water."

___B___ 4. "Ticonderoga! Crown Point! Send as many men as you can."

___F___ 5. "There is not a coward among our men or our women."

___C___ 6. "Please get a message to us somehow."

___E___ 7. "I bring a letter from the courier."

___A___ 8. "We are here in the name of the Great Jehovah and the Continental Congress!"

___F___ 9. "Men of Temple, we must march immediately."

___C___ 10. "Thank you for the offer of help, but the boys and I are able to get the work done."

▶**Choose the correct definition for the bold word.**

1. A courier, riding **posthaste,** came to a halt.
   - ○ slowly
   - ● speedily
   - ○ beautifully

2. Priest Trowbridge had a kindly but **unctuous** manner.
   - ○ characterized by understanding
   - ● characterized by insincerity
   - ○ hidden or secret

3. The boys collected potato bugs in a **pannikin.**
   - ● small metal cup
   - ○ large plate
   - ○ round pan

4. Jess was feeling **mirthful** because of what she glimpsed.
   - ○ a spice
   - ○ full of sorrow
   - ● full of gladness

5. The Green Mountain Boys had been **augmented** by men from Massachusetts.
   - ○ made fewer in number
   - ○ made weaker
   - ● made greater in number

6. It was a long process to **hatchel** the slender stalks.
   - ● separate fibers using a comb
   - ○ carry a small bag
   - ○ separate by using a machine

Reading 5: "We, the People," pp. 497–504, Lesson 142
Comprehension: comparing and contrasting character traits
Vocabulary: matching words and definitions

The Meaning Is

Name_____

▶Paraphrase or write in your own words each of these sentences from "We, the People."

Answers will vary.

1. The rooster was crowing as if a dozen dawns had burst on the world. _____
   _____*Possible answer: The rooster was crowing loudly.*_____

2. The fox rolled over, kicking convulsively before it lay still. _____
   _____*Possible answer: The fox kicked fiercely and then lay still.*_____

3. The June night was soft around them when they sat on the doorstone. _____
   _____*Possible answer: They sat on the step during the pleasant June night.*_____

4. Bleats and baas mingled with the shouts and laughter of the boys. ___*Possible answer:*___
   _____*You could hear the boys playing mixed with the sound of the goats and sheep.*_____

5. The lights from fireflies pricked the darkness around her as stars did the sky above her.
   _____*Possible answer: The fireflies twinkled in the darkness.*_____

▶Choose the correct definition for each bold word.

__a__ 1. Fifty-six men, wearing buckskin **jerkins,** gathered on the green.
   a. short jackets
   b. long pants

__a__ 2. The kernels of grain were waiting to be pounded into **hominy.**
   a. corn hulled and boiled as food
   b. peas shelled as food

__b__ 3. Jess used the **scythe** to make an early cut of the clover.
   a. long pair of scissors
   b. tool with a long, curved blade

__b__ 4. Jonas would skin the fox and **cure** his hide.
   a. to heal the wound
   b. to prepare and preserve

__b__ 5. People were in **dire straits.**
   a. tightly holding bonds
   b. urgent circumstances

__a__ 6. Liberty needed only a **croon** to keep her sleeping.
   a. humming or soft song
   b. soft blanket

__a__ 7. The boys put on their **hobnailed** boots.
   a. short nail used to protect the soles
   b. short fingernail

__b__ 8. Jonas had a **rent** in his jerkin.
   a. zipper
   b. tear

© 2002 BJU Press. Reproduction prohibited.

Reading 5: "We, the People," pp. 505-9, Lesson 143
Study skills: paraphrasing sentences to determine word meaning
Vocabulary: matching words and definitions

199

▶**Answer each question in a complete sentence.**

1. Why had the Colonies stopped buying goods from Britain? _____
   They didn't want to pay the taxes. / They wanted a voice in their government.

2. Why did Jonas not want to be a soldier? _____ *He enjoyed working the land. /*
   He had seen men die, houses burned, and fields destroyed.

3. How does the author let you know that Matthew and Mark do not understand the
   tragedies of the war? _____ *The boys played that they were Minute Men.*

4. What scene does the author describe to let you know that Jess did not always find
   comfort while Jonas was gone? _____ *She went to the field at night and cried.*

5. What was the outcome of the last battle that Jonas fought in?
   The British won but lost a lot of men.

6. Why did Jess send Matthew and Mark to help their
   father returning from the last battle?
   He was limping and didn't have much strength.

7. What document did the members of the Continental
   Congress sign in Philadelphia?
   They signed the Declaration of Independence.

▶**Write the correct word for each definition. You may use your glossary.**

imbue 1. to inspire

huzza 2. a shout of joy; a cheer

sluiceway 3. a man-made channel for water with a gate to control the flow

bestir 4. to encourage to action

cure 5. to prepare or preserve an animal skin for use

bestir
cure
huzza
imbue
sluiceway

Reading 5: "We, the People," pp. 510-14, Lesson 144
Comprehension: recalling facts and detail; drawing conclusions
Vocabulary: matching words and definitions
Study skills: using a glossary

Skill Day Lessons

This section of the worktext presents teaching and practice of each of the major reading subskills. The pages provide follow-up for the special skill lessons in the *READING 5 TEACHER'S EDITION.* The first Skill Day lesson (Lesson 4) comes after the first story in the reader.

These pages are located here so you can find them easily. You may find it beneficial to keep them in the worktext. They will serve as a reference to be used again as needed.

So to Speak

A. Write the nonliteral meaning of the shaded phrases in the sentences.

1. Blain is down in the dumps today.

   Blain is feeling sad today.

2. Keep that information under your hat.

   Don't tell anyone that information.

3. I know what you mean. We're both in the same boat.

   We both have that problem.

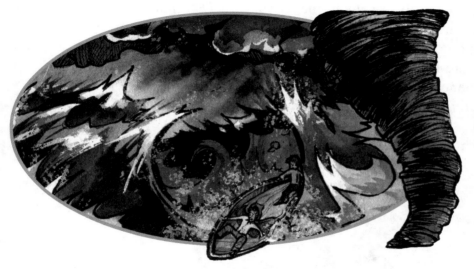

Idiom—a common expression whose meaning is different from the meanings of the individual words.

B. Finish rewriting each sentence with a gross exaggeration.

1. It's very cold.

   It's so cold outside that ___ *possible answer: my toes feel like* ___

   they have been in the refrigerator for a week .

2. Mother baked all morning.

   Mother baked enough cookies to ___ *possible answer: feed the entire Irish army* .

3. The hike was long.

   After the hike my feet ___ *possible answer:* ___

   felt as though they were on fire .

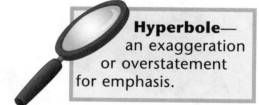

Hyperbole—an exaggeration or overstatement for emphasis.

C. Tell what you think the colored idiom means.

1. My little brother let the cat out of the bag. Now everyone knows that Dad has decided to coach the Pirates this season.

   gave away the secret

2. George decided to play on the Tigers' baseball team because he doesn't like the color of the Pirates' uniform. George is straining at a gnat and swallowing an elephant.

   paying attention to tiny

   details and overlooking

   the important facts

3. Our ball game was canceled yesterday. It was raining cats and dogs.

   raining very hard

4. Dad showed Mike how to hold the bat, but he liked his own way better. Dad sighed, "You can lead a horse to water, but you can't make him drink."

   tell someone how to do

   something, but you can't

   make him do it

5. Dad was ready to stack the wood. "Let's work shoulder to shoulder," he stated.

   close together

6. I didn't agree with the batting order, but I decided not to make any waves.

   upset people

7. I'd never played shortstop before. I had butterflies in my stomach!

   a nervous feeling in my stomach

8. The umpire didn't shout out the strikes and balls. He had a frog in his throat.

   a problem speaking

9. I struck out in the bottom of the ninth with two men on base. I'm now on the outs with the team.

   not very popular with my

   team right now

10. Dad says next week we're going to practice till the cows come home.

    for a long time

Codes & Ciphers

A. Use the sliding code to decode the message.
Circle the *VC/CV* pattern in each decoded word.

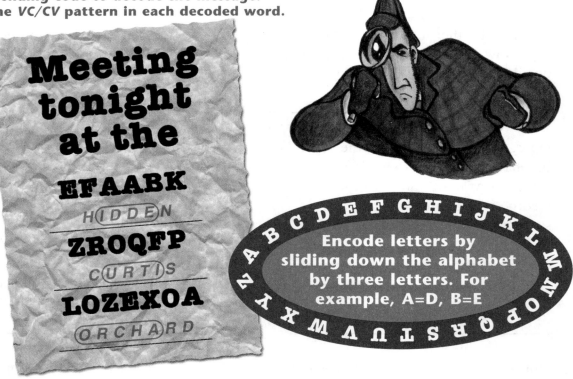

Meeting
tonight
at the

EFAABK
H(IDDE)N

ZROQFP
C(URTI)S

LOZEXOA
O(RCHA)RD

Encode letters by sliding down the alphabet by three letters. For example, A=D, B=E

B. Notice the vowel/consonant patterns in the lists of words.
Write a decoded word from above to match each set.

VC/CV	VC/CV	VC/CV
tamper	worthy	letters
practice	Richmond	cottage
contact	athlete	mirror
service	asphalt	valley
Curtis	*Orchard*	*Hidden*

C. Look at the words in the ovals. Notice how each word is divided.
When dividing words with a consonant digraph, where might
you divide the word?

● before the digraph

○ between the digraph

● after the digraph

ath•lete

Rich•mond

or•chard

as•phalt

Divide words between the consonants in the *VC/CV* pattern, even when one is a consonant digraph.

204

© 2002 BJU Press. Reproduction prohibited.

D. Circle the *VC/CV* pattern in each word. Remember that a consonant may be written as a consonant digraph. Place a dot to divide each word into syllables.

p u(r•c h a)s e   r(u n•n i)n g   s(e r•v a)n t

s(e r•v i)c e   w(o r•t h y)   (o r•p h a)n

w r(i t•t e)n   v(a l•l e)y   (a f•t e)r

f(a r•t h e)r   m(a s•t e)r   r e(a l•l y)

James Armistead Lafayette

E. Use words from above to complete the story.

1. James Armistead, a loyal Virginia slave, became a Revolutionary War

   spy for the Americans. He posed as a slave running from his ____**master**____.

2. British General Cornwallis paid James Armistead to be a ____**servant**____.
   At the same time Armistead was serving in the American army
   under General Lafayette.

3. James Armistead learned many British secrets for the Americans during

   his ____**service**____.

4. Later, the English recruited James Armistead to spy for them, never realizing

   that the runaway was ____**really**____ an American spy.

5. Once General Washington gave James Armistead a crumpled note that was

   ____**written**____ to mislead British General Cornwallis.

6. ____**After**____ the Revolutionary War, Armistead changed
   his name to James Armistead Lafayette because of his great admiration
   for General Lafayette.

7. In appreciation for Armistead's service, the Virginia Legislature declared

   him to be ____**worthy**____ of his freedom.

Reading 5: Skill Day, Lesson 21
Structural analysis: applying Syllable Division Rule 1—*VC/CV* pattern including consonant digraphs
Comprehension: understanding sentence closure

205

Who Says?

Verifying Sources for Facts

Five Senses:	sight		encyclopedia
	hearing		maps and globes
	touch		dictionary
	taste		books
	smell		the Bible

A. Identify each sentence as fact or opinion. If the sentence is factual, list at least one source you could use to verify it.

Fact or Opinion?

Answers will vary.
Verifying Source

1. Jeri Massi wrote "Lessons from Mr. Lee." (F) O *book*

2. The royal bodyguard of the Korean emperor developed the martial art *tae kwon do* over a thousand years ago. (F) O *encyclopedia*

3. The country of Korea is located near China and Japan. (F) O *map, globe, encyclopedia*

4. *Tae kwon do* is the (greatest) of the martial arts. F (O) _____

5. In the Korean language, *hwarang-do* means "the way of the flower of manhood." (F) O *dictionary, book*

6. An elbow strike received during *tae kwon do* training caused a large bump on the student's arm. (F) O *sense of touch, sight*

7. The martial arts are the (most) beneficial sport. F (O) _____

B. Circle any opinion signal words in the sentences above.

Signal Words for Possible Opinions

should	most, least,
think	greatest
probably	every, all
pleasant	better, best
always, never	very, only

Statements of **fact** can be proved by checking the information in another source. Statements of **opinion** are based on beliefs or feelings and cannot be proved.

C. Read each group of sentences. Choose the one that is a statement of fact in each group.

1. ○ Pinocchio is the most popular children's story.
   ● The story of Pinocchio was first written in Italian by C. Collodi.
   ○ This story will always be a favorite with children.

2. ○ It is always easier to write about puppets than to write about real children.
   ● The character, Pinocchio, is a jointed puppet, or marionette, controlled by strings and wires.
   ○ Operating a marionette is probably harder than riding a bicycle.

3. ○ Everyone enjoys watching marionette performances.
   ○ All puppeteers learn to operate marionettes very well.
   ● Puppeteers speak for the puppet to the audience.

D. Read the statements of fact. Write one source other than your reader that could be used to prove each.

Possible answers are shown.

1. Puppets were first used by church leaders to teach stories from the Bible. *encyclopedia, book*

2. The French word *marionette* means "little Mary." *dictionary, encyclopedia, book*

3. The flexible joints of puppets can be used to make movements that resemble the movements of people. *sense of sight, encyclopedia*

4. At a special marionette theater in Italy, tourists can hear and see beautiful operas performed by musicians and puppeteers. *sense of sight, sense of hearing, book*

5. The theater at the Schonbrun Castle is located in the southwest portion of Vienna. *map, encyclopedia, book*

6. Sculptors, mechanics, and costume makers work for about 130 hours to make each marionette for the operas. *encyclopedia, book*

Reading 5: Skill Day, Lesson 28
Comprehension: determining fact and opinion

Sky Spies

A. Write the compound word from each sentence. Divide the word with a dot. Mark the primary accent.

1. Carrier pigeons fitted with small cameras gathered valuable information on snapshots.

    snap´•shots

2. The pigeons had to make their flights during daylight hours.

    day´•light

3. Occasionally the birds' wingtips were seen in the pictures.

    wing´•tips

4. After the airplane was invented, pigeons were no longer used for spying.

    air´•plane

B. Answer the question.

How did the wingtips in the snapshot interfere with information?

Possible answer:

The wingtips hid parts of

the picture which may

contain important information.

C. Follow the steps to divide and accent the multisyllable compound words.

1. Divide between the base words. (Use a dot.)
2. Divide the two-syllable base word using the *VC/CV* rule.
3. Mark the primary accent in the first base word.
4. Mark the secondary accent in the second base word.

    p a s´•s a g e•w a y´

    c o t´•t o n•m o u t h´

    m a s´•t e r•p i e c e´

> **Compound words** are divided between the base words.
>
> In a compound word the **primary accent** is on or within the first base word. The **secondary accent** is on or within the second base word.

**D. Read both stories below. Circle the compound words.
Try to find eleven different words.**

Peppermint Soldiers

On June 6, 1944, when Allied troops hit the European beaches, everyone knew the attack would be a dangerous job. However, very few people knew about the possibility of an extra danger. Allied commanders suspected that Hitler's German forces would use radiation against Allied foot soldiers. The U.S. and Great Britain sent specially trained forces onto the seashores with their troops. The code name for these forces was "Peppermint Soldiers."

Peppermint soldiers had equipment to detect radiation and supplies to help troops if any radiation was present. No radiation was detected, and hardly anyone even knew there were peppermint soldiers on the beaches.

Coastwatchers

Coastwatchers served during WW II. These agents set up hidden stations in the Solomon and Bismarck Islands and watched for signs of Japanese troop movements. When coastwatchers learned about air raids, they quickly radioed Allied headquarters and reported them. Some missionaries were also coastwatchers. Throughout the war they helped rescue shipwrecked Allied soldiers and searched for information in Japanese plane crashes.

When Japanese soldiers learned where a coastwatcher's hideout was, they attacked. If a coastwatcher did not leave in time, he was tortured and killed. But history shows that the coastwatchers did valuable service for the Allied forces and helped to win the war.

E. Divide the words into syllables. Mark the primary and secondary accents.

seashore	*sea•shore´*	Peppermint	*Pep´•per•mint´*
hideout	*hide•out´*	headquarters	*head´•quar•ters*
shipwrecked	*ship•wrecked´*	butterfly	*but•ter•fly´*

Reading 5: Skill Day, Lesson 32
Structural analysis: applying Syllable Division Rules 1 and 2—*VC/CV* pattern and compound
words; applying Accent Rule 1—compound words

209

A. Underline the main idea of the paragraph.

My Family's Pets

Everyone in my family enjoys a different kind of pet. My brother likes sports and has a big dog, an active retriever that chases balls for him. A dog would never work for Mom. She does not have much time for pets, so she keeps a fish in a small bowl on the kitchen counter. She enjoys watching it sometimes, but she does not have to do much to care for it. My dad has a large, green parrot that squawks really loudly. A lady at the pet store helped me pick out a hedgehog! Spike has been perfect for me. He is pretty quiet and likes to curl up in my lap when I read.

B. Read the details listed. Check the correct column to tell if the detail is important to the main idea of the paragraph or if it is just a supporting detail.

Details	Important to Main Idea	Supporting Detail
1. My brother has a dog.	☑	☐
2. The dog chases balls.	☐	☑
3. Mom has a fish.	☑	☐
4. The fish's bowl is in the kitchen.	☐	☑
5. Dad has a green parrot.	☑	☐
6. A lady helped me pick out a hedgehog.	☐	☑
7. I have a hedgehog.	☑	☐

To summarize a paragraph, state the **main idea** and the **important details.**

C. Write a summary for the paragraph above.

Answers will vary.

Everyone in my family owns a different pet.

My brother has a dog, Mom has a fish,

Dad has a parrot, and I have a hedgehog.

C. Underline the main idea of the paragraph.

Water and Animals

<u>Water supplies meet many animals'</u> <u>needs.</u> Creeks, rivers, and streams provide homes for many species like frogs, fish, and turtles. Other animals like otters, jaguars, and many birds make their homes near waterways because they rely on them for at least part of their food. These animals find the fish and frogs very tasty! Many animals need the comfort of being in water. Elephants will bathe every day if the water is deep enough to allow it. The hippopotamus spends many hours each day in the refreshing water to keep cool. And of course, many animals trek to the water every day for the most common need—a drink!

D. Read the details listed. Check the correct column to tell if the detail is important to the main idea of the paragraph or if it is just a supporting detail.

Details	Important to Main Idea	Supporting Detail
1. Waterways provide homes for some animals.	☑	☐
2. Some animals find food in the water.	☑	☐
3. Fish and frogs are tasty.	☐	☑
4. Many animals need the comfort of being in water.	☑	☐
5. Elephants will bathe every day if possible.	☐	☑
6. Almost all animals use the water for drinking.	☑	☐

E. Write a summary for the paragraph above. *Answers will vary.*

Waterways are important to animals

because they provide homes, food, comfort, and drink.

Reading 5: Skill Day, Lesson 50
Study skills: summarizing a paragraph; identifying the main idea and supporting details of a paragraph

211

Character Search

A. Read the selection taken from "Lessons from Mr. Lee."

They stopped talking and watched me. Some of them started laughing. I kept walking with my head up. I could sense that they were imitating me, but I didn't look back at them this time. It was time to stop thinking more of older kids who picked on me than of what God thought of me. I just wanted to get to the karate school, test for my green belt, and tell Mr. Lee I had walked to class.

I passed the boys and walked on to Mr. Lee's. He was standing in the doorway. His hands were clasped behind his back.

"You early, Billy," he called.

"I started early," I said. "I walked."

"Boys pick on you?"

"I just kept walking, Mr. Lee. I never looked back." I swung my *gi* into my hand and looked up at his sparkling black eyes. "You were right. It wasn't important anymore."

1. Who are the characters? _____ Mr. Lee, Billy _____

2. Who is the first-person narrator telling the story? _____ Billy _____

3. What character did you learn more about and understand better? _____ Billy _____

B. Read the selection taken from "Runaway Friends."

I didn't see the rock. It was just a small rock, but when my foot landed on it, I knew I was going down hard. I heard myself scream. I felt my ankle twist sharply under me as I crashed onto the ground, landing hard. I closed my eyes. All Kyle would have to do now would be to trot slowly across the finish line, and his team would win. I had lost. In front of my grandparents and new friends, I had crashed. I couldn't wait for

summer so we could drive far away from Albuquerque and never come back.

"Rachel, you okay?"

I opened my eyes. There was Kyle standing over me! He was sweaty and breathing hard.

"Are you all right?" he said again.

"Go ahead, Kyle," I said. "Win the race. It's okay."

1. Who are the characters? _____ Rachel, Kyle _____

2. Who is the first-person narrator telling the story? _____ Rachel _____

3. Which character did you learn more about and understand better? _____ Rachel _____

A story told in **first-person point of view** may help you know the main character better.

C. Read the story excerpts from "The *Tal-Omega*." Write what each sentence reveals about the character. Then label the excerpt with the correct letter to identify how the author revealed the information.

> **A. by what the character says**   **B. by what the character does**
> **C. by what another character says**

___B___ 1. In a couple of minutes Captain Denton walked in, bowing   *Answers will vary.*
his head a little to avoid bumping it on the low bulkhead.

The captain is tall.

___A___ 2. "I just never thought it would come to roughing up a kid."
(said by Simmons)

Simmons had not thought about what

mutiny might mean. He is not a good thinker.

___C___ 3. "Joe Hands—I wouldn't trust him with my granny's glasses!"

Joe is considered to be dishonest.

> **Characters** are revealed by what they say, by what they do, and by what others say about them.

It's Set

A. Read the pages listed for each story. Focus on the author's choice of words used to describe the setting. Then complete the chart by choosing the place of setting, the time of setting, and the mood of each story's opening paragraphs.

Story Title	Setting (Place and time)	Mood
Lessons from Mr. Lee (pp. 25-26)	● real town ○ fanciful town ○ past ● present ○ future	○ somber and quiet ● hurried and upset ○ tired and worried
A Just Judge (p. 45)	● real city ○ fanciful city ● past ○ present ○ future	○ amused ● thoughtful ○ lighthearted
The Tal-Omega (pp. 124-25)	○ real spaceship ● fanciful spaceship ○ past ○ present ● future	● uneasy ○ hurried and excited ○ tired and sickly
Big Brother (pp. 84-85)	● real town ○ fanciful town ○ past ● present ○ future	○ lighthearted ○ frightened ● troubled

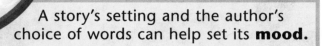

A story's setting and the author's choice of words can help set its **mood.**

Hunting Trip

Early in the morning, the men crept out of their sod house. Danny followed Pa and old Mr. Harris through the tangled underbrush. Behind him came Noah, his curly coated retriever, carrying the leather pouches with their lunch and two wooden decoys.

Pa and Mr. Harris carried Pa's canoe over their heads. When they reached the edge of the marsh, the men set the canoe soundlessly in the water and climbed in, Pa first.

Then they pulled their shotguns forward and settled themselves in the craft. Pa nodded to Danny. Danny quickly unbuckled the leather straps on Noah's pack and took out the decoys. Mr. Harris reached for them with a wink.

Noah took up his watch on the shore, every muscle ready to spring when a duck was brought down. Danny gave the canoe a little shove and stepped back, to wait. Only one more year, he thought, and I can hunt on my own to help provide food for the long winters.

B. Answer these questions.

1. Where did this story take place? ___*at a marsh*___

2. When did the story take place: past, present, or future? ___*in the past*___

3. List one clue that reveals the time period. ___*live in sod house; boy calls his*___ ___*father "Pa"; carry lunch in a leather pouch; hunt to provide food*___

4. What is the overall mood of the story: anger, humor, or quietness? ___*quietness*___

5. List one clue that reveals the mood. ___*soundlessly, nodded, wink*___

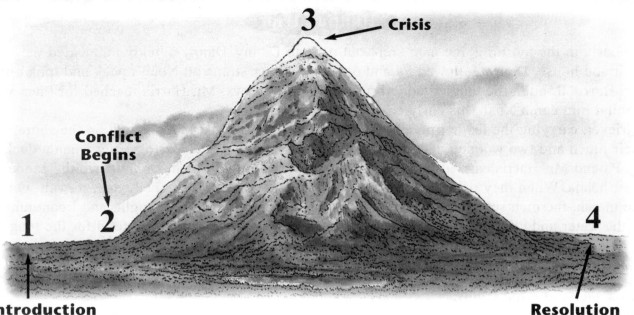

3 ← **Crisis**

Conflict Begins

1 **2** **4**

Introduction

Resolution (Final Outcome)

A. Number the events to match the plot diagram.

___4___ 1. Bruce will get to go to flight school.

___1___ 2. Denton prepares Bruce for surgery on his injured hand.

___2___ 3. While partly under anesthesia, Bruce learns about a mutiny plan.

___3___ 4. Bruce delivers explosives to the trapped loyal crew members by traveling through a treacherous, narrow, trash chute.

Plot is the sequence of important events in a story.

B. Match each story and poem from Unit 2 with its theme.

___D___ 1. "The *Tal-Omega*"

___A___ 2. "The Quarrel"

___E___ 3. "Adventure on Gull Island"

___C___ 4. "Big Brother"

___B___ 5. "No Longer a Slave"

A. Quarreling over who's right and who's wrong makes one "wrong."

B. Christ's forgiveness frees us from the slavery of sin.

C. Disabled people have feelings and can help others, just like everyone else.

D. Choosing the right loyalties is part of right living.

E. The Bible teaches us to love one another.

The **theme** of a story is its message.

C. Read the story. Use the plot diagram on page 216 to label the events.

Later Voyages of the *Tal-Omega*

Aboard the *Tal-Omega,* Lieutenant Finelli and Captain Denton completed the daily reports and sat talking about their young friend, Bruce. The computer interrupted, "Asteroid approaching on collision course. Large enough to destroy this vessel. Will collide in fifteen minutes."

"Lieutenant Finelli," Captain Denton ordered, "you'll have to destroy that asteroid."

The lieutenant caught his breath but said, "Aye, sir." He ran out and climbed into his space suit. He grabbed his equipment, but hesitated. During his space walk that day, debris had nicked his protective suit. Only threads had stood between him and certain death. Now he faced that danger again. When the asteroid explodes, debris will fly in all directions. He could die if he left the ship. But many would surely die if he did not. *If I can just quit focusing on the fear and concentrate on the job at hand,* he thought. The lieutenant took a deep breath and left the ship.

First he wedged himself between two handholds on the outside of the ship. Then he slung his laser gun down from his shoulder, aimed at the approaching asteroid, and shot. The asteroid disintegrated.

"Mission complete," he said into his transmitter.

"Well done, Lieutenant," said Captain Denton. "And Lieutenant, you showed great courage. Thank you."

____2____ 1. The computer announced a coming asteroid.

____4____ 2. Captain Denton congratulated Lieutenant Finelli.

____1____ 3. Captain Denton and Lieutenant Finelli sat talking about Bruce.

____3____ 4. The lieutenant left the ship to destroy the asteroid.

D. Choose the statement that best expresses the theme of the story above.

○ Courage is pretending there is no danger.

● Courage is not the absence of fear. It is doing what you have to do in spite of it.

○ Courage is the absence of fear. It is doing what you have to do!

Putting It Together

A. Place dots to show where to divide the words into syllables.

> Where should *VC/CV* pattern words be divided?
>
> frag•ment   mel•low   pan•ther

> Where should compound words be divided?
>
> good•will   four•square   sand•pit

B. Rewrite each word below. Place dots to show where to divide the words ending with *le*.

1. brindle   *brin•dle*

2. coddle   *cod•dle*

3. chortle   *chor•tle*

4. speckle   *speck•le*

5. hurtle   *hur•tle*

C. Rewrite these words and divide them into syllables. You will need to use several syllable division rules.

1. candlestick   *can•dle•stick*

2. entitle   *en•ti•tle*

3. tablecloth   *ta•ble•cloth*

4. turtleneck   *tur•tle•neck*

5. huckleberry   *huck•le•ber•ry*

> In words ending with a consonant + *le,* divide into syllables before the consonant + *le.* In words ending with the consonant digraph *ck* before the *le,* divide the word after the *ck.*

D. Place dots between the syllables of each word.

s p i n•d l e   g u r•g l e   c o u n•s e l

c o b•w e b   d r i b•b l e   p i g•g y•b a c k

c h i f•f o n   s t e e•p l e•c h a s e   f r e c k•l e

E. Use words found on page 218 or 219 to complete the puzzle.

Across
2. a rod for holding a spool of thread
6. to throw or hurl
7. a type of wild cat
8. a small brown dot on someone's skin
10. a holder for a light source made of wax

Down
1. fabric that is put on a table
3. drool
4. four sides with the same lengths and angles
5. a joyful laugh or chuckle
9. advice
11. a large hole in soft soil

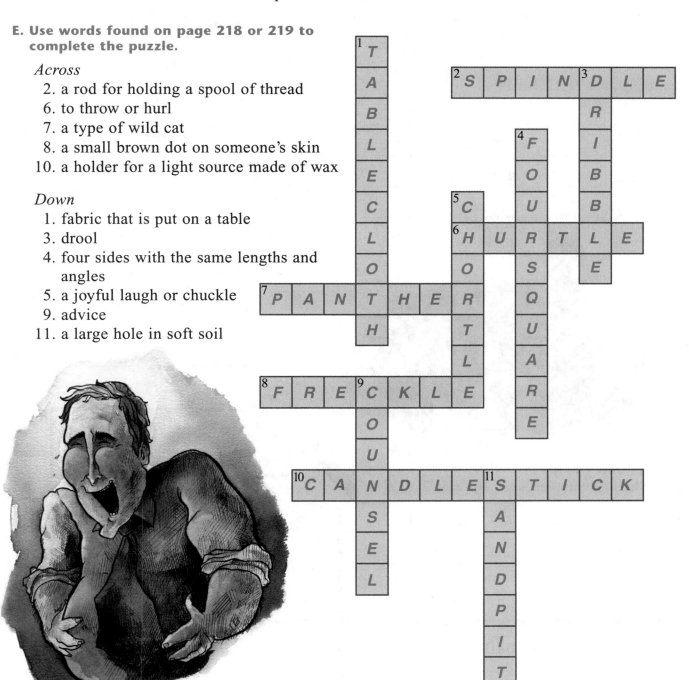

Reading 5: Skill Day, Lesson 65
Structural analysis: applying Syllable Division Rule 3—words ending with a consonant + *le* and words ending with *ck + le*; applying Syllable Division Rules 1 and 2—VC/CV pattern and compound words

219

A Class of Its Own

A. List four things that fit into each category.

Possible answers are shown.

Buildings

1. _apartment_
2. _barn_
3. _house_
4. _library_

Sports with balls

1. _baseball_
2. _tennis_
3. _soccer_
4. _football_

Boats

1. _canoe_
2. _kayak_
3. _sailboat_
4. _speedboat_

Books

1. _dictionary_
2. _encyclopedia_
3. _hymnal_
4. _Bible_

B. Narrow the group.
Classify your answers again.

> **Classifying** is grouping things that are related or alike in some way.

Answers will vary.
All spaces may not be filled.

Buildings where people might live

1. _____
2. _____

Engine-driven boats

1. _____
2. _____

Sports in which a ball is kicked

1. _____
2. _____

Books used in worship

1. _____
2. _____

stork
goose
goat
horse
swan
zebra
rhinoceros
penguin
giraffe
ostrich
duck
deer

C. Put each animal under the heading that describes it.

four legs, hooves

deer
_____
giraffe
_____
horse
_____
zebra
_____
goat
_____
rhinoceros
_____

feathers, two legs

swan
_____
goose
_____
penguin
_____
duck
_____
ostrich
_____
stork
_____

four legs, hooves, horns

goat
_____
deer
_____
giraffe
_____
rhinoceros
_____

feathers, two legs, can fly

swan
_____
goose
_____
duck
_____
stork
_____

Document the Evidence

A. Write any signal letters for each word. Write the number of syllables.

	Signal	Syllables		Signal	Syllables
planted	t	2	porches	ch	2
dreamed		1	cranes		1
tracked		1	grazes	z	2
branded	d	2	leashes	sh	2

B. Divide the words into syllables. Mark the accented syllable.

Rule 2	Rule 3	Rule 3
un•pack´	top•ic	for•give´
re•gain´	hum•ble	de•vote´
strength•en	mor•tar	rac•coon´
brand•ed	pick•le	sur•vive´

Accent Rule 2: In words with a prefix or suffix, the accent usually falls on the base word.

Accent Rule 3: In two-syllable words, the accent usually falls on the first syllable (bas´•ket).

The accent falls on the second syllable when the syllable contains two vowels (col•lapse´).

C. Divide each word. Mark the accented syllable. Use the words to complete the sentences.

F r a n k•l i n

e n•j o y´

w i t•t y

p u b•l i s h•e r

t r i e d´

s i g n e d´

i n•v e n t•e d

c a r•t o o n´

1. Benjamin Franklin is known for being a _____**publisher**_____, inventor, and statesman.

2. His newspaper, *The Pennsylvania Gazette,* was the first to print a _____**cartoon**_____.

3. The _____**witty**_____ sayings he published in *Poor Richard's Almanack* were wise and popular with readers everywhere. One saying was, "He that falls in love with himself will have no rivals."

4. Mr. Franklin _____**invented**_____ bifocal eyeglasses and the lightning rod.

5. Benjamin Franklin did not even try to make money from his inventions and discoveries. He wanted everyone to _____**enjoy**_____ their benefits.

6. Mr. Franklin went on to be of great service to his country. He was one of the men who _____**signed**_____ the Declaration of Independence.

7. While in France, he gathered important information and _____**tried**_____ to build a friendship between France and America.

8. Mr. _____**Franklin**_____ organized the first hospital in America and helped to establish a university.

Reading 5: Skill Day, Lesson 85
Structural analysis: applying Accent Rules 2 and 3; applying Syllable Division Rules 1-4

223

Keys to Research

A. Underline all the keyword(s) in each question.

1. What kinds of plants grow in the <u>Gobi</u>?
2. Where in <u>North America</u> did <u>Columbus</u> first land?
3. How far away is the <u>North Star</u>?
4. Where did the game of <u>soccer</u> originate?
5. What was <u>Thomas Jefferson</u>'s home like?
6. Where do we get <u>chocolate</u>?
7. Are there <u>lions</u> living in a natural habitat in <u>India</u>?
8. What kinds of animals live in the <u>Grand Canyon</u>?
9. Who are the <u>Aborigines</u> of <u>Australia</u>?
10. On what continents was <u>World War II</u> fought?

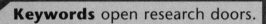

Keywords open research doors.

B. Match the article subheadings with the questions they will answer.

__B__ 1. What does a forest ranger do?
__A__ 2. Where are deciduous forests found?
__C__ 3. How can forest fires be prevented?

Forests
   A. Kinds of Forests
   B. Jobs in Forestry
   C. Man and the Forest

__D__ 4. What causes tidal waves?
__F__ 5. What is the biggest animal in the ocean?
__E__ 6. What is the continental shelf?

The Ocean
   D. Ocean Wave Movement
   E. The Ocean Floor
   F. Ocean Life

__H__ 7. What is family life like in Canada?
__G__ 8. Where was the first settlement in Canada?
__I__ 9. What languages do Canadian students learn in school?

Canada
   G. The History
   H. The People
   I. Education

Scanning the subheadings aids in research.

224

C. Answer the questions.

1. If you were researching horses, an encyclopedia index would first refer you to the *horse* entry. Where else might an index direct you?

Possible answers:

Transportation, Mammals, Rodeo

2. If you were researching *spying* or *espionage,* an encyclopedia index would first refer you to the *espionage* entry. Where else might an encyclopedia index direct you?

Possible answers:

Central Intelligence Agency,

Codes and ciphers, World War II

D. Refer to the index example to answer the questions.

1. How many articles give information about the FBI?

4

2. What is the entry word?

Intelligence service

3. What subheading titles are listed?

Central Intelligence Agency, Espionage,

Federal Bureau of Investigation

4. Under which subheading is Criminal investigation listed?

Federal Bureau of Investigation

Intelligence service: 707

Central Intelligence Agency
National security **C: 708**
National Security Council **C: 709**

Espionage
Foreign **E: 452**
Gathering information **E: 454**
Secret information **E: 459**

Federal Bureau of Investigation
Crime **F: 229**
Criminal investigation **F: 231**
FBI agents **F: 234**
History **F: 235**

For His Glory

March 12, 2002

I hiked back up the mountain today for another visit to Nimba's village. This time a few children crept out to stare at us, but none of the women appeared in the doorways of the huts. Even the dusty path down to the river looked deserted. I stood there for a minute, my eyes on the simmering jungle, and asked the Lord what to do next. A familiar voice interrupted my prayer—it was Nimba himself, calling excitedly and beckoning to me from where he stood in the shadow of the biggest tree.

He ran up to me. "Come now," he exclaimed; "the men are all here, waiting to hear about God's Book."

I don't know how much they understood of what I said—I'm still not very good at this language—but they listened carefully to the few verses of John that I've translated so far. Praise God! May He work in their hearts to His glory. The lamp's getting dim—better stop for now.

March 12, 2002

Well, tonight's game was the worst loss we've suffered so far. What kind of a coach am I, anyway? This basketball team never has been any good at shooting, and the guys missed a lot of shots. Just remembered several good things that happened, though—we prayed with the other team beforehand, as usual, and I could see that they were pretty surprised at that. They must have been even more surprised when they kept trying to foul Randy, and he just didn't get mad the way most guys would. I knew what Randy was after, though, and kept an eye on him.

He played a good clean game and then, sure enough, after the game he trotted over to congratulate the other team's big starting forward, Jim. I figured he was probably also asking Jim to go on a hike with his youth group next week, and I quickly prayed for them both. Jim nodded okay, still looking sort of surprised. Maybe he'll get saved too, like some of the others Randy's been working on. Another game to God's glory—I realize it wasn't really a loss after all.

Compare by showing how things are similar. **Contrast** by showing how things are different.

A. Complete the sentences to *compare* the two journal entries on page 226.

| experience | Christian | glory |
| prayer | spiritual | |

1. The first author, as well as the second author, must be a _____*Christian*_____.

2. Both accounts centered on an _____*experience*_____ that the author had that day.

3. The coach, like the missionary, showed a concern for the _____*spiritual*_____ needs of others.

4. The power of _____*prayer*_____ was evident in the first entry and in the second entry too.

5. Both journals told about something that God did for His own _____*glory*_____.

B. Complete the sentences to *contrast* the two journal entries on page 226.

preaching	jungle natives	Christlike
basketball players	missionary	coach
foreign	mountain village	

1. One country was _____*foreign*_____, but the other was not.

2. The first setting was a _____*mountain village*_____; however, the second was a gym.

3. The first author was a _____*missionary*_____, but the second was a _____*coach*_____.

4. The first journal told about a _____*preaching*_____ testimony and the second about the testimony of a _____*Christlike*_____ example.

5. The first author's ministry was to _____*jungle natives*_____; however, the second had a ministry to _____*basketball players*_____.

Special Careers

A. Underline the schwa syllables in each of the words.

cas´•<u>tle</u>   em´•<u>bas</u>•sy

law´•<u>yer</u>   pris´•<u>on</u>

har´•<u>bor</u>   ca•reer´

ri´•val   spe´•<u>cial</u>

B. Write the schwa vowel. Mark the accented syllable.

___*o*___ sec•ond   ___*a*___ cym•bal

___*a*___ com•ma   ___*e*___ hap•pen

___*e*___ prob•lem   ___*o*___ eb•on•y

___*o*___ meth•od   ___*i*___ fos•sil

___*a*___ a•gree´   ___*e*___ e•mer•gen•cy

C. Rewrite these words. Divide them into syllables and mark the accented syllable.

1. fumble   *fum´•ble*

2. piggyback   *pig´•gy•back*

3. remaining   *re•main´•ing*

D. Divide the words into syllables. Write each word under the title that applies to that word.

r i d•d l e

s i g•n a l

s h a m•b l e s

c h u c k•l e

s k e p•t i c

s h a c k•l e

b l i s•t e r

w e a l•t h y

Rule 1

signal

skeptic

blister

wealthy

Rule 3

riddle

shambles

chuckle

shackle

Division Rule 1: Divide words into syllables between the consonants *(dol´•phin)*.

Division Rule 3: In words ending with a consonant + *le,* divide into syllables before the consonant + *le (Bi´•ble).* In words ending with *ck + le,* divide after the *ck (buck´•le).*

E. Place the accent mark on the correct syllable in the words.

com•mon   sur•prise´

serv•er   tem•per

car•toon´   in•crease´

tai•lor   rib•bon

scal•pel   bam•boo´

di•vine´   tres•pass

Accent Rule 3: In two-syllable words the accent usually falls on the first syllable *(bas´•ket).* The accent falls on the second syllable when that syllable contains two vowels *(col•lapse´).*

Accent Rule 4: The accent never falls on a syllable with a schwa *(pen´•cil).*

Reading 5: Skill Day, Lesson 107
Structural analysis: dividing words into syllables and placing primary accent marks;
applying Syllable Division Rules 1 and 3; applying Accent Rules 3 and 4

229

Use the PQ3R method to study the informational text on this page. Write your responses on the next page.

More Than a Pet

Wild Dog to Shepherd

Wild dogs once roamed the fields and hillsides of Europe. It didn't take shepherds long to realize that some of these wild dogs could be tamed and trained to work. They taught one type of dog to become an "assistant shepherd." The dog's courage and ability made him an excellent guard dog. He warned the shepherd of attacks by wild animals and herded sheep in the direction the shepherd commanded.

The dog quickly displayed the ability to work independently. The shepherds, pleased with the dog's progress, allowed it more responsibility. Finally, the dog began working alone. Sometimes the shepherds would leave a *cache* of food for the dog. The food allowed the dog to stay with the sheep and to keep the sheep in a pasture for several days without leaving the flock. The fame of this rough *shepherd* dog spread throughout Europe.

German shepherds carried valuable supplies in backpacks.

Becoming a Spy

Many of the German people were impressed by the shepherd dog's ability to learn. As a result, the Germans established canine schools to train the shepherd dogs. By the time the dogs graduated from school, their ability to learn and their keen sense of smell made it possible for them to track burglars and to ferret out smugglers.

Their uncanny hearing also fit them to become sentries in wartime. After being trained, a dog either accompanied his master or patrolled an area alone. When patrolling in enemy territory, the dog was trained to keep quiet. The dog responded to danger by growling deep in his throat without a sound being heard. His master caught the signal by placing his hand on the dog's throat and feeling the vibration of the suppressed growl.

Having progressed from shepherd to war hero, the **German shepherd** performs each job well. Is it any wonder, then, that the German shepherd is known as "more than a pet"?

A. Follow the first step in the PQ3R method as you look over the article on page 230. Check each box as you complete the step.

PREVIEW

❑ 1. What will you look at as you preview?

title, subheadings, illustrations, captions, and bold and italicized words

❑ 2. What do you think the article will be about?

German shepherds, sheep-herding dogs

B. Follow the middle three steps in the PQ3R method as you read each section of the article on page 230.

QUESTION

❑ 3. Make a question from the subheading: "Wild Dog to Shepherd."

Possible answer: How did wild dogs become shepherds?

READ

❑ 4. Think about your question as you read silently.

RECITE

❑ 5. Tell yourself the answer to the question you wrote in number 3 above.

QUESTION AGAIN

❑ 6. Make a question from the second subheading: "Becoming a Spy."

Possible answer: How can dogs become spies?

READ

❑ 7. Think about your question as you read silently.

RECITE

❑ 8. Tell yourself the answer to the question you wrote in number 6.

C. Complete the last step in the PQ3R study method.

REVIEW

❑ 9. Look back at the title and subheadings of the article.
Think about the information you learned.

Early National Endeavors

Event	Date	Nations Involved	Outcome
First permanent settlement at Jamestown, Virginia	1607	England	Colony prospered after a hard beginning
Colony established at Plymouth, Massachusetts	1620	England	Colony prospered
French and Indian War	1754-63	France vs. England	France lost control of Canada
Signing of the Declaration of Independence	1776	United States	Colonies declared themselves separate from England
War for American Independence	1775-83	United States vs. England	Freedom to establish an independent government
Louisiana Purchase	1803	United States and France	Size of United States doubled
War of 1812	1812-15	United States vs. England	United States recognized as a world power
Texas joins the Union	1845	United States and Mexico	Mexican War
Mexican War	1846-48	United States vs. Mexico	New territory added to United States
War Between the States	1862-65	Northern United States vs. Southern United States	Slavery was abolished
Purchase of Alaska	1867	United States and Russia	Size of United States expanded
First transcontinental railroad	1869	United States	States unified; communication improved
First telephone	1876	United States	Communication improved
Electric light developed	1879	United States	Quality of life improved
Spanish-American War	1898	United States vs. Spain	United States gained Guam, Puerto Rico, and the Philippines

Use the table on the previous page to answer the questions.

1. When was a colony established at Plymouth, Massachusetts? _____ *1620* _____

2. What was completed in 1869 that connected different areas of the United States?

    _____ *the first transcontinental railroad* _____

3. What was the outcome of the War of 1812? _____

    _____ *The United States was recognized as a world power.* _____

4. What countries fought each other in the French and Indian War? _____

    _____ *France and England* _____

5. What colony had a rough beginning but later began to prosper? ___ *Jamestown* ___

6. In what war did the United States gain Guam? ___ *Spanish-American War* ___

7. Where did the United States get Alaska? ___ *from Russia* ___

8. What year did the War for American Independence end? ___ *1783* ___

9. What was a result of the War Between the States? _____

    _____ *Slavery was abolished.* _____

10. Which country was at war with the United States more than the others?

    _____ *England* _____

11. Which war lasted the longest?

    _____ *French and Indian War* _____

12. Which was developed first, the

telephone or the electric light? ___ *telephone* ___

Tables present details in a concise format.

Reading 5: Skill Day, Lesson 123
Study skills: getting information from a table
Comprehension: comparing and contrasting information

Information Delivery

A. Read the pairs of words. Mark the accented syllables in each word. Notice the shift in the accent.

ter•mi•nate	prov•i•dence	cal•cu•late
ter•mi•na•tion	prov•i•den•tial	cal•cu•la•tion
his•to•ry	of•fice	con•ti•nent
his•tor•i•cal	of•fi•cial	con•ti•nen•tal

Adding **suffixes** to some longer words often shifts the primary accent to the syllable before the suffix.

B. Use the definitions to decide which word is being used in the sentences. Write the divided, accented word in the space.

in´•va•lid (n.)
a person disabled because of an injury or an illness

in•val´•id (adj.)
having no value

1. The spy's passport license became ⎯⎯⎯ *in•val´•id* ⎯⎯⎯ when the forgery was discovered.

2. A spy in a story I read posed as an ⎯⎯⎯ *in´•va•lid* ⎯⎯⎯ and hid documents in his wheelchair.

con´•duct (n.)
the way a person acts

con•duct´ (v.)
to manage or control

3. A diplomat is trained to ⎯⎯ *con•duct´* ⎯⎯ himself with dignity.

4. The spy was careful to mimic the ⎯⎯ *con´•duct* ⎯⎯ of a diplomat.

The accent often shifts when the meaning of a word changes.

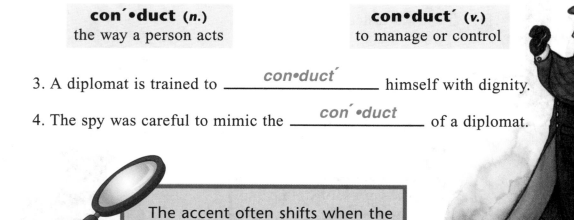

C. Read the definitions for each set of words.
   Write a sample sentence for each definition.

Answers will vary.

---

rec´•ord

—*noun* A written account of facts or events

re•cord´

—*verb* To preserve or to save in some way (for example, to write facts down)

---

1. _____

2. _____

---

ob´•ject

—*noun* Something that has shape and can
   be seen or felt

ob•ject´

—*verb* To express an opposite opinion or argument

---

3. _____

_____

4. _____

_____

---

pro´•duce

—*noun* Fruits, vegetables, and other farm products

pro•duce´

—*verb* To make or build something

---

5. _____

_____

6. _____

_____

_____

Author Scrapbook

Tennyson

David

Harris

Entries

Joel Chandler Harris
Rudyard Kipling
David McCord
Alfred, Lord Tennyson
Author of the Psalms
Emma Lazarus

Kipling

McCord

Lazarus

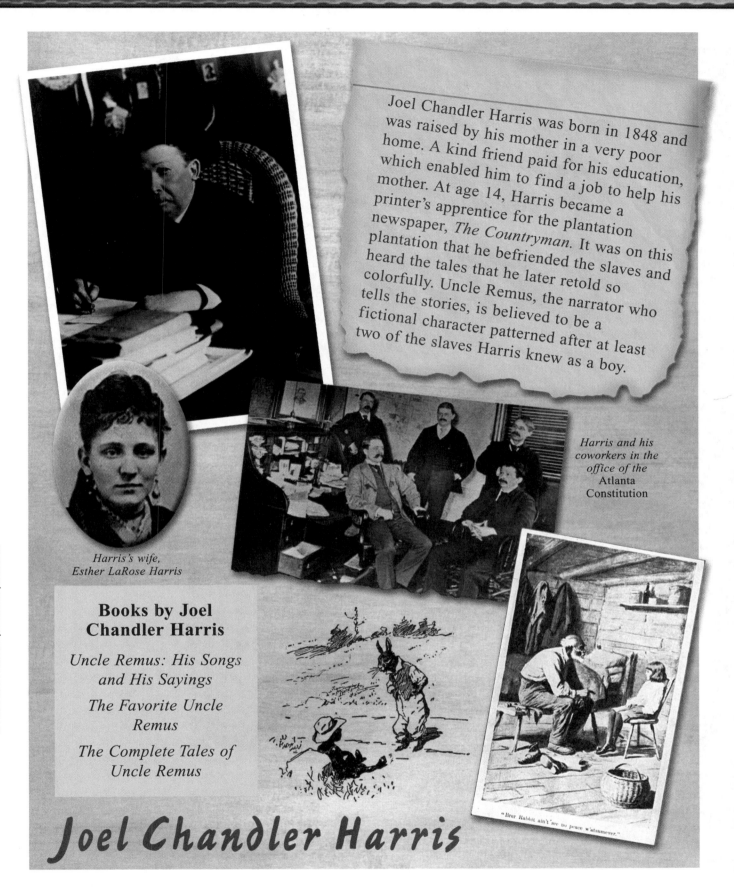

Joel Chandler Harris was born in 1848 and was raised by his mother in a very poor home. A kind friend paid for his education, which enabled him to find a job to help his mother. At age 14, Harris became a printer's apprentice for the plantation newspaper, *The Countryman*. It was on this plantation that he befriended the slaves and heard the tales that he later retold so colorfully. Uncle Remus, the narrator who tells the stories, is believed to be a fictional character patterned after at least two of the slaves Harris knew as a boy.

Harris and his coworkers in the office of the Atlanta Constitution

Harris's wife, Esther LaRose Harris

Books by Joel Chandler Harris

Uncle Remus: His Songs and His Sayings

The Favorite Uncle Remus

The Complete Tales of Uncle Remus

Joel Chandler Harris

Evidence . . .

what you already know about the subject.

Ask . . .

what you hope to learn as you listen.

Reach . . .

toward the source by listening carefully. Sit up, look at the source, think, and pick out key pieces of information.

Sum up . . .

the important things you learned.

Tip for the Day

"Watch" yourself listen.

The Wren's Nest

 **Evidence** What do you know about The Wren's Nest?

Possible answers: It is the home of Joel Chandler Harris.

It is located outside of Atlanta, Georgia.

 **Ask** Write two questions about what you hope to learn about The Wren's Nest.

Possible answers:

1. _____

How did the house get its name? / Why did Mr. Harris decide to live there?

2. *How many children lived in the house? / Is the house the same today as*

it was when Mr. Harris lived in it? / Who lives there now?

Reach Look and listen carefully as your teacher reads some information about The Wren's Nest.

The Wren's Nest: Home of Joel Chandler Harris outside of Atlanta, Georgia

Reading 5: "Author Scrapbook: Joel Chandler Harris," Lesson 15
Study skills: E.A.R.S. Listening Strategy

S **um up** Write the important things you learned.

1. Did you learn the answers to your questions? _____

2. If so, what was the answer to one of them? _____

_____

3. What are the three most interesting things you learned about The Wren's Nest?

a. _____

_____

b. _____

_____

c. _____

_____

Life span of J. C. Harris
1848-1908

| 1800 | 1820 | 1840 | 1860 | 1880 | 1900 | 1920 | 1940 | 1960 | 1980 | 2000 | 2020 |

1848 First Gold Rush

1906 First radio program with voice *and* music

1876 Invention of the telephone

1861-1865 Civil War
Abraham Lincoln becomes president
D. L. Moody ministers to soldiers

Reading 5: "Author Scrapbook: Joel Chandler Harris," Lesson 15
Study skills: E.A.R.S. Listening Strategy

Name_____

Young "Ruddy," accompanied
by Indian servants

Rudyard Kipling was born in Bombay, India, on December 30, 1865. He lived there until he was sent to school in England at age six. Although Kipling returned to India, he later lived in England, Vermont, and South Africa. Many of Kipling's writings are military-related since he was often a war correspondent. However, he is best known for his children's books and short stories.

Just So Stories for Little Children
"Wee Willie Winkie" and Other Child Stories
Captains Courageous
Second Jungle Book
The Jungle Book
Books by Rudyard Kipling

Rudyard Kipling

E vidence . . .

what you already know about the subject.

A sk . . .

what you hope to learn as you listen.

R each . . .

toward the source by listening carefully. Sit up, look at the source, think, and pick out key pieces of information.

S um up . . .

the important things you learned.

Tip for the Day

Take notes or make drawings.

1. Write only facts that deal with the main idea or that answer your questions.

2. Write words or groups of words instead of whole sentences.

3. Make only simple sketches as reminders, not detailed drawings.

Reading 5: "Author Scrapbook: Rudyard Kipling," Lesson 49
Study skills: E.A.R.S. Listening Strategy

Name_____

Evidence — What do you know about Rudyard Kipling's childhood?

Possible answers: He was born in India;

he went to school in England.

Ask — Write two questions about what you hope to learn about Rudyard Kipling's childhood.

1. *Possible answers: Why was he born in India?*

2. *Why did he have to go to school in England? Was he Indian?*

Reach — Look and listen carefully as your teacher reads some information about Rudyard Kipling. Take notes or make drawings as you listen. Review the tips on note taking before you get started.

"Ruddy's Idea of Heaven" drawn by John Lockwood Kipling, Rudyard Kipling's father

Sum up   Write the important things you learned.

1. Did you learn the answers to your questions? _____

2. If so, what was the answer to one of them? _____

   _____

3. Look at the notes you took. Write the three most important things you learned as you

   listened.

   a. _____

   _____

   b. _____

   _____

   c. _____

   _____

Life span of J. C. Harris

**Life span of Rudyard Kipling
1865-1936**

| 1800 | 1820 | 1840 | 1860 | 1880 | 1900 | 1920 | 1940 | 1960 | 1980 | 2000 | 2020 |

1861-1865
Civil War

1926 Invention of the helicopter

1867 Invention of
the typewriter

1914-1919 World War I

1865 Abraham Lincoln assassinated

1903 The Wright brothers'
first airplane flight

Reading 5: "Author Scrapbook: Rudyard Kipling," Lesson 49
Study skills: E.A.R.S. Listening Strategy

David McCord was born in 1897 in New York, N.Y. When he was twelve years old, his family moved to Oregon. An only child, he spent much time playing alone outdoors. He learned to observe and appreciate nature. As a result, nature is a common theme in his poetry. He attended Harvard University and served a short time in World War I, although he was never sent overseas. Most of his adult life was spent at Harvard. He edited the *Harvard Magazine* and directed Harvard's fundraising program, the Harvard College Fund. Above all, he was a poet. David McCord died in 1997 when he was ninety-nine years old.

Poetry by David McCord

The Star in the Pail

One at a Time: His Collected Poems for the Young

Fake Sky: More Rhymes of the Never Was and Always Is

Evidence . . .

what you already know about the subject.

Ask . . .

what you hope to learn as you listen.

Reach . . .

toward the source by listening carefully. Sit up, look at the source, think, and pick out key pieces of information.

Sum up . . .

the important things you learned.

Tip for the **Day**

**Review—
Take notes or
make drawings.**

1. Write only the facts that deal with the main idea or answer your questions.
2. Write words or groups of words instead of whole sentences.
3. Make only simple sketches as reminders, not detailed drawings. Remember to pick out only the important things.

Reading 5: "Author Scrapbook: David McCord," Lesson 72
Study skills: E.A.R.S. Listening Strategy

Name_____

*E*vidence   What do you know about David McCord?

Possible answers: He lived in

Oregon; he wrote poems;

he liked nature; he was

ninety-nine when he died.

_____

_____

*A*sk   Write two questions about what you hope to learn about David McCord.

1. *Possible answers: What were*

some of his nature poems about?

_____

2. *Was he very famous?*

_____

_____

*R*each   Look and listen carefully as your teacher reads some information about Mr. McCord.

Sum up   Write the important things you learned.

1. Did you learn the answers to your questions? _____

2. If so, what was the answer to one of them? _____

   _____

3. Write the three most interesting things you learned about Mr. McCord.

   a. _____

   _____

   b. _____

   _____

   c. _____

   _____

   _____

Life span of J. C. Harris

Life span of Rudyard Kipling

Life span of David McCord 1897-1997

| 1800 | 1820 | 1840 | 1860 | 1880 | 1900 | 1920 | 1940 | 1960 | 1980 | 2000 | 2020 |

1981 First space shuttle, *Columbia,* launched

1896 Invention of the electric stove

1938-1945 World War II

1897 Rudyard Kipling writes *Captains Courageous*

1914-1919 World War I

1906 Invention of the electric washing machine

Alfred, Lord Tennyson

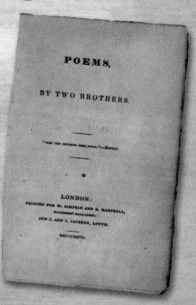

Poems, by Two Brothers *is the first volume of poetry published by the Tennyson boys. Though the title indicates only "two brothers," which were Alfred and Charles, it was discovered that Frederick wrote four of the poems. Alfred wrote over half of the poems.*

Alfred Tennyson was born in 1809 in Somersby, England. He started writing poetry at an early age and published his first volume of poetry when he was eighteen years old. His poetry became very popular, and in 1850, the same year that he married Emily Sellwood, the queen appointed him to the position of Poet Laureate. This position is given to one who is expected to write verses for official occasions. Alfred and Emily had two sons, Hallam and Lionel. After his father's death in 1892, Hallam wrote the first biography of Alfred Tennyson.

Poet Laureate: The position originated with the medieval custom of minstrels in the king's court and the need for poetic verse. The title comes from an ancient Greek and Roman custom of crowning important individuals with a laurel wreath.

Queen Victoria bestowed the title of Poet Laureate on Alfred, Lord Tennyson. She also made him a baron.

Evidence . . .

what you already know about the subject.

Ask . . .

what you hope to learn as you listen.

Reach . . .

toward the source by listening carefully. Sit up, look at the source, think, and pick out key pieces of information.

Sum up . . .

the important things you learned.

Tip for the Day

Separate the facts from the opinions as you listen.

Name_____

Evidence What do you know about Alfred Tennyson?

Possible answers: He wrote poetry when he was

young; he was Poet Laureate in England; he loved

dogs and books; he married and had two sons.

Ask Write two questions about what you hope to learn about Alfred Tennyson.

Possible answers: What was life like when Tennyson lived?

1._____

_____

How did he learn to write such great poetry?

2._____

_____

Reach Look and listen carefully as your teacher reads some information about Alfred Tennyson. Separate the facts from the opinions as you listen.

Young Tennyson was an enthusiastic writer.

Sum up   Write the important things you learned.

1. Did you learn the answers to your questions? _____

2. If so, what was the answer to one of them? _____

   _____

3. Look at the notes you took. Write the three most important things
   you learned as you listened.

   a. _____

   _____

   b. _____

   _____

   c. _____

   _____

Life span of J. C. Harris

Life span of Rudyard Kipling

Life span of David McCord

Life span of Alfred, Lord Tennyson
1809-1892

| 1800 | 1820 | 1840 | 1860 | 1880 | 1900 | 1920 | 1940 | 1960 | 1980 | 2000 | 2020 |

1837 Invention of the telegraph

1809 Birth of Abraham Lincoln, Louis Braille, and Charles Darwin

1803 Invention of the steam locomotive

Reading 5: "Author Scrapbook: Alfred, Lord Tennyson," Lesson 91
Study skills: E.A.R.S. Listening Strategy

דָּוִד

(David)

David plays for Saul

Jonathan
warns David

David as
a soldier

**Hymns or songs that are based
on the Psalms:**

Hiding in Thee (Psalm 61)

*The King of Love My Shepherd Is
(Psalm 23)*

The Lord Is My Shepherd (Psalm 23)

*O God, Our Help in Ages Past
(Psalm 90)*

Under His Wings (Psalm 91)

Whiter than Snow (Psalm 51)

*Glorious Things of Thee Are Spoken
(Psalm 87)*

David and his true
friend, Jonathan

Reading 5: "Author Scrapbook: Author of the Psalms," Lesson 102
Study skills: E.A.R.S. Listening Strategy

Evidence . . .

what you already know about the subject.

Ask . . .

what you hope to learn as you listen.

Reach . . .

toward the source by listening carefully. Sit up, look at the source, think, and pick out key pieces of information.

Sum up . . .

the important things you learned.

Tip for the Day

Listen to complete an outline.

1. Look over the outline to see what key words you are listening for.
2. Fill in the missing information using short phrases or abbreviations so that you can continue listening and not miss anything.
3. Be sure your handwriting is legible and your abbreviations are logical.

Reading 5: "Author Scrapbook: Author of the Psalms," Lesson 102
Study skills: E.A.R.S. Listening Strategy

 **vidence**   What do you know about David? _____

Answers will vary.

_____

 **sk**   Write two questions about what you hope to learn about David.

Answers will vary.

1. _____

2. _____

Reach   Look and listen carefully as your teacher reads some information about David. Fill in the blanks as you listen using the tips given for completing an outline.

David, an Old Testament Author

I. Reasons that people write poetry

   A. To play with _____*language*_____

   B. To express their _____*feelings*_____

   C. To share an event that _____*changed*_____ them

   D. To communicate _____*truth*_____

II. Reasons that David wrote the Psalms

   A. To communicate _____*truth*_____ about _____*God*_____

   B. To play with _____*language*_____

   C. To express his _____*feelings*_____ toward _____*God*_____

     1. To express excitement—psalms of _____*praise*_____

     2. To express brokenheartedness—psalms of _____*sorrow*_____ and

       _____*repentance*_____

     3. To express sadness or anger—psalms asking God to _____*judge*_____ his enemies

Sum up   Write the important things you learned.   *Answers will vary.*

1. Did you learn the answers to your questions? _____

2. If so, what was the answer to one of them? _____

_____

3. Write the three most interesting things you learned about David. These can be points included in your outline, as well as other information you learned.

a. _____

_____

b. _____

_____

c. _____

_____

Life span of David
1040-970 B.C.

| 1100 | 1080 | 1060 | 1040 | 1020 | 1000 | 980 | 960 | 940 | 920 | 900 | 880 |

B.C.

930 B.C. Kingdom divided

1010 B.C. David became king

966-959 B.C. Building of Temple

1020 B.C. David fought Goliath

992 B.C. Solomon is born

1052-1010 B.C. Saul is king

1100-1050 B.C. Samson

Reading 5: "Author Scrapbook: Author of the Psalms," Lesson 102
Study skills: E.A.R.S. Listening Strategy

Name_____

Emma Lazarus was the daughter of a wealthy sugar merchant. She was born in 1849 in New York City. She was a frail child and could not attend school. She studied under private tutors, spending much time learning other languages and reading works of classic poets. When Emma was a teenager, her father published her first volume of poetry for her. She went on to publish many more poems as an adult. Her fame today rests on only one poem, "The New Colossus." Emma Lazarus died at age 37 from Hodgkin's disease, a form of cancer.

Immigrants found great hope in the freedom that the Statue of Liberty represented.

Evidence . . .

what you already know about the subject.

Ask . . .

what you hope to learn as you listen.

Reach . . .

toward the source by listening carefully. Sit up, look at the source, think, and pick out key pieces of information.

Sum up . . .

the important things you learned.

Tip for the **Day**

Determine a purpose for listening.

Name_____

 **vidence** What do you know about Emma Lazarus?

Possible answers: She wrote "The New Colossus"; she wrote poetry;

she died when she was 37; her father was wealthy.

 **sk** Write two questions about what you hope to learn about Emma Lazarus.

1. _____*Possible answers: Why did she*_____

_____*write "The New Colossus"?*_____

_____

2. _____*Why weren't her other poems*_____

_____*famous?*_____

_____

 **each** Look and listen carefully as your teacher reads some information about Miss Lazarus.

S um up

Write the important things you learned.

1. Did you learn the answers to your questions? _____

2. If so, what was the answer to one of them? _____

   _____

3. Write the three most interesting things you learned about Miss Lazarus.

   a. _____

   _____

   b. _____

   _____

   c. _____

   _____

Life span of Alfred, Lord Tennyson

Life span of J. C. Harris

Life span of Rudyard Kipling

Life span of David McCord

Life span of Emma Lazarus 1849-1887

| 1800 | 1820 | 1840 | 1860 | 1880 | 1900 | 1920 | 1940 | 1960 | 1980 | 2000 | 2020 |

1850 Alfred, Lord Tennyson named Poet Laureate

1861-1865 Civil War

1877 Invention of the phonograph

1887 The first Sherlock Holmes story published in England

1886 The Statue of Liberty brought to the U.S. from France

Reading 5: "Author Scrapbook: Emma Lazarus," Lesson 128
Study skills: E.A.R.S. Listening Strategy

Phonics Critters

This section of the worktext provides optional teacher-guided review and/or independent practice of phonics for fifth-grade students who would benefit from the instruction. We recommend using these pages at the beginning of the year to provide maximum benefit.

Additional information for teaching phonics is presented in the Phonics section of the Introduction in the *READING 5 Teacher's Edition*. Also, a list of the phonics generalizations applied on these worktext pages is included in the appendix of the *READING 5 Teacher's Edition*.

These pages are located here so that you can find them easily. You may find it beneficial to keep them in the worktext. They will serve as a reference to be used again as needed.

/ă/ as in dragon

▶Read the words.

stand	match	math	
grand	hatch	path	
plant	quack	grab	clap
slant	shack	grass	clasp
drag	flash	clamp	branch
shag	splash	class	brass

The short *a* sound is usually in a closed syllable.

▶Circle the correct answers.

1. What vowel sound do you hear in each of the words above?

   long ā   (short ă)   short ŏ

2. What comes after the vowel?

   (a consonant)   a vowel

A **closed syllable** ends with one or more consonants.

▶Read the two-syllable words.
Circle each closed syllable with the short *a* sound.

(wag)•on	(mas)•ter	(band)•(stand)	(ram)•ble	(bash)•ful	(grand)•(dad)
(han)•dle	(af)•ter	(blan)•ket	(flap)•(jack)	(crash)•ing	(can)•dy
(hand)•(craft)	(cat)•tle	(lad)•der	(pat)•tern		

What vowel makes the short *a* sound in a closed syllable?

   o   e   (a)   i   u

264

▶**Read each sentence. Circle the word with the short *a* sound that has the correct meaning in the sentence.**

1. It is important for the Komodo dragon to (catch, save) a big meal.

2. Animals such as mice and rats are only a small (sandwich, snack).

3. A Komodo dragon can run (farther, faster) than 15 miles per hour.

4. He will chase after a goat or deer if it gets in his (way, path).

5. His sharp teeth help him (match, clasp) the food in his mouth.

6. This lizard spends time both in the water and on the (grand, island).

7. If you look up into a big tree, you might spot him taking a (nap, flash).

8. When he swims, he creates a very large (splash, wave).

9. There are very few of these (creatures, dragons) still alive today.

▶**Write a rhyming word for each of the short *a* words. You may choose words from the top of page 264.**   *Answers will vary.*

stamp _____   wrath _____

crash _____   brag _____

grant _____   smack_____

grasp _____   pass _____

Komodo Dragon

The island of Komodo in Southeast Asia is home to this 8- to 10-foot-long lizard. By flicking its forked tongue, it can detect scents as far as 5 miles away.

▶**Read the words.**

rest	sent	left	blend
nest	rent	theft	trend

crept	them	egg	spell
slept	stem	end	sped
drench	then	else	spend
bench	when	edge	speck

stepped	helped	swelled
pecked	begged	webbed

The short *e* sound is usually in a closed syllable.

▶**Circle the correct answers.**

1. What vowel sound do you hear in each of the words above?

    short ŏ   long ē   (short ĕ)

2. What comes after the vowel in each word?

    a vowel   (a consonant)

A **closed syllable** ends with one or more consonants.

▶**Read the two-syllable words.**
Circle each closed syllable with the short *e* sound.

(peb)•ble	(pen)•ny	(dead)•ly	(heav)•y
(treas)•ure	(set)•tle	(jel)•ly	(head)•ing
(spread)•ing	(stead)•fast	(trem)•ble	(pep)•py

Sometimes *ea* makes the short *e* sound.

What vowels make the short *e* sound in a closed syllable?

    a   (e)   i   o   u   (ea)

▶Help Benjamin Penguin slide down the iceberg and find his supper by drawing a fish around all the words with the short *e* sound. The first one is done for you.

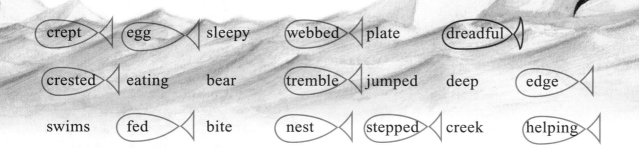

crept   egg   sleepy   webbed   plate   dreadful

crested   eating   bear   tremble   jumped   deep   edge

swims   fed   bite   nest   stepped   creek   helping

▶**Complete the sentences using the short *e* words on the iceberg above.**

1. After the _____*egg*_____ hatches, Father stays with little Benjamin while Mother hunts for fish and squid.

2. One day Benjamin's father takes him to the _____*edge*_____ of the rocks.

3. They will use their _____*webbed*_____ feet to swim quickly through the water.

King Penguins

Standing at a height of about three feet, King penguins are the second largest penguins in the world. After King penguins lay an egg, they roll it onto their feet and tuck it into a fold of their skin to keep it warm. The male and female take turns caring for the egg 5 days at a time, until it hatches 55 days later.

/ĭ/ as in fish

▶ **Read the words.**

The short *i* sound is usually in a closed syllable.

thick	fish
stick	swish

chill	sprint
drill	mint

print	swift	which	twins
prince	drift	whip	twist

fist	slipped	itched	trimmed
wrist	kicked	spilled	grinned

▶ **Circle the correct answers.**

1. What vowel sound do you hear in each of the words above?

   short ă   long ī   (short ĭ)

2. What comes after the vowel in each word?

   a vowel   (a consonant)

A **closed syllable** ends with one or more consonants.

▶ **Read the two-syllable words.**
  Circle each closed syllable with the short *i* sound.

(lit)•tle	(mis)•print	sys•tem	sig•nal
(dip)•per	sym•bol	dis•play	(dish)•es
(hym)•nal	(rid)•dle	(kitch)•en	symp•tom
(sim)•ple	(fin)•(ish)	(vis)•(it)	(pic)•(nic)

Sometimes *y* is a vowel.

Sometimes *y* makes the short *i* sound.

What vowels make the short *i* sound in a closed syllable?

   (i)   o   (y)   a   e

▶**Complete the puzzle.**

Crossword puzzle:

Row 1: ¹T I P

²F (down)

³I N H A B I T

H, I, N (down from T)

N (down from F)

⁴S W I ⁵M

Down from I: N C H E

⁶F ⁷I S H

Down from I (7): N J U R Y

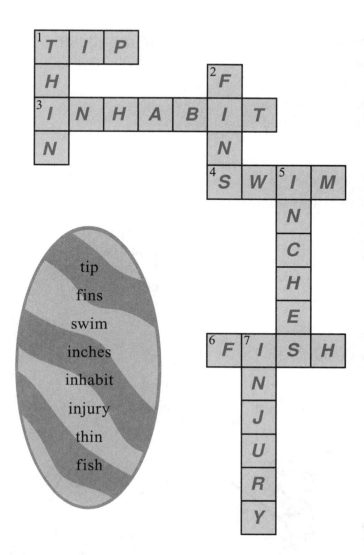

tip
fins
swim
inches
inhabit
injury
thin
fish

Lionfish

Lionfish are known for their brightly colored featherlike fins that can deliver a painful and poisonous sting. These fish are usually found in caves and under ledges of coral.

Across

1. If a diver steps on a lionfish, the sharp ____ of the lionfish's fin will sting the diver.
3. Lionfish ____ many of the coral reefs in the oceans.
4. Lionfish can ____ very quickly.
6. The lionfish sucks and gulps small ____ alive.

Down

1. The lionfish uses his long, ____ fins to corner his prey.
2. The ____ of a lionfish can be harmful.
5. Lionfish can grow up to 15 ____ in length.
7. The poison in their fins can cause ____.

▶**Read the words.**

frost	blot	fond	chop
cost	trot	blond	prop
lost	knot	pond	crop

tromp	shocks	docked	blocked
trod	shops	stomped	robbed

The short *o* sound is usually in a closed syllable.

▶**Circle the correct answers.**

1. What vowel sound do you hear in each of the words above?

　　short ă　　　long ō　　　(short ŏ)

2. What comes after the vowel?

　　(a consonant)　　　a vowel

A **closed syllable** ends with one or more consonants.

▶**Read the two-syllable words.**
Circle each closed syllable with the short *o* sound.

(chop)•sticks	(stop)•per	(pock)•et	(spot)•ted	(trop)•ics
back•(stop)	(gos)•pel	(rock)•et	(odd)•est	(box)•ing
sling•(shot)	(slosh)•es	(hot)•test		(frost)•ing
(top)•(knot)	(cross)•es			

What vowel makes the short *o* sound in a closed syllable?

　　e　　i　　u　　(o)　　oa

Name_____

▶ For each line, color the letters that spell the word that is given.
Write the leftover letters in the blanks to make a new word.

tropic	s	t	r	o	p	h	i	o	c	t	_s_ _h_ _o_ _t_
log	s	p	l	o	o	t	t	g	e	d	_s_ _p_ _o_ _t_ _t_ _e_ _d_
frog	b	o	t	f	r	t	o	o	g	m	_b_ _o_ _t_ _t_ _o_ _m_
rocket	r	o	c	b	l	k	o	e	b	t	_b_ _l_ _o_ _b_
pot	p	l	o	o	b	s	t	t	e	r	_l_ _o_ _b_ _s_ _t_ _e_ _r_
tromp	r	o	t	r	o	c	m	k	p	s	_r_ _o_ _c_ _k_ _s_

▶ Use the short *o* words you found in the puzzle above to complete the sentences.

1. Ollie the octopus lives at the _____bottom_____ of the ocean in warm, shallow waters.

2. During the day, Ollie hides in a hole or a crevice in the _____rocks_____.

3. One night Ollie decided he wanted some _____lobster_____ for supper.

4. He changed the color of his skin to match the _____spotted_____ ocean floor and settled down to wait.

5. Later, as a plump lobster walked past, Ollie _____shot_____ ink into the water.

6. The _____blob_____ of ink confused the lobster, and soon Ollie was enjoying a delicious supper!

Common Octopus

God has equipped the octopus with many ways to protect itself from its enemies. First, it is able to change its skin color and blend in with its surroundings. Second, it can flatten its body and squeeze through tiny holes to escape its enemies. Finally, if an enemy is approaching, an octopus can squirt ink into the water, as well as another liquid that numbs the enemy's sense of smell, and make a quick getaway.

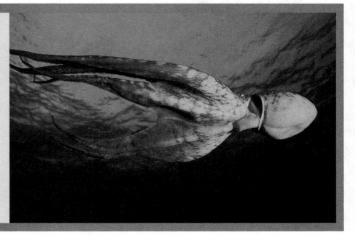

Reading 5
Phonics: using letter-sound association for /ŏ/

271

/ŭ/ as in bug

▶**Read the words.**

bug	thump	must	lung	hutch
chug	stump	thrust	stung	Dutch
smug	plump	crust	strung	clutch

▶**Circle the correct answers.**

1. What vowel sound do you hear in each of the words above?

   (short ŭ)   long ē   short ŏ

2. What follows the vowel?

   a vowel   (a consonant)

▶**Read the words with the /ŭ/ as in *bug*.**

won	touch	rough
son	young	Doug

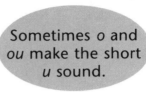

Sometimes *o* and *ou* make the short *u* sound.

The short *u* sound is often in a closed syllable.

▶**Read the two-syllable words.**
Circle each closed syllable with the short *u* sound.

(hon•)ey	(coun•)try	(un•)done	(broth•)er
pea•(nut)	hand•(cuff)	(crutch•)es	(un•)wrap
(cov•)er	(pun•)ished	(puzz•)ling	(but•)ter•(cup)
(stum•)ble	(clut•)tered	(punch•)ing	mid•(sum•)mer

What vowels make the short *u* sound in a closed syllable?

(u)   e   (o)   a   (ou)

▶**Write the correct word for each definition.**

1. humorous, comical _____*funny*_____

2. roar, rumbling noise _____*thunder*_____

3. to put in place _____*tuck*_____

4. to laugh quietly _____*chuckle*_____

5. a prop, support _____*crutch*_____

6. chubby, overweight _____*plump*_____

7. to fall _____*stumble*_____

8. push, shove _____*thrust*_____

9. a liquid made by bees _____*honey*_____

10. not gentle or careful _____*rough*_____

thrust	thunder
chuckle	rough
stumble	crutch
tuck	funny
plump	honey

▶**The words you wrote above are hidden in the puzzle. Find and circle each one.**

```
A T P U M T T P G U O R B L C A Q M
P L U M P O H W O D C H U C R K L E
T H S C D T U N R A N G I R U B D F
U G D F K M N I E O N U C R U T C H
D F N K P U D F P K U C H P S Y J O
S T U M B L E U D S R G E T I C K N
N E S N C P R N K B T C H U C K L E
E O N U N A T N Z Q S V B E V P T Y
J L H O U Y U E O T H R U S T E O P
R C M R T C S G T H U N D E Z Q H U
```

Harlequin Bug

If not controlled, the Harlequin bug has the ability to destroy an entire crop of cabbage. The bug sucks out the plant's juices, causing the plant to wither and eventually die. This shield-shaped bug usually lays about twelve eggs that resemble white barrels arranged side by side.

Review of short vowels

▶**Read the words.**

cat•tle	crept	han•dle	pic•nic
trick	rid•dle	trem•ble	chuck•le
gos•pel	knot	splash	grand•dad
set•tle	top•knot	thrust	sprint
stum•ble	plump	stem	frost

When there is one vowel letter in a closed syllable, it usually has a short vowel sound.

▶**Write the above words under the correct short vowel sound.**

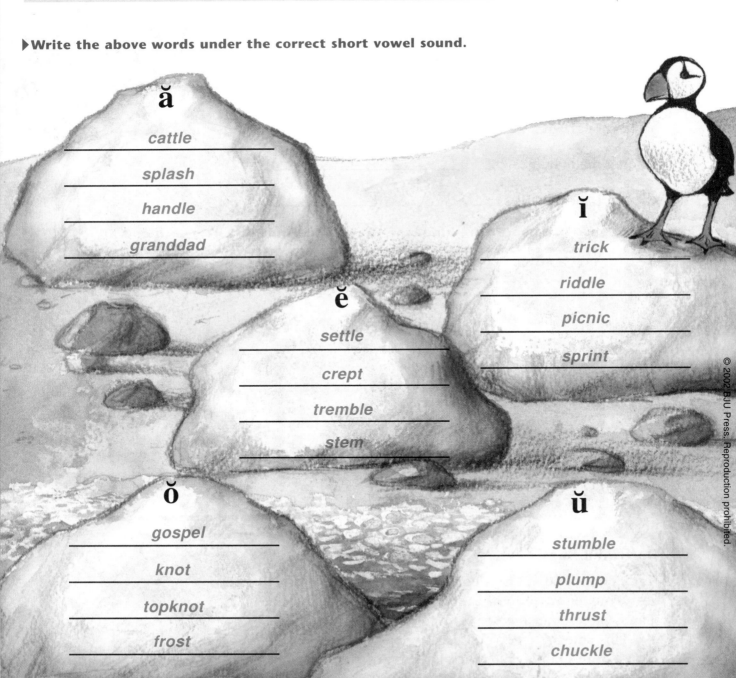

ă
cattle
splash
handle
granddad

ĭ
trick
riddle
picnic
sprint

ĕ
settle
crept
tremble
stem

ŏ
gospel
knot
topknot
frost

ŭ
stumble
plump
thrust
chuckle

▶**Complete the puzzle.**

puffin
bat
duck   skunk
ostrich   pelican
bug   fox
fish   octopus
    dragon

¹**D U C K**
R
A   ²**P**
A   ³**O**   ⁴**S K U N K**
⁵**B U G**   **C**   **F**
A   ⁶**O S T R I C H**   ⁷**F O X**
T   **N**   **O**   **I**
    ⁸**P E L I C A N**
    U
⁹**F I S H**

Across
1. water bird with a flat bill, short legs, and webbed feet
4. animal with black-and-white fur and a smelly spray
5. an insect
6. largest living bird with long legs and a long neck
7. member of dog family with a long, bushy tail
8. sea bird with wingspan of 7-10 feet, a long bill, and a pouch
9. an animal that has fins and lives in the water

Down
1. usually pictured as a giant lizard with wings and claws
2. a plump black-and-white bird with a brightly colored bill
3. a sea animal with eight parts that look like arms
5. a small animal with thin, leathery wings; sleeps during the day

Puffin

Puffins have triangular-shaped beaks. During the spring breeding season, their beaks become very colorful. Because of this, puffins have been called "parrots of the sea."

/ā/ as in snake

▶**Read the words.**
Circle the correct answers.

trail	brain	paid	paint	clay	stray
snail	stain	maid	faint	pray	spray

Sometimes y is a vowel.

1. How many vowel letters are in each word above?

   ②   3   1

2. What one long vowel sound do you hear?

   long ī   short ĭ   (long ā)   short ă

Silent e pattern
a_e
ame
ace
ade

shave	stage	crane	draped	scales
frame	grace	shade	chased	skates

3. What long vowel is in each of the words above?

   ⓐ   e

4. What vowel is silent?

   a   ⓔ

they	weight	reigns	beige
hey	freight	veins	sleigh

The long a sound is heard in special vowel pairs.

5. What two special vowel pairs are in the words above?

   ae   ie   ⓔⓘ   ⓔⓨ   ay

▶**Read the multisyllable words.**
Circle each open syllable with the long a sound.

ⓒⓐ•ble   ⓟⓐ•per   ⓑⓐ•bies
ⓝⓐ•tion   ⓰ⓡⓐ•vy   ⓕⓐ•mous
in•fla•tion   lo•ca•tion   ⓜⓐ•jor
im•pa•tient   ⓒⓡⓐ•dle   ⓑⓐ•sin

*An **open syllable** ends with a vowel.*

The long a sound is often in an open syllable.

What letters make the long a sound?

   ⓐ_ⓔ   i   ⓐⓘ   ⓐ   ye

   ⓔⓘ   ⓔⓨ   ⓐⓨ

276

▶Read the definitions on the snake.
Write the correct word on the line below its definition.

cradle   stray   brain   snail   famous
beige   painter   frame   shave   scale

1. a light shade of tan   2. the human mind   3. a small bed for a baby

4. an artist

1. _____beige_____   2. _____brain_____   3. _____cradle_____

4. _____painter_____

7. a border around a picture   6. a lost animal   5. an instrument for weighing

5. _____scale_____   6. _____stray_____   7. _____frame_____

8. well known   9. to remove with a razor   10. a slow-moving animal

8. _____famous_____

9. _____shave_____   10. _____snail_____

Rhinoceros Viper

The rhinoceros viper is named for the two or three small sharp horns on its nose. This highly poisonous African snake has fangs so long they will not fit in its closed mouth. Therefore, God gave the viper teeth that actually fold up when it closes its mouth.

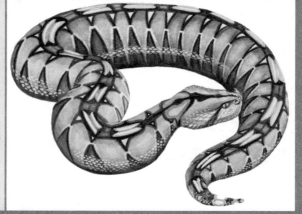

/ē/ as in anteater

▶**Read the words. Circle the correct answers.**

eat	greed	team	wheel
treat	bleed	dream	kneel

1. How many vowel letters are in each word above?

    1   3   (2)

2. What one long vowel sound do you hear?

   (long ē)   short ĕ   long ā   short ă

The long e sound is heard in special vowel pairs.

field	grief	mon•key
yield	thief	chim•ney
shield	chief	hock•ey

3. What long vowel pairs make the long *e* sound in the words above?

   (ie)   ei   ae   (ey)

push•y	sun•ny	frost•y	ba•by
trick•y	hun•gry	rain•y	po•ny
quick•ly	twen•ty	stud•y	la•zy

4. What sound does *y* make at the ends of the words above?

   long ī   (long ē)   short ĭ   short ĕ

▶**Read the words with open syllables.**
Circle each open syllable with the long *e* sound.

(he)   (e)•vil   (me)•ter

(ze)•bra   may•be   (cre)•a•tion

(e)•ven   se•cret

An **open syllable** ends with a vowel.

The long e sound is often in an open syllable.

What letters make the long *e* sound?

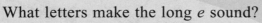

(e)   (ea)   (ee)   (ey)   (ie)   (y)

▶**Read the sentences. Choose the correct long *e* word to match the clue and complete the sentence.**

secret	teeth	wheel	hungry	thief	twenty	maybe	shady	treat	tree

1. One summer (eve,) (Pete,) the (anteater,) climbed up a ___*shady*___ (tree.)
(giving shade)

2. (He) wrapped his two-foot-long tail around a limb of the ___*tree*___.
(large bush)

3. (Pete) had a ___*secret*___ (he) could not (keep.)
(something hidden)

4. (He) was looking for a (real) (anteater) ___*treat*___.
(special delight)

5. ___*Maybe*___ there was a fine (meal) (here.)
(Possibly)

6. But his long slender snout had no ___*teeth*___ for (eating.)
(used to chew)

7. Surprise! More than ___*twenty*___ ants and termites disappeared by (only) the
(ten + ten)
lick of (Pete's) (sticky) tongue.

8. Did you ever wonder how much a ___*hungry*___ (anteater) can (eat?)
(wanting food)

▶**Read the sentences again. Circle the other long *e* words you find in the sentences.**

Giant Anteater

Some giant anteaters are over 6 feet in length, which includes a 2½-foot-long tail. They use their strong front claws to rip open ant nests. Then they push their sticky 2-foot-long tongue into the nest to collect their insect meal.

Reading 5
Phonics: using letter-sound association for /ē/

/ī/ as in butterfly

▶Read the words. Circle the correct answers.

drive	slice	die	spied	white
thrive	twice	lie	tried	write

1. How many vowel letters are in each word above?

    4   3   ②   1

2. What one long vowel sound do you hear?

    (long ī)   short ĕ   long ē

The long i sound is often formed by *igh* and *y*.

shy	high	tight	spy
cry	sigh	light	why

3. What special patterns make the long *i* sound in the words above?

    ey   Ⓨ   ei   (igh)   ay

▶Read the multisyllable words. Circle each syllable that has the long *i* sound.

ar•(rive)   al•(ly)   (fright)•en   (fire•fly)
in•(vite)   ap•(ply)   sat•is•(fy)   head•(line)
sup•(ply)   (tight)•er   (high)•way   (like•wise)

(Fri)•day   (spi)•der   (sci)•ence   dy•na•(mite)
(i)•tem   (pi)•lot   (qui)•et   (mi)•nor
(i)•de•a   (si)•lent   (spy)•glass   (sky•line)

The long *i* sound is often in an open syllable.

What letters make the long *i* sound?

    ei   (ie)   (i_e)   (i)   (y)   (igh)

▶**Write an antonym for each word.**
You may find the words on page 280.

dark
light

loose
tight

black
white

live
die

laugh
cry

outgoing
shy

gave up
tried

noisy
quiet / silent

truth
lie

low
high

leave
arrive

major
minor

Butterflies

Butterflies have two forewings and two hindwings that are held together during flight, functioning as one wing. The coloration of butterflies' wings varies and serves many different purposes. For example, the Australian leafwing butterfly is shaped and colored like a leaf, allowing it to blend into its surroundings and hide from its enemies.

/ō/ as in koala

▶ **Read the words.**

toe	drove	goat	broke	glow
hoe	throne	cloak	vote	show
foe	home	coast	rode	blow

> Sometimes *w* is a vowel.

▶ **Mark the correct answers.**

1. What vowel sound do you hear in the words above?

　　　long ē　　　(long ō)　　　long ā　　　short ă

2. Cross out the silent vowel in each word in the list above.

▶ **Read the special pattern words with the long *o* sound.**

gold	roll	post	colt	folk
sold	scroll	host	bolt	yolk

▶ **Read the two-syllable words.**
Circle the syllables that have the long *o* sound.

el•bow　　　soak•ing　　　sea•coast
pil•low　　　toast•er　　　hail•stone
un•fold　　　slow•ly

▶ **Circle the open syllables with the long *o* sound.**

fro•zen　　　yo•del
spo•ken　　　o•val
po•lar　　　lo•ca•tion

no•ble　　　quo•ta•tion
mo•ment　　　bo•nus
lo•cal　　　o•mit

> The long *o* sound is often in an open syllable.

> An **open syllable** ends with a vowel.

What letters make the long *o* sound?

　　　(oa)　　　(oe)　　　oi　　　oy

　　　(ow)　　　(o_e)　　　(o)

▶**Complete the puzzle.**

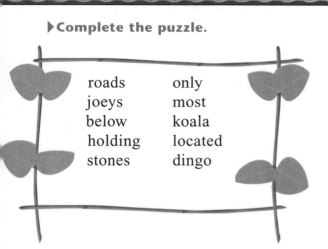

roads   only
joeys   most
below   koala
holding located
stones   dingo

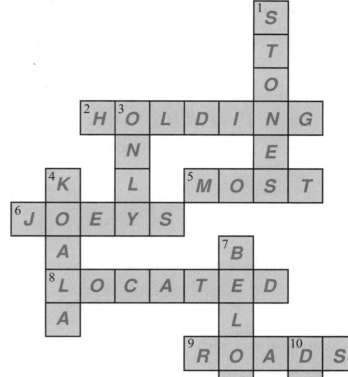

Across

2. Koalas are often shown ___ onto the trunk or limb of a eucalyptus tree.

5. Koalas sleep during ___ of the day and are active during the night.

6. Kangaroos live in Australia with their babies called ___.

8. There are many kinds of eucalyptus trees ___ in the Australian forests.

9. Koala crossing signs are posted along ___ near eucalyptus forests.

Down

1. On the ground koalas may eat dirt and ___, which help digest the leaves.

3. Koalas live ___ in the eucalyptus forests of Australia.

4. A koala never leaves the tree for water; the name ___ means "no water."

7. A koala may move to another tree by going down to the ground ___.

10. A ___ is a wild dog that is the koala's enemy.

Koala

Have you ever smelled a eucalyptus cough drop? Koalas eat so much eucalyptus that they smell like the strong-flavored eucalyptus. An adult koala eats two to three pounds of leaves daily.

▶ **Read the words. Circle the correct answers.**

mule	cute	dune	cube
rule	flute	tune	tube

1. How many vowel letters are in the words above?

    4   ②   1

The long u is heard in special vowel pairs.

2. What one vowel sound do you hear?

    short ĕ   long ō   (long ū)

troop	threw	newest	true	suit	goose
bloom	chew	jewel	clue	fruit	smooth

3. What vowel pairs make the long *u* or *oo* sound in the words above?

    ai   (oo)   (ew)   a   (ui)   (ue)   ou

▶ **Read the two-syllable words.**
Circle the syllables with the long *u* or *oo* sound.

a•(new)	(fruit)•ful	toad•(stool)	car•(toon)
a•(muse)	(tooth)•less	snow•(suit)	val•(ue)
a•(cute)	(use)•ful	ty•(phoon)	is•(sue)

The long u or oo sound has many spellings.

▶ **Read the words with open syllables.**
Circle the open syllables with the long *u* sound.

(u)•nit	(u)•su•al	so•lu•tion
(u)•nite	(pu)•pil	(mu)•sic
(u)•ten•sil	stu•dent	fu•ner•al

The long u sound is often in an open syllable.

What letters make the long *u* sound?

(u)   (ui)   (oo)   (u_e)

a   (ew)   (ue)

▶ **Look at the pattern of each word on the left. Circle all the other words in each row that follow the same pattern for the long _u_ sound.**

1. *oo* as in *loop*	(troop)	clown	(zoo)	floor
2. *u* as in *flu*	trust	(unite)	fun	(music)
3. *u_e* as in *cute*	(flute)	jump	grunt	(tube)
4. *ew* as in *crew*	check	(chew)	before	(flew)
5. *ue* as in *glue*	mud	(Sue)	stuck	(clue)

▶ **Circle all the long _u_ or _oo_ words in the story.**

As Mother (Baboon) climbs the jagged rocks, Baby (Baboon) clings closely to her. Each day Baby (Baboon) stuffs the pouches in his cheeks with the (fruit) his mother gives him. He enjoys (chewing) on a variety of tree (roots) for his (afternoon) snack.

Sometimes he gets another (baboon) to pick his fur, or (groom) him. (Grooming) is an activity that relaxes and (unites) members of the (troop). Some day Baby (Baboon) will have a thick gray mane to (groom).

▶ **Choose the long _u_ or _oo_ words for the sentences.**

1. Baboons live together in groups called ((troops), tons).

2. Large males (rust, (rule)) the group.

3. Baboons eat insects, small mammals, grasses, and (rots, (roots)).

4. A baboon in danger may bark loudly and show its ((huge,) bug) teeth.

5. Baboons (roughly, (usually)) sleep on cliffs rather than in trees.

Hamadryas Baboon

One adult male and one to nine females live in the family groups of the Hamadryas baboons. As many as 700 baboons may gather to rest on a single cliff at night.

Review of long vowels

▶Read the words.

acute	pie	faint	bleed	spyglass
cable	coast	jewel	firefly	useful
hockey	quickly	pillow	music	chosen
throne	spider	chased	spray	zebra

▶Write the above words under the correct long vowel sound.

ā

cable

faint

chased

spray

> When a syllable has two vowels together, the first vowel is often long and the second one is silent.

> When a syllable ends with a vowel, it usually has a long sound.

> When a syllable has the final silent e pattern, the vowel is usually long.

ē

hockey

quickly

bleed

zebra

ī

pie

spider

firefly

spyglass

ō

throne

coast

pillow

chosen

ū

acute

jewel

music

useful

▶ **The animals below can be found in the Florida swamps. Circle all the words with a long vowel sound. Hint: there are 24 words.**

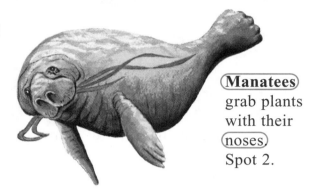

(Snail)(kites)(eat) apple (snails) with their curved bills. (Locate) 4.

Manatees grab plants with their (noses) Spot 2.

(**Raccoon**) tracks look (like)(human) hand-prints and footprints. (Find) 5 (raccoons)

(**Zebra**) (**butterflies**) (lay) eggs on pawpaw (tree)(leaves) (Find) 6.

(**Garpike**) have sharp (teeth) on their long snout. Spot 3.

Cottonmouth (snakes) mouths are (white)(inside) (Locate) 5

Reading 5
Phonics: using letter-sound association for /ā/, /ē/, /ī/, /ō/, /ū/, /yo͞o/, and /o͞o/

/är/ as in star

▶**Read the words.**

arch	hard	barn	part	arm	dark
starch	yard	yarn	large	charm	shark
march	card	dart	barge	farm	

▶**Circle the correct answers.**

1. What vowel is in all the words above?

   (a)   e   i   o   u

2. What consonant follows the vowel?

   m   g   k   d   (r)

> When *r* follows a vowel, it usually influences the vowel's sound.

▶**Read the words.**
Circle the syllables that have the /är/ as in *star*.

(dark)•ness   (smart)•est   (start)•ing   (par)•ty   (gar)•den
(hard)•ness   (harsh)•est   (park)•ing   (marsh)•y   (sharp)•en

(barn)(yard)   (mar)•ble   (par)•don
sky•(lark)   (mar)•ket   (art)•ist
(star)•fish   (car)•pet   un•(chart)•ed
(dar)•ling   (far)•ther   de•(part)•ment

Which letters make the /är/ as in *star*?

   ir   ur   (ar)   er   or

▶**Find the letters from the code and write them in the blanks.**

⭐	s	a	b	c	j
✳	e	l	r	y	m
✴	g	p	i	k	t
⭐	n	h	d	f	q
	1	2	3	4	5

1. (✳, 2) (⭐, 2) (✳, 3) (✴, 1) (✳, 1) = _____ *large* _____

2. (⭐, 1) (✴, 2) (⭐, 2) (✳, 3) (✴, 4) (✳, 2) (✴, 3) (⭐, 1) (✴, 1) = _____ *sparkling* _____

3. (✳, 4) (⭐, 2) (✳, 3) (⭐, 3) = _____ *yard* _____

4. (⭐, 1) (⭐, 2) (⭐, 2) (✳, 3) (✴, 4) = _____ *shark* _____

5. (⭐, 4) (⭐, 2) (✳, 3) = _____ *far* _____

6. (⭐, 3) (⭐, 2) (✳, 3) (✴, 5) (✴, 3) (⭐, 1) (✴, 1) = _____ *darting* _____

▶**Use the words you found above to complete the sentences.**

1. Marvin sat on the swing in the _____ *yard* _____ and thought about his family's vacation.

2. He could almost smell the salt air and see the

   sunlight _____ *sparkling* _____ on the pale blue water.

3. Marvin and his family had spent a week at a

   beach _____ *far* _____ from their home.

4. Marvin was snorkeling one day and saw

   a _____ *large* _____ school of fish _____ *darting* _____

   around in the water.

5. Suddenly, a small _____ *shark* _____ charged through
   the fish and snatched a few for his lunch.

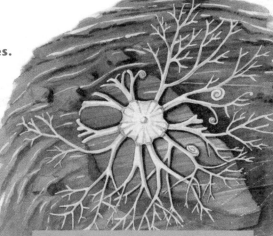

Basket Star

At first glance the basket star may be identified as a plant; however, the basket star is a relative of the starfish. It uses its branches to trap tiny fish and push them to its mouth for a tasty snack.

▶**Read the words.**

fork	more	sort	torch
cork	shore	sport	porch
stork	score	short	scorn
pork	snore	port	sworn

▶**Circle the correct answers.**

1. What vowel is in every word above?

   a   e   i   (o)   u

2. What consonant follows the vowel?

   t   (r)   p   k   c

When *r* follows a vowel, it usually influences the vowel's sound.

▶**Read the multisyllable words.**
Circle the syllables that have the /or/ as in *scorpion*.

a•(shore)	be•(fore)	(cor)•ner	(tor)•na•do
ig•(nore)	(north)•east	af•(ford)	im•(port)•ant
a•(dore)	(for)•mal	(fore)•cast	(tor)•pe•do
(for)•ty	(scor)•ing	(or)•der	re•(cord)•er
(storm)•y	(for)•est	ex•(port)	(sword)•fish

Which letters make the /or/ as in *scorpion*?

ar   ur   ir   er   (or)

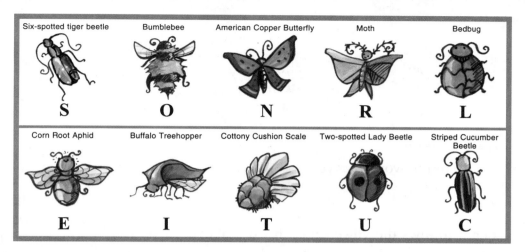

▶ **Fill in the missing letters using the code to reveal what happens to the scorpion when he is exposed to ultraviolet light.**

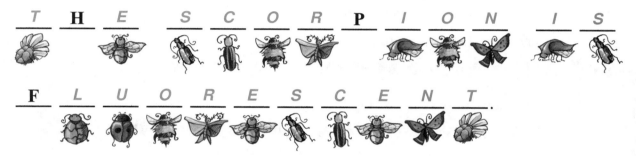

T   H   E   S   C   O   R   P   I   O   N   I   S

F   L   U   O   R   E   S   C   E   N   T .

▶ **Write an /or/ word for each definition. You will find the words on page 290.**

1. _____*forty*_____   comes after thirty-nine

2. _____*forecast*_____   prediction

3. _____*sport*_____   soccer

4. _____*sort*_____   to separate into groups

5. _____*adore*_____   to love

6. _____*tornado*_____   strong whirlwind

7. _____*corner*_____   where two lines meet

8. _____*before*_____   ahead of

Scorpion
The scorpion, although a small animal, is well-equipped to protect itself. At the end of its tail are two glands that put out a poison. Its sting is very painful, but it rarely causes death.

/ûr/ as in urchin

▶**Read the words.**

shirt	perk	birth	church	surf
squirt	clerk	chirp	burst	urge
twirl	germ	stern	nurse	
whirl	term	verse	curve	

▶**Circle the correct answers.**

1. What vowels are in the words above?

   a   (e)   (i)   o   (u)

2. What consonant follows the vowel in each word above?

   b   (r)   l   k   n

3. Which letters usually make the /ûr/ as in urchin?

   ar   (er)   (ir)   or   (ur)

When *r* follows a vowel, it usually influences the vowel's sound.

▶**Read the words.**
Circle the syllables that have the /ûr/ as in *urchin*.

(ker)•nel	(sur)•ger•y	birth•day	(tur)•key
(mer)•cy	(hur)•dle	ob•(serve)	(thir)•ty
(ser)•vant	(cir)•cus	re•(serve)	(burst)•ing

▶**Read the special pattern words.**

pearl	earth	worm	worse
early	heard	worth	worship
learn	search	work	world

When *or* follows *w*, it usually makes the /ûr/ as in *urchin*.

What letters make the /ûr/ as in *urchin*?

(w)or   (ear)   (er)   (ir)   ar   (ur)

▶ **Circle the correct rhyming word for each sentence.**

1. Gene watches a (nurse, purse) shark swimming at the aquarium.

2. Gene (burns, turns) right at the next exhibit.

3. In the marine habitat there are sand dollars and sea (urchins, merchants).

4. The sea urchins (stir, fir) on the ocean floor using their spines.

5. The spines also offer the (burst, first) method of defense.

6. Gene (churns, learns) that sea urchins can climb up rocks using their tube-feet.

7. Their tube-feet (nerve, serve) an important role in feeding and breathing.

8. Gene (observes, reserves) more creatures in the next exhibit.

▶ **Color all the squares that have words with the *ur* sound to find the name of the shell or skeleton that protects the sea urchin.**

sir	nerve	first
brag	birth	score
ramp	fir	brown
chill	churn	chip
torn	thirst	round

perk	serve	term
twirl	twig	trip
burst	third	rest
stern	grass	short
fur	whirl	nurse

clerk	purse	burn
stir	north	rain
smart	spur	beet
cry	chew	learn
surf	bird	urge

squirt	germ	curve
chop	chirp	cheek
drive	dirt	part
free	fern	face
pride	girl	star

Sea Urchin

Long, movable spines cover the body of a sea urchin. The spines grow from a shell that rests just under the skin. The shell protects the soft body of the sea urchin.

/âr/ as in bear

▶**Read the words.**
  Circle the letters in each word that make the /âr/ as in *bear*.
  (Hint: There should be two vowels and one consonant in each pattern.)

b(ear)   (air)   fl(are)

p(ear)   p(air)   h(are)

w(ear)   st(air)   p(are)

                   h(air)   sh(are)

                                      st(are)

When *r* follows a vowel, it usually influences the vowel's sound.

▶**Read the words.**
  Circle the syllable in each word that makes the /âr/ as in *bear*.

(care)   (tear)•ing   com•(pare)   (fair)•ly

(care)•ful•ly   (wear)•ing   be•(ware)   (fair)•er

(care)•less   a•(ware)   (fair)•est

(care)•ful

(rare)   (stare)   (scare)

(rar)•er   (star)•ing   (scar)•ing

(rar)•est

(rare)•ly

Remember that silent *e* is dropped when adding *-ing, -er,* or *-est.*

What letters make the /âr/ as in *bear*?

ace   (are)   (air)   ey   re   (ear)

wears
canary
tears
careful
hair
library
glare
square
beware
February

Sloth Bear

The big and shaggy sloth bear lives in the rocky canyons and hills of India and Sri Lanka. The sucking noise of the bear eating termites can be heard 200 yards away! The sloth bear, which has a short temper, can be dangerous when it is approached.

▶**Write the word that matches each definition.**

1. look angrily _____*glare*_____

2. watchful _____*careful*_____

3. a month _____*February*_____

4. covering of mammals _____*hair*_____

5. a bird _____*canary*_____

6. pull into pieces _____*tears*_____

7. be careful or cautious _____*beware*_____

8. a collection of books _____*library*_____

9. a four-sided figure _____*square*_____

10. be clothed in; have on _____*wears*_____

▶**Choose the correct word for each sentence.**

1. The only bear with long _____*hair*_____ on its ears is the sloth bear.

2. It _____*wears*_____ a white or yellow *Y* on its chest.

3. _____*Beware*_____ ! A sloth bear can gallop faster than a person can run.

4. They are _____*careful*_____ climbers, but they don't climb trees to escape danger.

5. A sloth bear finds a termite or ant mound and _____*tears*_____ it open with its claws.

▶**Circle the third letter in each set of letters to show a favorite food of the sloth bear. Write the word.**

ei(o)su

omh(y)i

rc(e)on

drn(u)a

qxy(y)zp

h o n e y
_ _ _ _ _

/îr/ as in meerkat

▶**Read the words.**

tier
fierce
pierce

hear
near
dear
gear
spear

deer
peer
cheer
steer
sheer

here
sphere

▶**Circle the correct answers.**

1. What vowel pairs are in the words above?

(ie)   (ea)   ui   ae   (ee)

2. What consonant follows each vowel pair?

e   f   (r)   l   n

> When *r* follows a vowel, it usually influences the vowel's sound.

▶**Read the words.**
Circle the syllables that contain vowels influenced by *r*.

(cheer)•ful   (steer)•ing   (pierced)   (dear)•est

(near)•ing   sin•(cere)•ly   (mere)•ly

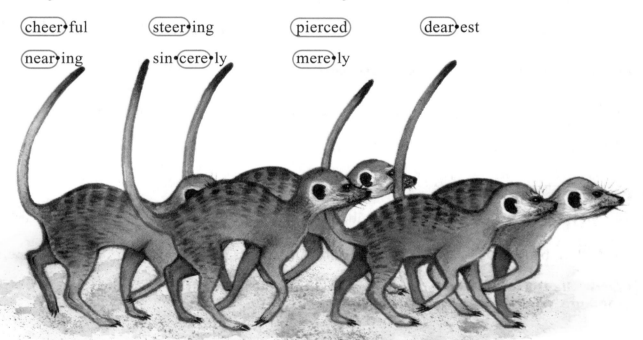

Which letters make the /îr/ as in *meerkat*?

air   (ear)   (eer)   ire   (ere)   (ier)

▶**Write an antonym for each word.**

1. gentle   _fierce_

2. there   _here_

3. far   _near_

4. fake   _sincere_

5. unhappy   _cheerful_

cheerful	fierce
sincere	near
here	

▶**Fill in the blanks with one of the words from the word bank.**

1. The meerkat, a sociable creature, is quite _cheerful_.

2. The meerkat is _sincere_ in his role as a parent.

3. Working together in colonies, meerkats fight off _fierce_ prey.

4. If an intruder comes _near_ the burrows, a group of meerkats will advance toward him.

5. It is _here_ the meerkats will perform a series of false attacks.

▶**Circle every fourth letter and write it on the lines to find out the life span of the meerkat.**

e r p ⓣ u w b ⓔ d g u ⓝ r g a ⓨ n s v ⓔ w v i ⓐ t c n ⓡ x a p ⓢ

_t_ _e_ _n_   _y_ _e_ _a_ _r_ _s_

Meerkat

What a unique animal the meerkat is! It can dig through a pile of sand equal to its own weight in just seconds. The meerkat is immune to the poison from a scorpion or a snake. Its tail is used for balance and as a signal.

Review of r-controlled vowels

▶ **Read the words.**

charm	snore	rarely	merely	export
fairest	starfish	before	thirty	careful
dearest	servant	parking	market	search
turkey	fierce	staircase	cheerful	scoring

▶ **Write the above words under the correct *r*-controlled vowel sound.**

> When *r* follows a vowel, it usually influences the vowel's sound.

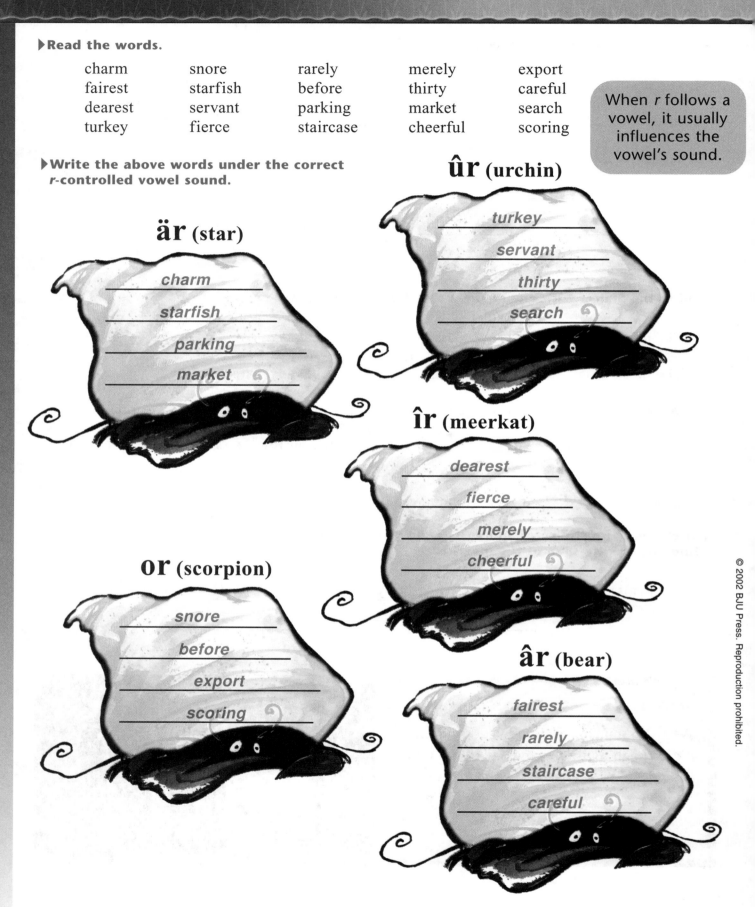

är (star)
charm
starfish
parking
market

ûr (urchin)
turkey
servant
thirty
search

îr (meerkat)
dearest
fierce
merely
cheerful

or (scorpion)
snore
before
export
scoring

âr (bear)
fairest
rarely
staircase
careful

▶ **Read the clues. Write the correct words on the blanks.**
When you are finished, the shaded letters will tell you another
characteristic of the hermit crab.

1. Hermit crabs are ___ that eat the remains of dead or dying plants and animals.
2. They use the small antennae between their eyes to detect ___ and to find food.
3. About one month after hermit crabs hatch, they begin to ___ for a shell to cover their soft bodies.
4. Hermit crabs can live one year without any food or ___.
5. A hermit crab may spend several hours ___ examining a new shell before moving into it.
6. Giant hermit crabs often prey upon ___ and mollusks.
7. After hermit crabs molt or shed their outer covering, it generally takes about ten days for their skin to ___ again.
8. They use their last ___ of legs to hold their shell or hollow object in place.
9. As hermit crabs grow ___, they look for more spacious shells.

scavengers
harden
pair
larger
search
carefully
odors
water
worms

1. S C A V E N G E R S
2. O D O R S
3. S E A R C H
4. W A T E R
5. C A R E F U L L Y
6. W O R M S
7. H A R D E N
8. P A I R
9. L A R G E R

Hermit Crab

Hermit crabs use empty snail shells or other hollow objects such as broken coconut shells to protect their soft abdomens. When hermit crabs are frightened or attacked, they retreat into their shell and use their larger claw to close the entrance.

/ô/ as in hawk

▶**Read the words. Circle the correct answers.**

haul	drawl	yawn	claw
maul	shawl	dawn	thaw
Saul	crawl	fawn	squaw

pause	staunch	fault	caught
cause	launch	vault	taught

Sometimes vowels have special sounds when they are with other letters.

1. What vowel pairs are in the words above?

e   ou   a   (au)   o   (aw)

stall	salt	chalk	bald
fall	malt	stalk	scald

2. What consonant follows the letter *a* in the words above?

k   w   t   (l)   d

▶**Read the multisyllable words.**
Circle the syllables that have the /ô/ as in *hawk*.

(au)•thor	(flaw)•less	(laun)•dry
(al)•tar	(fau)•cet	(au)•to•graph
(aw)•ful	(thaw)•ing	ap•(plause)

(fault)•y	(wal)•rus	(au)•di•o
(au)•tumn	(law)•yer	(auc)•tion
ex•(alt)	(awn)•ing	(au)•to•work•er

Which letters make the /ô/ as in *hawk*?

ei   (aw)   i   (a(l))   (au)   ow

300

▶**Find the letters from the code and write them in the blanks.**

1. __S__ __M__ __A__ __L__ __L__

2. __C__ __L__ __A__ __W__ __S__

3. __C__ __A__ __U__ __S__ __E__ __S__

4. __A__ __W__ __F__ __U__ __L__

5. __L__ __A__ __U__ __N__ __C__ __H__

6. __T__ __A__ __L__ __L__

▶**Fill in the blanks using the words above.**

1. The red-tailed hawk's main weapons are its _____*claws*_____ called talons.

2. The hawk eats _____*small*_____ creatures such as rabbits, snakes, and lizards.

3. In March the hawk builds its nest in the forks of _____*tall*_____ trees.

4. When defending its nest, the hawk cries an _____*awful*_____ scream.

5. A baby hawk demands much food, which _____*causes*_____ both parents to keep busy.

6. A young hawk perches on the edge of the nest, flapping its wings and preparing

   to _____*launch*_____ into the air.

Red-tailed Hawk

The red-tailed hawk is the most common hawk in North America. Its eyesight is eight times as powerful as a human's eyesight. When this hawk is flying toward someone, it looks as though it has a pair of headlights on its wings.

/ou/ as in owl

▶**Read the words.**

prowl	pound	clown	blouse
scowl	sound	drown	spouse

grouch	ounce	trout	cloud	count
slouch	bounce	shout	proud	mount

> Sometimes vowels have special sounds when they are together.

▶**Circle the correct answers.**

1. What vowel pairs are in the words above?

      oe   (ou)   oa   oo   (ow)

2. Which letter is acting like a vowel instead of a consonant?

      t   n   d   (w)   s

▶**Read the multisyllable words. Circle the syllables that have the /ou/ as in *owl*.**

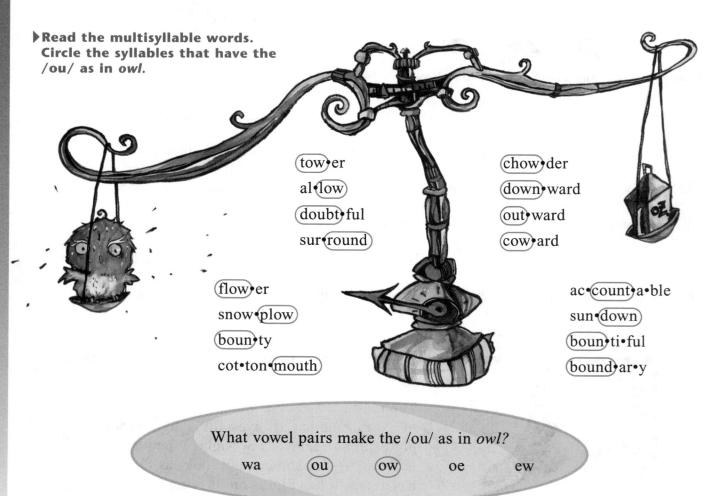

(tow)•er
al•(low)
(doubt)•ful
sur•(round)

(chow)•der
(down)•ward
(out)•ward
(cow)•ard

(flow)•er
snow•(plow)
(boun)•ty
cot•ton•(mouth)

ac•(count)•a•ble
sun•(down)
(boun)•ti•ful
(bound)•ar•y

What vowel pairs make the /ou/ as in *owl*?

      wa   (ou)   (ow)   oe   ew

▶**Circle the /ou/ words to find the places where the elf owl lives.**

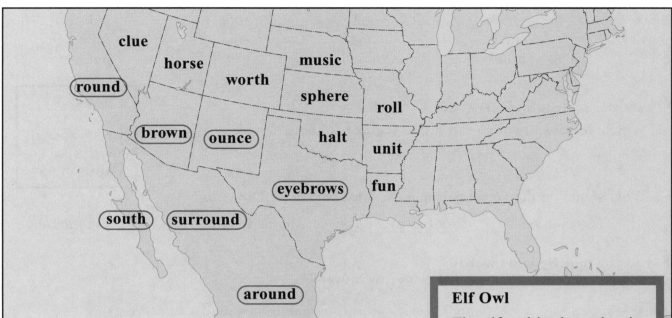

clue
horse
music
worth
round
sphere
roll
brown
ounce
halt
unit
eyebrows
fun
south
surround
around

▶**Use the /ou/ words from above to complete the sentences.**

1. The elf owl weighs a little over an _____ounce_____.

2. Spots of white speckle the owl's _____brown_____ feathers.

3. An elf owl's round head has white _____eyebrows_____ above its yellow eyes.

4. Circles of feathers _____surround_____ each eye, giving the owl a wide-eyed look.

5. An owl cannot move its eyes like you can. It must move its entire head to look _____around_____.

6. The elf owl flies _____south_____ for the winter.

Elf Owl

The elf owl is about the size of a large sparrow and is the smallest owl in North America. It lives in saguaro cactuses, mesquite trees, and even in fence posts. The owl's eggs are about the size of a jellybean. The elf owl can be distinguished from other owls by its small size, yellow eyes, short tail, and its voice.

/ŏŏ/ as in woolly

▶ **Read the words.**

push	crook	hood	foot	pull
bush	shook	wood	soot	full
	brook	stood		put

▶ **Circle the correct answers.**

1. Which vowel and vowel pair are in the words above?

(oo)   ow   (u)   ew   ui   a   i

> Sometimes vowels have special sounds when they are together.

2. What sound do the vowel pair and the vowel make in the words?

/ōō/ as in *boot*   (/ŏŏ/ as in *look*)   /ou/ as in *cloud*   /ŭ/ as in *puzzle*

▶ **Read the multisyllable words.**
Circle the syllables that have the /ŏŏ/ as in *woolly*.

(bush)•el	(wood)•en	neigh•bor•(hood)	(pul)•ley
(cook)•ie	un•der•(stood)	(wool)•en	(push)•y
o•ver•(look)	(pul)•pit	(crook)•ed	(push)•up
am•(bush)	book•shelf	(foot)•ball	in•(put)

What letters make /ŏŏ/ as in *woolly*?

oi   ow   (oo)   o   (u)

▶**Read the paragraph. Find all the words in color in the puzzle.**

Early Americans depended on their food crops. They understood that harsh winters took extra preparation. Folks looked at how plants and animals prepared for cold weather. In the autumn they observed the woolly bear caterpillar on its way to hibernate under wooden boards, in crooks, and in crevices. The bands or segments at the ends of the woolly bear are black. The ones in the middle are reddish-brown. According to legend the fuller the reddish-brown band, the milder the winter. If it had a narrow middle band, it would be a harsh winter. Some people put faith in such myths.

E	N	W	C	W	O	O	Y	F	D
L	O	O	K	E	D	A	L	P	U
U	C	O	R	C	B	D	L	S	T
U	N	D	E	R	S	T	O	O	D
D	W	E	F	O	O	D	O	R	A
C	N	N	O	O	F	L	W	E	K
F	T	O	O	K	S	P	U	T	O
O	R	O	P	S	W	K	B	B	U
W	R	E	L	L	U	F	O	K	P

▶**Use the /o͝o/ words from above to write synonyms for the words.**

1. furry _____woolly_____

2. grabbed _____took_____

3. wider _____fuller_____

4. stared _____looked_____

5. learned _____understood_____

6. set _____put_____

7. bends _____crooks_____

Woolly Bear Caterpillar

The woolly bear caterpillar is covered with short, stiff bristles of hair. When disturbed, it curls into a tight bristly ball and "plays dead." As a result, it is called the hedgehog caterpillar. The woolly bear is the larva of the Isabella tiger moth.

/oi/ as in oyster

▶**Read the words.**

coil	coin	boy
soil	join	soy
spoil	point	joy
toil	joint	toy

voice	noise	moist
choice	poise	hoist

▶**Circle the correct answers.**

1. Which vowel pairs are in the words above?

    ow   io   oo   (oy)   (oi)

Sometimes vowels have special sounds when they are together.

2. What sound do the vowel pairs make in the words?

    /ou/ as in *about*   (/oi/ as in *coin*)   /o͞o/ as in *shook*

▶**Read the multisyllable words.**
Circle the syllables that have the /oi/ as in *oyster*.

en•(joy)	(voy)•age	dis•ap•(point)	(loy)•al
(roy)•al	en•(joy)•ment	de•(stroy)	re•(joice)
em•(ploy)•er	em•(ploy)	(oil)•can	(nois)•y
a•(void)	cow•(boy)	tin•(foil)	(poi)•son
an•(noy)	(joy)•ous	(oys)•ter	pin•point

What letters make the /oi/ as in *oyster*?

    oo   ou   (oi)   (oy)   ow

▶ **Circle the words with the *oi* sound in these Bible verses.**
Some verses have more than one word.

1. "Make a (joyful) (noise) unto God" (Psalm 66:1).

2. "(Rejoice) in the Lord alway" (Philippians 4:4).

3. "Thou (anointest) my head with (oil;) my cup runneth over" (Psalm 23:5).

4. "Trust in the living God, who giveth us richly all things to (enjoy)" (I Timothy 6:17).

▶ **Complete the sentences.**

1. A little _____*boy*_____ gathered shells along the shore.

2. He found two shells _____*joined*_____ together by a hinge.

3. The soft-bodied _____*oyster*_____ was no longer in the shell.

4. Some people _____*enjoy*_____ eating oysters fried;

   others like them _____*boiled*_____.

5. A grain of sand or other _____*annoying*_____ substance can enter an oyster's shell.

6. The oyster _____*toils*_____ many years, coating the grain of sand with a shiny substance and forming a pearl.

toils
enjoy
oyster
annoying
boy
joined
boiled

Oyster

An oyster is one of the most nourishing of all seafoods. An oyster takes in water through its gills. It filters out oxygen and floating algae which it uses for food. A large oyster may filter more than a barrel of water in a day. The edible oyster does not produce pearls because it lacks a lining of mother-of-pearl.

Review of special sounds

▶**Read the words.**

launch	wooden	understood	flower	poison
cartoon	bedroom	tinfoil	groove	thawing
crown	laundry	bookshelf	loyal	overlook
enjoy	outside	flawless	moody	grouch

▶**Write the above words under the correct special sound.**

> When a syllable has two vowels together, they may make a special sound.

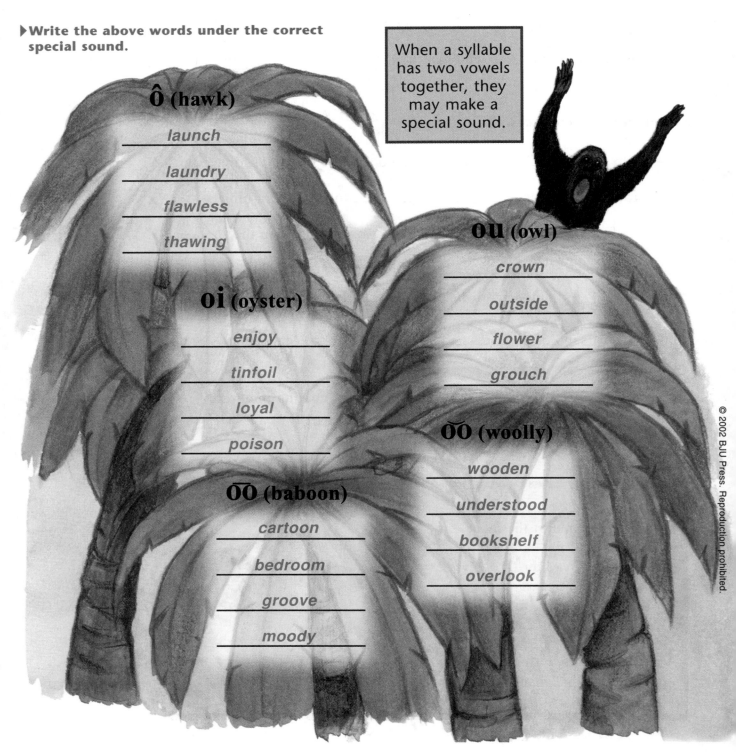

ô (hawk)

launch

laundry

flawless

thawing

oi (oyster)

enjoy

tinfoil

loyal

poison

o͞o (baboon)

cartoon

bedroom

groove

moody

ou (owl)

crown

outside

flower

grouch

o͝o (woolly)

wooden

understood

bookshelf

overlook

▶ **Read the clues. Write the correct words on the blanks. When you are finished, the shaded letters will tell you the habitat of the black howler monkey.**

loud	brown	destroyed
sounds	around	powerful
flowers	stouter	
voices	allow	

1. The male black howler monkey is black, but the female and babies are ___.

2. The adult howlers ___ the young monkeys to jump and climb on them.

3. They defend their territory by using their ___.

4. Their howling is one of the loudest animal ___.

5. The howler monkey enjoys eating fruits, leaves, and ___.

6. The ___ calls can be heard two to three miles away.

7. These monkeys spend a lot of their time lounging ___ or sleeping.

8. Their ___ tails are strong enough to hold their entire body weight.

9. Their legs are shorter and ___ than those of the spider monkeys.

10. Some land is protected so that their food trees will not be ___ to make way for pasture.

Black Howler Monkey

The black howler monkey is among the largest of the American monkeys and is known as the baboon in Belize. Its body hair is coarse, but its face is hairless. The monkeys live and travel in small troops and sleep high in the trees at night.

1. B R O W N

2. A L L O W

3. V O I C E S

4. S O U N D S

5. F L O W E R S

6. L O U D

7. A R O U N D

8. P O W E R F U L

9. S T O U T E R

10. D E S T R O Y E D

/s/ as in centipede

▶ **Read the words.**

price	cell	circle	cycle
spice	cent	circus	cyclone
twice	cease	citrus	cymbal

▶ **Circle the correct answers.**

1. What sound does the letter *c* usually make?

/z/   /s/   (/k/)   /sh/

2. What vowels follow the letter *c* in the words above?

(e)   (i)   a   o   (y)

3. What sound does the letter *c* make in the words above?

/ch/   (/s/)   /k/   /sh/

> The letter *c* usually says its **soft** sound when followed by *e, i,* or *y.*

▶ **Read the words.**
Circle all the syllables with soft *c*.

prac•(tice)	spe•(cies)	con•(vince)	(ce)•ment
(cit)•i•zen	pen•(cil)	de•(cide)	(ce)•dar
(civ)•il	(cyl)•in•der	(cer)•tain	(ce)•re•al
dis•(tance)	of•fi•(cer)	(ceil)•ing	(cel)•er•y
tri•(cy)•cle	ad•(vance)	(cel)•lar	o•be•di•(ence)

What letter patterns make the /s/ as in *centipede?*

ca   (ce)   (ci)   co   cu   (cy)

▶**Circle the rhyming words.**

1. plant   (lace)   plow   (place)   pluck

2. spill   (spice)   (nice)   stool   mail

3.(bell)   beach   blank   (cell)   clue

4. spark   symbol   (spider)   stay   (cider)

5. middle   (mice)   mitten   meadow   (twice)

6.(face)   fiddle   fact   fat   (grace)

▶**Complete the sentences.**

| centimeters | mice | sliced | centipede | crevices | face |

1. The giant desert centipede is one of the world's largest and prettiest species of

   _____*centipede*_____ .

2. The centipede can grow to about 12 inches or 30 _____*centimeters*_____ in length.

3. It can be found in cracks and _____*crevices*_____ of rocks and under flat objects.

4. Adults will eat large crickets, cockroaches, and even tiny _____*mice*_____ .

5. When a centipede's leg is _____*sliced*_____ off, it will grow again.

6. Would you like to come face to _____*face*_____ with one of these creatures?

Giant Desert Centipede

The giant desert centipede lives in the southwestern United States, emerging at night or in cool, cloudy weather and on rainy days. Its first pair of legs are called poison jaws. These legs contain venom that it uses to kill its prey. Its bite is not usually deadly to humans, although it is quite painful.

/j/ as in giraffe

▶ **Read the words.**

giant	hedge	edge	gem	smudge
ginger	pledge	ledge	gene	grudge
bridge	lodge	change	germ	huge
hinge	dodge	strange	gym	plunge

▶ **Circle all the correct answers.**

1. What vowels follow the letter *g* in the words above?

   o   (e)   (i)   a   (y)

2. What sound does the letter *g* make in the words above?

   /qu/   /f/   /g/   (/j/)

The letter *g* usually says its **soft** sound when followed by *e, i,* or *y.*

▶ **Circle all the syllables with soft g in the words.**

(gen)•tle   (ger)•bil   dam•(age)   (Ger)•ma•ny

(gen)•er•ous   (gi)•gan•tic   re•(gion)   lug•(gage)

(gym)•nast   (gyp)•sy   en•(gine)   en•er•(gy)

(gel)•a•tin   (Ger)•man   col•(lege)   in•ter•(change)

What letter patterns make the /j/ as in *giraffe*?

   ga   (ge)   (gi)   go   gu   (gy)

▶**Find the way to the entrance of the Giraffe's Exchange by drawing a path under the words with the _j_ sound.**

START

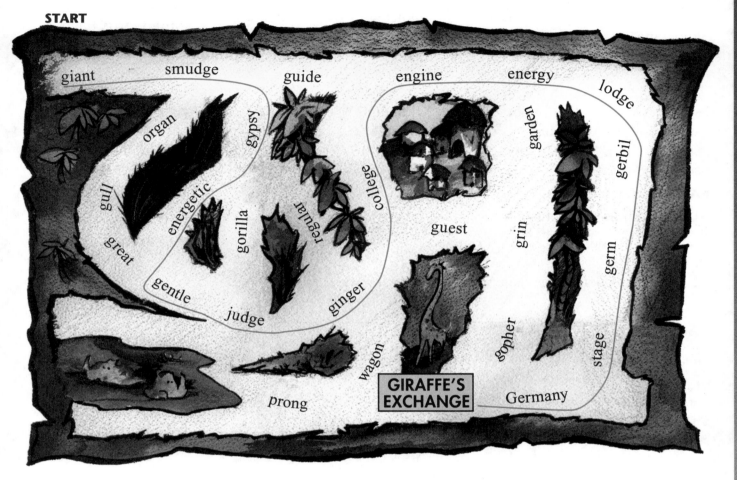

giant   smudge   guide   engine   energy   lodge

organ   gypsy   garden   gerbil

gull   energetic   college   grin   germ

great   gorilla   regular   guest

gentle   judge   ginger   gopher   stage

wagon

prong   **GIRAFFE'S EXCHANGE**   Germany

Giraffe

A baby giraffe is called a *calf*. At birth, calves are about six feet tall. A calf is born with horns that are flat against its head. These become upright during the giraffe's first week of life. Despite the horns, giraffes are rather peaceful animals.

Silent Consonants

▶**Read the words.**

knee	wrong	match	debt
knuckle	wrecked	moisten	doubt
knocking	wrinkle	fasten	plumber
knife	wrapper	listen	climbed

> Some words have silent consonants.

scene	brought	although	calf	gnat
science	taught	through	walk	design
scent	naughty	thought	almond	campaign
scepter				

▶**Answer the questions.**

1. What kinds of sounds do the shaded letters above make?

   soft sounds   (no sounds)   hard sounds

2. Write the silent consonants from the lists above.

   __k__   __w__   __t__   __b__   __c__   __gh__   __l__   __g__

▶**Read and complete the sentences.**

wrinkled	calves
listened	often
watching	knife
designed	doubt
knobs	

1. A twelve-foot-long rhinoceros lumbered toward the water

   hole as we stood _____*watching*_____.

2. As we _____*listened*_____ to the science teacher, we
   learned that humans are the only enemy of adult rhinos.

3. However, tigers may attack and kill the young rhinos or _____*calves*_____.

4. The Creator _____*designed*_____ the rhino to wallow in mud
   to protect it from sunburn.

5. The mud also protects it from getting insects in the folds of its

   _____*wrinkled*_____ skin.

6. The Indian rhino appears to wear an armor plate because of the many round

   _____*knobs*_____ under its skin.

7. Even with the knobs, a sharp _____*knife*_____ or bullet can
   still pierce the rhino.

8. Poachers _____*often*_____ hunt rhinos to sell their horns and skin.

9. The rhino is without a _____*doubt*_____ an interesting creature.

Rhinoceros

Although a rhino may weigh up to two tons, it can charge at frightening speed. The Indian rhino has one stubby horn. Both white and black rhinos have two horns. Horns are made of hairlike fibers and will grow back if broken off. The longer front horn averages twenty inches; however, the white rhino's horn may grow as much as five feet long!

A Message to Parents

Ways You Can Help

Many parents ask the question "How can I help my child become a good reader?" Reading outside the instructional setting is an essential ingredient for his success. You can make a difference.

- *Read to your child.* Children of all ages benefit as they listen to an adult read. When a child hears material that is *above his own reading level,* his vocabulary is stretched and enriched, and he hears the more interesting syntax patterns that he will encounter in his own reading in the future. When a child hears material *at his present reading level,* he is given a model for the fluency that he needs to attain. When a child hears material that is *easy for him to read,* he is invited to take up that very book and read it for himself.

- *Visit the library with your child.* Help him to select easy, interesting books for his independent reading and more difficult, appealing books for you to read aloud to him.

- *Read the newspaper with your child.* Study the weather map and compare the map to the forecast given. Look at the sports page. If a sports article is particularly interesting to a child, he will read it eagerly. If any articles or editorials have content a child can understand, discuss the facts and opinions given after you and your child have read it.

- *Ask your child to read to other family members.* Any homework that turns into family time has double benefits. A child's oral reading fluency will improve as he entertains younger children or elderly relatives by reading easy material to them.

- *Encourage meaningful writing.* Writing builds reading. Help your child to keep a journal of family trips. Enhanced with photographs or original art, it can become a record of his childhood that he will value all his life. Encourage him to write long letters to grandparents or aunts and uncles who live in other cities. (Keep copies for yourself.)

- *Show interest in your child's school papers.* Look with interest at the worktext pages that he has completed. Give value to his pages by commenting on their content rather than concentrating only on the incorrect answers. If he knows you are interested in his thinking, he will become more diligent in his efforts.

- *Be enthusiastic about the stories in your child's reader.* After your child has completed the reading lessons for a story in his reader, he will benefit from some good follow-up.

  1. Read some of the selections yourself and then carry out a discussion that resembles a relaxed dinner table conversation. Some of the stories with strong messages will provide wonderful opportunities for discipling your child.

  2. Ask him to read the most exciting paragraphs aloud. Praise him specifically if he makes you hear the character's voice, if he communicates fear or other emotions, or if he changes the pace or pauses to show suspense. (Sometimes children at this age, although they have had good oral reading skills in the past, develop poor habits.)

Things to Avoid

Sometimes well-meaning parents cause problems unintentionally. Avoid practices that may become obstacles.

- *Allowing your child to read ahead in his reader is not a good teaching technique.* This will harm the book's effectiveness as a tool for teaching reading comprehension.

- *Avoid making your questions sound like a quiz.*

- *Don't allow your child to read his whole story aloud in a meaningless drone or in a hurried manner.* Good oral reading always communicates the message of the author.

- *Use caution as you correct misread words.* A child who reads fluently may say slightly different words. For example, the sentence *Jessie put her many toys away* might be read *Jessie put all her toys away.* This happens when his eyes begin moving across the text faster than his speaking voice can interpret it. In his mind the author's words and his own thoughts have become one. This is a sign of a good reader. It is the way you read. If you insist on asking him to go back to get each specific word, you are asking him to revert to being a word-by-word reader rather than a fluent phrase-by-phrase reader.

Tools for the Job

READING for Christian Schools emphasizes comprehension and develops phonics systematically. These materials provide the tools not only to teach reading well but also to encourage growth in Christian character. A variety of selections—family stories, adventure stories, Christian realism, historical fiction, Bible accounts retold, biographies, information articles, folktales, poems, and plays—offer engaging reading that provides both pleasure and understanding. Notice especially the author pages in his worktext and help him find works by these authors in the library.

We trust your child will enjoy the school year as he uses his fifth grade reading materials to become a confident, eager reader—one who will continue to read all his life.

—Bob Jones University Press

Fifth-Grade Summer Reading List

Rising sixth graders demonstrate a wide range of ability levels and represent an even wider range of interest levels. Not every book on the following list will appeal to your child. The annotations will help you to choose books he may find interesting, but you need to evaluate the difficulty level to determine if it fits your child. It is important that you keep your child reading during the summer months. His continued success in reading depends on it.

The books we choose for young people should possess two characteristics: literary excellence and high moral tone. A book that is poorly written, even though it teaches noble Christian precepts, may hinder a child's love for the worthy literature he will encounter in the future; on the other hand, a well-crafted book with a subtle undermining of biblical principles may quietly undermine a child's faith. The books on this list have been evaluated in the light of the two characteristics mentioned above by Christians who care about books and children. In the end, however, each parent must be the final judge of the books his child reads.

Brammer, Deb. *Peanut Butter Friends in a Chop Suey World.* Amy can't wait to be a missionary with her family in Taiwan! Then she finds out it's hard to make friends with people with whom you can't communicate. An eye-opener for all kids who want to serve the Lord and trust Him more completely. (Bob Jones University Press, 1995)

Brink, Carol. *Caddie Woodlawn.* In this pioneer story, redheaded tomboy Caddie and her brother have friendly encounters with the Indians and find them to be compassionate and unbiased. (Macmillan, 1973)

Burnett, Frances. *The Secret Garden.* Illus. Michael Hague. Mary returns to England after her parents' untimely deaths in India. She realizes how unruly she has been when she meets her pampered cousin, Colin. Mary and Colin begin to change when they discover an abandoned garden that once belonged to Colin's deceased mother. A robin and a boy who loves nature also become part of the children's new world. (H. Holt, 1987)

Cleary, Beverly. *The Mouse and the Motorcycle.* Illus. Louis Darling. Ralph, the mischievous mouse, rides a mouse-sized motorcycle through the hotel corridors. Keith, the owner of the toy, becomes good friends with Ralph in this classic imaginative tale. (W. Morrow, 1965)

Coerr, Eleanor. *Mieko and the Fifth Treasure.* Mieko's hand is injured as a result of flying glass when Nagasaki is bombed at the end of WWII. Her hand is scarred—and so is her spirit and the beauty she holds within. Friendship makes it blossom again, though, and her beautiful calligraphy flows onto the rice paper as it did before the war. (G.P. Putnam's Sons, 1993)

Conrad, Pam. *Pedro's Journal.* Illus. Peter Koepper. We roll along the ocean swells with Christopher Columbus and his crew—one of whom records the entire adventure in journal form. This artful story has actual historical events for the enjoyment of all readers. (Scholastic, 1992)

DeJong, Meindert. *Hurry Home, Candy.* Illus. Maurice Sendak. This story traces the unhappy, hungry existence of Candy, a dog briefly loved by two children and separated from them by a terrible storm. He does finally find a friend and a home with the old sea captain. Great dog story! (Harper, 1953)

———. *The Wheel on the School.* Illus. Maurice Sendak. Children from the Dutch village of Shora learn that storks once perched on the roofs of the people's houses. The children begin a campaign to get the storks back. They influence the whole village with their efforts and determination. Superb illustrations! (Harper & Row, 1972)

Farley, Walter. *The Black Stallion.* Shipwreck lands Alec and the black Arabian stallion on a deserted island. The friendship they forge there only grows stronger—even after they are rescued. (Random House, 1969)

Field, Rachel. *Calico Bush.* Illus. Allen Lewis. Courage, grit, and grace mark young Marguerite, or Maggie. Her life as a bound-out girl is hard. And yet it is Maggie who speaks French with the marauding Indians and saves the family and the children she has come to love. (Collier Macmillan, 1966)

Fritz, Jean. *The Cabin Faced West.* Illus. Maureen Hyde. Since coming to the Western country, Ann Hamilton has been lonely and homesick for Gettysburg and her cousin Margaret. Only boys and babies live in the nearby cabins around her. Mother promised that on a special day they would have a party—and the day finally comes when General George Washington visits her home! (G.P. Putnam's Sons, 1958)

———. *Early Thunder.* Whig or Tory? This question is on the lips of the townspeople of Salem, Massachusetts, in the early Revolutionary days. Daniel West watches as his loved ones have to decide where their convictions lie—and then he makes his own important choice. (Coward-McCann, 1967)

Gates, Doris. *Blue Willow.* Illus. Paul Lantz. "It takes a lot of courage to live like we do," Pa said. Life was hard for migrant workers and their families who followed the crops—but Jamie had the blue willow plate, and that made all the difference in the world. (Viking Press, 1966)

Hambrick, Sharon. *Arby Jenkins.* Arby and the events in his sixth-grade world represent a lot of kids getting ready to enter junior high. He meets the new challenges with honesty and humor. Sequels are *Arby Jenkins, Mighty Mustang; Arby Jenkins, Ready to Roll; Stuart's Run to Faith;* and *Arby Jenkins Meets His Match.* (Bob Jones University Press, 1996)

———. *The Year of Abi Crim.* Could a year be any more different than the one Abi had planned out in her hopes? She finds it to be a year of growth, understanding, and step-taking on all fronts. (Bob Jones University Press, 2000)

Hammett, Evelyn Allen. *I, Priscilla.* Priscilla kept a diary of her family's arduous journey to the new colony in Connecticut. Indians, snow, sickness—the hardships were worth the struggle, and she became one of the founding citizens of the new settlement. (Macmillan, 1961)

Hawse, Alberta. *Vinegar Boy.* The lonely vinegar boy carries the liquid he is named for to Crucifixion hill. He will never forget the words he hears there or the man who dies on the center cross. His heart leaps with hope as the centurion exclaims, "Surely, this was the Son of God." (Moody Press, 1989)

Henry, Marguerite. *Misty of Chincoteague.* Illus. Wesley Dennis. Each year ponies from the island of Chincoteague in the Chesapeake Bay are sold. This is the story of Phantom, one of these wild freedom-loving ponies, and her foal, Misty. Both are tamed by Paul and Maureen. (Rand McNally, 1975)

Howard, Milly. *Brave the Wild Trail.* Josh and his dad join a cattle drive through Florida's fearful wilderness after the Civil War. Their adventures heighten their awareness of God's protection and direction in their lives. (Bob Jones University Press, 1987)

Jacques, Brian. *Redwall.* The story begins in Mossflower Wood at Redwall Abbey where the gentle mice and their woodland friends have gathered to celebrate a year of peace and plenty. But Cluny is on the way. Cluny the Scourge—a terrible bilge rat and his gang. The only hope for his defeat lies in the legendary sword of Martin the Warrior. (Philomel Books, 1998)

Latham, Jean Lee. *Carry On, Mr. Bowditch.* A sea story, set in the 1770s, portrays an exciting historical figure, Nathaniel Bowditch. (Houghton Mifflin, 1983)

Leppard, Lois. *Mandie and the Secret Tunnel.* Mandie is heartbroken when her beloved father dies. Then when she is hired out to a neighbor family, her despair seems all-encompassing. With Uncle Ned's help she returns to her father's childhood home and finds her birth mother and the true story of her heritage. Some of the sequels are *Mandie and the Cherokee Legend, Mandie and the Forbidden Attic, Mandie and the Trunk's Secret,* and *Mandie and the Midnight Journey.* (Bethany House Publishers, 1983)

Lewis, C. S. *The Lion, the Witch, and the Wardrobe.* In this, the first of Lewis's seven Narnia stories, Lucy, Susan, Peter, and Edmund discover the world of Narnia, and Aslan dies to save the traitorous Edmund from death. Sequels are *Prince Caspian, The Voyage of the Dawn Treader, The Silver Chair, The Horse and His Boy, The Magician's Nephew,* and *The Last Battle.* (Macmillan, 1988)

Lowell, Susan. *I Am Lavina Cumming.* Illus. Paul Mirocha. Lavina Cumming loves the Bosque Ranch in Arizona Territory where she's always lived with Father, Mother, and her five brothers—until Mother dies. Now she must go to Aunt Agnes in Santa Cruz, California, learn to be a lady, and get an education. The Great San Francisco Earthquake changes Lavina's mind and plans. (Milkweed Editions, 1993)

Massi, Jeri. THE BRACKEN SERIES: *The Bridge.* Princess Rosalynn flees for her life when Bracken is invaded. Her time with the wise woman teaches her much about giving to others and what true bravery is. Sequels are *Crown and Jewel* and *The Two Collars.* (Bob Jones University Press, 1986)

————. THE PEABODY ADVENTURE SERIES: *Derwood, Inc.* In this humorous story a brother and sister detective team find adventure and mystery as close as the local mattress store. Sequels are *A Dangerous Game, Treasure in the Yukon, Courage by Darkness, Llamas on the Loose,* and *Abandoned.* (Bob Jones University Press, 1986)

McSwigan, Marie. *Snow Treasure.* Illus. Andre LaBlanc. The brave children of a Norwegian village carry nine million dollars in gold bullion via their sleds to a fishing vessel that takes the gold to America—under the noses of the Nazis. Their adventures, close calls of near discovery, and the bravery of an unexpected friend make an excellent story. (Recorded Books, 1999)

Miller, Marvin. *You Be the Jury.* Illus. Bob Roper. This book is comprised of ten "mind-stretchers," giving two different sides of a case and the evidence a jury would consider in making a decision about who is guilty. Interesting—lends itself to short dramatic or skit adaptation. (Scholastic, 1987)

Repp, Gloria. *Mik-Shrok: Adventures of an Arctic Missionary.* Steve and Liz Bailey, pioneer missionaries, run into difficulties as soon as they arrive at the small Eskimo town of Koyalik. If only they had a dog team, Steve thinks, they could haul their own wood and water and perhaps travel to other villages. He and Liz pray for a good team of huskies, and the Eskimos watch to see what the white man's God will do. (Bob Jones University Press, 1999)

————. *The Secret of the Golden Cowrie.* Connie Lawrence listens eagerly when Aunt Laura shares a puzzling secret with her about the rare golden shell in her uncle's collection. What has become of it? (Bob Jones University Press, 1988)

St. John, Patricia. *Star of Light.* Miss St. John's experience as a Christian missionary brings vivid detail and compassion to this compelling story of children in a Muslim culture in Morocco. (Moody Press, 1953)

————. *Treasures of the Snow.* Set in beautiful Switzerland, this story of love, bitterness, and forgiveness quietly teaches important Christian truths. Even children who may have seen a film based on this book will enjoy reading Miss St. John's story again for themselves. A surprise kitten, which arrives on a sad snowy Christmas Eve, becomes the center of young Dani's life. His older sister, Annette, in an effort to love and protect him, finds herself in an unhappy state that only forgiveness can remedy. (Moody Press, 1950)

Thomson, Andy. *Renegade in the Hills.* Josiah Eagle tries to escape being captured by a greedy rancher. If only Pa were different and could help him. (Bob Jones University Press, 1989)

Walley, Susan. *Best of Friends.* Katie Crawford wants to be friends with Renee, the talented new girl in town—but Renee is harboring a secret that needs desperate attention. (Bob Jones University Press, 1989)

Wilkie, Katherine E. *Helen Keller: From Tragedy to Triumph.* Illus. Robert Doremus. Helen was not only blind but also deaf. The world was dark and frustrating to this intelligent little girl until Teacher came into her life, giving her the key to understanding. (Bobbs-Merrill, 1983)

Yates, Elizabeth. *A Place for Peter.* Peter grows up and seeks to prove himself. Can he face the rattlesnakes on the hill? Sequel to *Mountain Born.* (Bob Jones University Press, 1997)

Index

Photo Credits

The following agencies and individuals have furnished materials to meet the photographic needs of this textbook. We wish to express our gratitude to them for their important contribution.

American Jewish Historical Society

1999-2001 © www.arttoday.com

Bateman's, Burwash, Sussex

© David Chopin, www.crapemyrtles.com

Corel Corporation

Creation Science Foundation, Ltd., Australia

Digital Stock

divegallery.com

The Emory Magazine

Emory University Library

Peter B. Kaplan

Library of Congress

Ron Magill

Courtesy of David T. W. McCord

NASA

National Archives

National Oceanic and Atmospheric Administration

National Portrait Galley, London

The Phoenix Zoo

PhotoDisc, Inc.

© Tony Rath Photography 2001, www.trphoto.com

H. Roger-Viollet, Paris

The Tennyson Research Centre

UK National Trust for Places of Historic Interest or Natural Beauty, from the Kipling Papers at the University of Sussex Library

Unusual Films

Kay Washer

YIVO Institute for Jewish Research

COVER—Digital Stock (girl reading book); PhotoDisc, Inc. (paper)

FRONT MATTER—PhotoDisc, Inc. (paper) title page

UNIT 1—Corel Corporation 30 (both); Unusual Films 31, 32

UNIT 2—Corel Corporation 43, 45, 46; PhotoDisc, Inc. 48, 61; NASA 49, 52 (both); © David Chopin, www.crapemyrtles.com 57; 1999-2001 © www.arttoday.com 58

UNIT 3—1999-2001 © www.arttoday.com 74; National Archives 91

UNIT 4—PhotoDisc, Inc. 105, 108, 114, 118, 119; 1999-2001 © www.arttoday.com 109

UNIT 5—Unusual Films 129, 130, 132; Digital Stock 138, 140 (all); PhotoDisc, Inc. 146; Corel Corporation 149

UNIT 6—PhotoDisc, Inc. 171, 177, 197; Digital Stock 172; National Archives 180 (all), 181 (all)

SKILL DAY LESSONS—PhotoDisc, Inc. 206, 210, 211, 220 (both), 221 (all), 228 (all); 1999-2001 © www.arttoday.com 209, 223; Corel Corporation 217; Digital Stock 226

AUTHOR SCRAPBOOK—PhotoDisc, Inc. 237

Lesson 15 (Harris): Emory University Library 238, 239 (middle both) 241, 242; PhotoDisc, Inc. 239 (background); *The Emory Magazine* 239 (top left); 1999-2001 © www.arttoday.com 239 (bottom both)

Lesson 49 (Kipling): H. Roger-Viollet, Paris 238, 243 (middle); PhotoDisc, Inc. 239 (back right, background); Bateman's, Burwash, Sussex 243 (top left); Library of Congress 243 (bottom); Reproduced with permission of the UK National Trust for Places of Historic Interest or Natural Beauty, from the Kipling Papers at the University of Sussex Library 245

Lesson 72 (McCord): Courtesy of David T. W. McCord 238, 247 (all), 250; PhotoDisc, Inc. 247 (background)

Lesson 91 (Tennyson): The Tennyson Research Centre, Lincoln, by permission of Lord Tennyson and the Lincolnshire Library Service 238, 251 (top), 254; Library of Congress 251 (bottom); 1999-2001 © www.arttoday.com 253 (top); PhotoDisc, Inc. 251 (bottom); 1999-2001 © www.arttoday.com 253 (top); PhotoDisc, Inc. 251 (background); By courtesy of the National Portrait Gallery, London 253 (bottom)

Lesson 102 (David): Corel Corporation 255; PhotoDisc, Inc. 255 (background)

Lesson 128 (Lazarus): Library of Congress 238, 259 (middle), 262; American Jewish Historical Society 259 (top); YIVO Institute for Jewish Research 259 (bottom); PhotoDisc, Inc. 259 (left and background), 261

PHONICS CRITTERS—Ron Magill 265; PhotoDisc, Inc. 267, 269, 275, 280, 281 (top), 285, 286, 297, 301 (both), 315; divegallery.com 271; Creation Science Foundation, Ltd., Australia 273, 281 (bottom), 283; The Phoenix Zoo 279; Unusual Films 291; National Oceanic and Atmospheric Administration 293, 299, 307; 1999-2001 © www.arttoday.com 295, 311; ©Copyright Tony Rath Photography 2001, www.trphoto.com 309; Kay Washer 313